PERGAMON INTERNATIONAL LIBRARY
of Science, Technology, Engineering and Soci°'
The 1000-volume original paperback lih⸗
training and the enjoyment of leisure
Publisher: Robert Maxwell, M.C.

HIGH-VOLTAGE ENGINEERING

Fundamentals

THE PERGAMON TEXTBOOK INSPECTION COPY SERVICE

An inspection copy of any book published in the Pergamon International Library will gladly be sent to academic staff without obligation for their consideration for course adoption or recommendation. Copies may be retained for a period of 60 days from receipt and returned if not suitable. When a particular title is adopted or recommended for adoption for class use and the recommendation results in a sale of 12 or more copies, the inspection copy may be retained with our compliments. The Publishers will be pleased to receive suggestions for revised editions and new titles to be published in this important International Library.

APPLIED ELECTRICITY AND ELECTRONICS

General Editor: P. HAMMOND

Other titles of interest in the

PERGAMON INTERNATIONAL LIBRARY

ABRAHAMS & PRIDHAM
Semiconductor Circuits: Theory Design and Experiment
Semiconductor Circuits: Worked Examples
BADEN FULLER
Engineering Field Theory
Worked Examples in Engineering Field Theory
BINNS & LAWRENSON
Analysis and Computation of Electric and Magnetic Field Problems, 2nd Edition
BROOKES
Basic Electric Circuits, 2nd Edition
CHEN
Theory and Design of Broadband Matching Networks
COEKIN
High Speed Pulse Techniques
DUMMER
Electronic Inventions and Discoveries, 3rd Edition
FISHER & GATLAND
Electronics—From Theory into Practice, 2nd Edition
GARLAND & STAINER
Modern Electronic Maintenance
GATLAND
Electronic Engineering Application of Two Port Networks
GUILE & PATERSON
Electrical Power Systems Volume 1, 2nd Edition
Electrical Power Systems Volume 2, 2nd Edition
HAMMOND
Applied Electromagnetism
Electromagnetism for Engineers, 2nd Edition
HANCOCK
Matrix Analysis of Electrical Machinery, 2nd Edition
HARRIS & ROBSON
The Physical Basis of Electronics
HINDMARSH
Electrical Machines and Their Application, 4th Edition
Worked Examples in Electrical Machines and Drives
MURPHY
Thyristor Control of AC Motors
RODDY
Introduction to Microelectronics, 2nd Edition
YORKE
Electric Circuit Theory

HIGH-VOLTAGE ENGINEERING

Fundamentals

E. KUFFEL
Dean of Engineering, University of Manitoba, Canada

W. S. ZAENGL
Professor in Electrical Engineering, Swiss Federal Institute of Technology, Zurich, Switzerland

PERGAMON PRESS
OXFORD . NEW YORK . TORONTO . SYDNEY . PARIS . FRANKFURT

U.K.	Pergamon Press Ltd., Headington Hill Hall, Oxford OX3 0BW, England
U.S.A.	Pergamon Press Inc., Maxwell House, Fairview Park, Elmsford, New York 10523, U.S.A.
CANADA	Pergamon Press Canada Ltd., Suite 104, 150 Consumers Rd., Willowdale, Ontario M2J 1P9, Canada
AUSTRALIA	Pergamon Press (Aust.) Pty. Ltd., P.O. Box 544, Potts Point, N.S.W. 2011, Australia
FRANCE	Pergamon Press SARL, 24 rue des Ecoles, 75240 Paris, Cedex 05, France
FEDERAL REPUBLIC OF GERMANY	Pergamon Press GmbH, Hammerweg 6, D-6242 Kronberg-Taunus, Federal Republic of Germany

---

Copyright © 1984 E. Kuffel and W. S. Zaengl

All Rights Reserved. No part of this publication may be reproduced, stored in a retrieval system or transmitted in any form or by any means: electronic, electrostatic, magnetic tape, mechanical, photocopying, recording or otherwise, without permission in writing from the publishers.

First edition 1984

Library of Congress Cataloging in Publication Data

Kuffel, E.
High voltage engineering.
(Applied electricity and electronics) (Pergamon international library of science, technology, engineering, and social studies)
Includes bibliographical references and index.
1. Electric engineering. 2. High voltages.
I. Zaengl, W. S. II. Title. III. Series. IV. Series:
Pergamon international library of science, technology, engineering, and social studies.
TK153.K8 1983 621.31 83-13340

British Library Cataloguing in Publication Data

Kuffel, E.
High voltage engineering.—(Applied electricity and electronics)
1. Electric power distribution—High tension
I. Title II. Zaengl, W. S. III. Series
621.31′042 TK452

ISBN 0-08-024213-8 (Hardcover)
ISBN 0-08-024212-X (Flexicover)

Printed in Great Britain by A. Wheaton & Co. Ltd., Exeter

CONTENTS

PREFACE

The need for an up-to-date textbook in High Voltage Engineering fundamentals has been apparent for some time. The earlier text of Kuffel and Abdullah published in 1970, although it had a wide circulation, was of somewhat limited scope and has now become partly outdated.

In this book an attempt is made to cover the basics of high voltage laboratory techniques and high voltage phenomena together with the principles governing design of high voltage insulation.

Following the historical introduction the chapters 2 and 3 present a comprehensive and rigorous treatment of laboratory, high voltage generation and measurement techniques and make extensive references to the various international standards.

Chapter 4 reviews methods used in controlling electric stresses and introduces the reader to modern numerical methods and their applications in the calculation of electric stresses in simple practical insulations.

Chapter 5 includes an extensive treatment of the subject of gas discharges and the basic mechanisms of electrical breakdown of gaseous, liquid and solid insulations.

Chapter 6 deals with modern techniques for discharge detection and measurement. The final chapter gives an overview treatment of systems overvoltages and insulation coordination.

It is hoped the text will fill the needs of senior undergraduate and graduate students enrolled in high voltage engineering courses as well as junior researchers engaged in the field of gas discharges. The in-depth treatment of high voltage techniques should make the book particularly useful to designers and operators of high voltage equipment and utility engineers.

The authors gratefully acknowledge Dr. M. M. Abdullah's permission to reproduce some material from the book *High Voltage Engineering*, Pergamon Press, 1970.

E. KUFFEL, W. S. ZAENGL
March 1984

Chapter 1

INTRODUCTION

1.1 GENERATION AND TRANSMISSION OF ELECTRIC ENERGY

The potential benefits of electrical energy supplied to a number of consumers from a common generating system were recognized shortly after the development of the "dynamo", commonly known as the generator.

The first public power station was put into service in 1882 in London (Holborn). Soon a number of other public supplies for electricity followed in other developed countries. The early systems produced direct current at low voltage, but their service was limited to highly localized areas and were used mainly for electric lighting. The limitations of d.c. transmission at low voltage became readily apparent. By 1890 the art in the development of an a.c. generator and transformer had been perfected to the point when a.c. supply was becoming common, displacing the earlier d.c. system. The first major a.c. power station was commissioned in 1890 at Deptford, supplying power to central London over a distance of 28 miles at 10,000 V. From the earliest "electricity" days it was realized that to make full use of economic generation the transmission network must be tailored to production with increased interconnection for pooling of generation in an integrated system. In addition, the potential development of hydro-electric power and the need to carry that power over long distances to the centres of consumption were recognized.

Power transfer for large systems, whether in the context of interconnection of large systems or bulk transfers, led engineers invariably to think in terms of high system voltages. Figure 1.1 lists some of the major a.c. transmission systems in chronological order of their installations, with tentative projections to the end of this century.

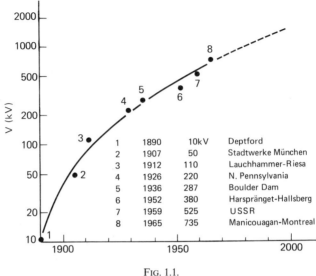

1	1890	10kV	Deptford
2	1907	50	Stadtwerke München
3	1912	110	Lauchhammer-Riesa
4	1926	220	N. Pennsylvania
5	1936	287	Boulder Dam
6	1952	380	Harspränget-Hallsberg
7	1959	525	USSR
8	1965	735	Manicouagan-Montreal

FIG. 1.1.

The electric power (P) transmitted on an overhead a.c. line increases approximately with the surge impedance loading or the square of the system's operating voltage. Thus for a transmission line of surge impedance Z_L ($\simeq 250\ \Omega$) at an operating voltage V, the power transfer capability is approximately $P = V^2/Z_L$, which for an overhead a.c. system leads to the following results:

V (kV)	400	700	1000	1200	1500
P (MW)	640	2000	4000	5800	9000

The rapidly increasing transmission voltage level in recent decades is a result of the growing demand for electrical energy, coupled with the development of large hydroelectric power stations at sites far remote from centres of industrial activity and the need to transmit the energy over long distances to the centres.

Although the bulk of the world's electric transmission is carried on a.c. systems, recent progress in high-voltage direct current (HVDC) technology has enabled the development of large-scale d.c. transmission by overhead lines and submarine cables which have become economically attractive in long-distance transmission of large bulk of power. HVDC permits a higher power density on a given right-of-way than a.c. transmission and thus helps

TABLE 1.1
Estimated Optimum Voltages and Currents for HVDC Transmissions

Bipolar power capability (MW)	Line voltage (kV)	Direct current (A)
500–1000	±400	600–1250
1000–2500	±500	1000–2500
2500–4000	±600	2100–3300
4000–6000	±700	2150–4300
6000–9000	±800	2800–5600

the electric utilities in meeting the environmental requirements imposed on the transmission of electric power.

Table 1.1 summarizes the estimated optimum voltages for HVDC overhead transmission. Some of the major HVDC schemes in service or under construction are listed in Fig. 1.2 in order of their in-service dates. At present the prevailing views are that voltages in excess of ±800 kV are unlikely to be required for HVDC transmissions.

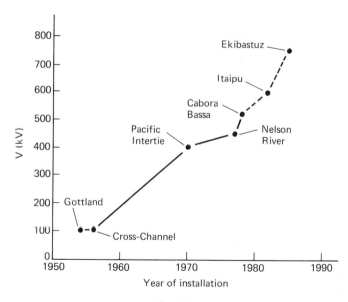

Fig. 1.2.

1.2 VOLTAGE STRESSES

Normal operating voltage does not severely stress the power system's insulation and only in special circumstances, for example under pollution conditions, may operating voltages cause problems to external insulation. Nevertheless, the operating voltage determines the dimensions of the insulation which forms part of the generation, transmission and distribution equipment. The voltage stresses on power systems arise from various overvoltages. These may be of external or internal origin. External overvoltages are associated with lightning discharges and are not dependent on the voltage of the system. As a result, the importance of stresses produced by lightning decreases as the operating voltage increases. Internal overvoltages are generated by changes in the operating conditions of the system such as switching operations, a fault on the system or fluctuations in the load or generations.

Their magnitude depends on the rated voltage, the instance at which a change in operating conditions occurs, the complexity of the system and so on. Since the change in the system's conditions is usually associated with switching operations, these overvoltages are generally referred to as switching overvoltages.

In designing the system's insulation the two areas of specific importance are:

(i) determination of the voltage stresses which the insulation must withstand, and

(ii) determination of the response of the insulation when subjected to these voltage stresses.

The balance between the electric stresses on the insulation and the dielectric strength of this insulation falls within the framework of insulation coordination and will be discussed in Chapter 7.

1.3 TESTING VOLTAGES

Power systems equipment must withstand not only the rated voltage (V_m), which corresponds to the highest voltage of a particular system, but also overvoltages. Accordingly, it is necessary to test h.v. equipment during its development stage and prior to commissioning. The magnitude and type of test voltage varies with the rated voltage of a particular apparatus. The standard methods of measurement of high voltage and the basic techniques for application to all types of apparatus for alternating voltages, direct voltages, switching impulse voltages and lightning impulse voltages are laid down in the relevant national and international standards.

1.3.1 Testing with Power Frequency Voltages

To assess the ability of the apparatus's insulation withstand under the system's power frequency voltage the apparatus is subjected to the 1-min test under 50 Hz or 60 Hz depending upon the country. The test voltage is set at a level higher than the expected working voltage in order to be able to simulate the stresses likely to be encountered over the years of service. For indoor installations the equipment tests are carried out under dry conditions only. For outdoor equipment tests may be required under conditions of standard rain as prescribed in the appropriate standards.

1.3.2 Testing with Lightning Impulse Voltages

Lightning strokes terminating on transmission lines will induce steep rising voltages in the line and set up travelling waves along the line and may damage the system's insulation. The magnitude of these overvoltages may reach several thousand kilovolts, depending upon the insulation. Exhaustive measurements and long experience have shown that lightning over-voltages are characterized by short front duration, ranging from a fraction of a microsecond to several tens of microseconds and then slowly decreasing to zero. The standard impulse voltage has been accepted as an aperiodic impulse that reaches its peak value in 1.2 μsec and then decreases slowly (in about 50 μsec) to half its peak value. Full details of the waveshape of the standard impulse voltage together with the permitted tolerances are presented in Chapter 2, and the prescribed test procedures are discussed in Chapter 7.

In addition to testing equipment, impulse voltages are extensively used in research laboratories in the fundamental studies of electrical discharge mechanisms, notably when the time to breakdown is of interest.

1.3.3 Testing with Switching Impulses

Transient overvoltages accompanying sudden changes in the state of power systems, e.g. switching operations or faults, are known as switching impulse voltages. It has become generally recognized that switching impulse voltages are usually the dominant factor affecting the design of insulation in h.v. power systems for rated voltages of about 300 kV and above. Accordingly, the various international standards recommend that equipment designed for voltages above 300 kV be tested for switching impulses. Although the waveshape of switching overvoltages occurring in the system may vary widely, experience has shown that for flashover distances of practical interest the lowest withstand values are obtained with surges with front times between 100 and 300 μsec. Hence, the recommended switching surge voltage has been designated to have a front time of about 250 μsec and half-value time of 2500 μsec. Full details relating to generation, measurements and test procedures in testing with switching surge voltages will be found in Chapters 2, 3 and 7.

1.3.4 D.C. Voltages

In the past d.c. voltages have been chiefly used for purely scientific research work. Industrial applications were mainly limited to testing cables with relatively large capacitance, which take a very large current when tested with a.c. voltages, and in testing insulations in which internal discharges may lead to degradation of the insulation under testing conditions. In recent years, with the rapidly growing interest in h.v. d.c. transmission, an increasing number of industrial laboratories are being equipped with sources for producing d.c. high voltages. Because of the diversity in the application of d.c. high voltages, ranging from basic physics experiments to industrial applications, the requirements on the output voltage will vary accordingly. Detailed description of the various types of HVDC generators is given in Chapter 2.

Chapter 2

GENERATION OF HIGH VOLTAGES

A fundamental knowledge about generators and circuits which are in use for the generation of high voltages belongs to the background of work on h.v. technology.

Generally commercially available h.v. generators are applied in routine testing laboratories; they are used for testing equipment such as trans-formers, bushings, cables, capacitors, switchgear, etc. The tests should confirm the efficiency and reliability of the products and therefore the h.v. testing equipment is required to study the insulation behaviour under all conditions which the apparatus is likely to encounter. The amplitudes and types of the test voltages, which are always higher than the normal or rated voltages of the apparatus under test, are in general prescribed by national or international recommendations, and therefore there is not much freedom in the selection of the h.v. testing equipment. Quite often, however, routine testing laboratories are also used for the development of new products. Then even higher voltages might be necessary to determine the factor of safety over the prospective working conditions and to ensure that the working margin is neither too high nor too low. Most of the h.v. generator circuits can be changed to increase the output voltage levels, if the original circuit was properly designed. Therefore, even the selection of routine testing equipment should always consider a future extension of the testing capabilities.

The work carried out in research laboratories varies considerably from one establishment to another, and the type of equipment needed varies accordingly. As there are always some interactions between the h.v. generating circuits used and the test results, the layout of these circuits has to be done very carefully. The classes of tests may differ from the routine tests, and therefore specially designed circuits are often necessary for such laboratories. The knowledge about some fundamental circuits treated in this chapter will also support the development of new test circuits.

Finally, high voltages are used in many branches of natural sciences or other technical applications. The generating circuits are often the same or similar to those treated in the following sections. It is not the aim, however, of this introductory text to treat the broad variations of possible circuits, due to space limitation. Not taken into account are also the differing problems of electrical power generation and transmission with high voltages of a.c. or d.c., or the pure testing technique of h.v. equipment. Power generation and transmission problems are treated in many modern books, some of which are listed within the bibliography of a very recent report.[1]*

This chapter discusses the generation of the following main classes of voltages: direct voltages, alternating voltages, transient voltages.

2.1 DIRECT VOLTAGES

In h.v. technology direct voltages are mainly used for pure scientific research work and for testing equipment related to HVDC transmission systems. There is still a main application in tests on HVAC power cables of long length, as the large capacitance of those cables would take too large a current if tested with a.c. voltages (see, however, 2.2 Series resonant circuits). Though such d.c. tests on a.c. cables are more economical and convenient, the validity of this test suffers from the experimentally obtained stress distribution within the insulating material, which differs considerably from the normal working conditions where the cable is transmitting power at low-frequency alternating voltages.

High d.c. voltages are even more extensively used in physics (accelerators, electron microscopy, etc.), electromedical equipment (x-rays), industrial applications (precipitation and filtering of exhaust gases in thermal power stations and cement industry; electrostatic painting and powder coating, etc.), or communications electronics (TV; broadcasting stations). Therefore, the requirements on voltage shape, voltage level, current rating, short- or long-term stability for every HVDC generating system may differ strongly from each other. With the knowledge of the fundamental generating principles it will be possible, however, to select proper circuits for a special application.

---

* Superscript numbers are to References at the end of the chapter.

In IEC Publication 60-2[2] or IEEE Stand. 4-1978[3] the value of a direct test voltage is defined by its arithmetic mean value, which will be designated as $\bar{V}$. Therefore, this value may be derived from

$$\bar{V} = \frac{1}{T} \int_0^T V(t)\,dt, \qquad (2.1)$$

where T equals a certain period of time if the voltage $V(t)$ is not constant, but periodically oscillating with a frequency of $f = 1/T$. Test voltages as applied to test objects then deviate periodically from the mean value. This means that a ripple is present. The amplitude of the ripple, δV, is defined as half the difference between the maximum and minimum values, or

$$\delta V = 0.5\,(V_{max} - V_{min}). \qquad (2.2)$$

The ripple factor is the ratio of the ripple amplitude to the arithmetic mean value, or $\delta V/\bar{V}$. For test voltages this ripple factor should not exceed 5% unless otherwise specified by the appropriate apparatus standard or be necessary for fundamental investigations.

The voltages are generally obtained by means of rectifying circuits applied to a.c. voltages or by electrostatic generation. A treatment of the generation principles according to this subdivision is appropriate.

2.1.1 A.C. to D.C. Conversion

The rectification of alternating currents is the most efficient means of obtaining HVDC supplies. Though all circuits in use have been known for a long time, the cheap production and availability of manifold solid state rectifiers has facilitated the production and application of these circuits fundamentally. Today there is no longer a need to employ valves, hot cathode gas-filled valves, mercury pool or corona rectifiers, or even mechanical rectifiers within the circuits, for which the auxiliary systems for cathode heating, etc., have always aggravated the application. The state of the art of such circuits may be found in the work of Craggs and Meek,[4] which was written in 1954. Most of the rectifier diodes used now adopt the Si-type, and though the peak reverse voltage is limited to less than about 2500 V, rectifying diode units up to tenths and hundredths of a kV can be made by series connections if appropriate means are applied to provide equal voltage distribution during the non-conducting period. One may treat and simulate, therefore, a rectifier within the circuits—independently of the voltage levels—simply by the common symbol for a diode.

The theory of rectifier circuits for low voltages and high power output is discussed in many standard handbooks. Having the generation of high d.c. voltages in mind, we will restrict the treatment mainly to single-phase a.c. systems providing a high ratio of d.c. output to a.c. input voltage. As, however, the power or d.c. output is always limited by this ratio, and also very simple rectifier circuits are in use, we will treat only selected examples of the many available circuits.

Simple Rectifier Circuits

For a clear understanding of all a.c. to d.c. conversion circuits the *single-phase half-wave rectifier* with voltage smoothing is of basic interest (Fig. 2.1). If we neglect the leakage reactance of the transformer and the small internal impedance of the diodes during conduction—and this will be done throughout unless otherwise stated—the (storage) reservoir capacitor C is charged to the maximum voltage $+V_{max}$ of the a.c. voltage $V_\sim(t)$ of the h.t. transformer, if D conducts. This is the case as long as $V < V_\sim(t)$ for the polarity of D assumed. If $I = 0$, the output load being zero $(R_L = \infty)$, the d.c. voltage across C remains constant $(+V_{max})$, whereas $V_\sim(t)$ oscillates between $\pm V_{max}$. The diode D must be dimensioned, therefore, to withstand a peak reverse voltage of $2V_{max}$. This would also be the case if the h.t. transformer is grounded at the terminal b instead of terminal a. Such a circuit is known as voltage doubler due to Villard, for which the useful output voltage would be taken across D. This d.c. voltage, however, oscillates between zero and $+2V_{max}$ and is needed for the cascade circuit.

The output voltage V does not remain any more constant if the circuit is loaded. During one period, $T = 1/f$, of the a.c. voltage a charge Q is transferred to the load R, which is represented as

$$Q = \int_T i_L(t)\,dt = \frac{1}{R_L} \int_T V(t)\,dt = IT = \frac{I}{f}. \tag{2.3}$$

I is therefore the mean value of the d.c. output $i_L(t)$, and $V(t)$ the d.c. voltage which includes a ripple as shown in Fig. 2.1b. If we introduce the ripple factor δV from eqn. (2.2), we may easily see that $V(t)$ now varies between

$$V_{max} \geqslant V(t) \geqslant V_{min}; \quad V_{min} = V_{max} - 2(\delta V). \tag{2.4}$$

The charge Q is also supplied from the transformer within the short conduction time $t_c = \alpha T$ of the diode D during each cycle. Therefore, Q

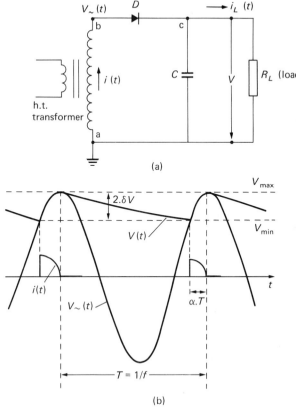

FIG. 2.1. Single-phase half-wave rectifier with reservoir capacitance C. (a) Circuit. (b) Voltages and currents with load R_L.

equals also to

$$Q = \int_{\alpha T} i(t)\, dt = \int_{T} i_L(t)\, dt. \tag{2.5}$$

As $\alpha \ll T$, the transformer current $i(t)$ is pulsed as shown idealized in Fig. 2.1b and is of much bigger amplitudes than the direct current $i_L \sim I$ The ripple δV could be calculated exactly for this circuit based upon the exponential decay of $V(t)$ during the discharge period $T(1-\alpha)$. As, however, for practical circuits the neglected voltage drops within transformer and rectifiers must be taken into account, and such calculations are found elsewhere,[3] we may assume that $\alpha = 0$. Then δV is easily found from the charge Q transferred to the load, and therefore

$$Q = 2\delta VC = IT; \quad \delta V = \frac{IT}{2C} = \frac{I}{2fC}. \tag{2.6}$$

This relation shows the interaction between the ripple, the load current and circuit parameter design values f and C. As, according to eqn. (2.4), the mean output voltage will also be influenced by δV, even with a constant a.c. voltage $V_\sim(t)$ and a lossless rectifier D, no load-independent output voltage can be reached. The product fC is therefore an important design factor.

For h.v. test circuits, a sudden voltage breakdown at the load ($R_L \rightarrow 0$) must always be taken into account. Whenever possible, the rectifiers should be able to carry either the excessive currents, which can be limited by fast, electronically controlled switching devices at the transformer input, or they can be protected by an additional resistance inserted in the h.t. circuit. The last method, however, increases the internal voltage drop.

Half-wave rectifier circuits have been built up to voltages in the megavolt range, in general by extending an existing h.v. testing transformer to a d.c. current supply. The largest unit has been presented by Prinz,[5] who used a 1.2-MV cascaded transformer and 60-mA selenium-type solid state rectifiers with an overall reverse voltage of 3.4 MV for the circuit. The voltage distribution of this rectifier, which is about 12 m in length, is controlled by sectionalized parallel capacitor units, which are small in capacitance value in comparison with the smoothing capacitor C (see Fig. 2.15). The size of such circuits, however, would be unnecessarily large for pure d.c. supplies.

The other disadvantage of the single-phase half-wave rectifier concerns the possible saturation of the h.t. transformer, if the amplitude of the direct current is comparable with the nominal alternating current of the transformer. The biphase half-wave rectifier shown in Fig. 2.2 overcomes this disadvantage, but it does not change the fundamental efficiency, considering that two h.t. windings of the transformer are now available. With reference to the frequency f during one cycle, now each of the diodes D_1 and D_2 is conducting for one half-cycle with a time delay of $T/2$. The ripple factor according to eqn. (2.6) is therefore halved. It should be mentioned that the real ripple will also be increased if both voltages $V_{1\sim}$ and $V_{2\sim}$ are not exactly equal. If $V_{2\max}$ would be smaller than $(V_{1\max} - 2\delta V)$ or $V_{\min}$, this h.v. winding would not charge the capacitance C. The same effect holds true for multiphase rectifiers, which are not treated here.

Thus single-phase full-wave circuits can only be used for h.v. applications

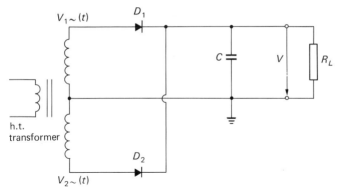

FIG. 2.2. Biphase half-wave rectifier circuit with smoothing condenser C.

if the h.t. winding of the transformer can be earthed, at its midpoint, and if the d.c. output is single-ended grounded. More commonly used are single-phase voltage doublers, a circuit of which is contained in the voltage multiplier of Fig. 2.5 (circuit D_1, D_2, C_1, C_2, T). Though in such a circuit grounding of the h.v. winding is also not possible, if asymmetrical d.c. voltages are produced, the potential of this winding is fixed. Therefore, there is no danger due to transients followed by voltage breakdowns.

Cascade Circuits

The demands from physicists for very high d.c. voltages forced the improvement of rectifying circuits quite early. It is obvious that every multiplier circuit in which transformers, rectifiers and capacitor units have only to withstand a fraction of the total output voltage will have great advantages. Today there are many standard cascade circuits available for the conversion of modest a.c. to high d.c. voltages. However, only some basic circuits will be treated, the last of which ("Engetron" or Deltatron) is quite new.

In 1920 Greinacher, a young physicist, published a circuit[6] which was improved in 1932 by Cockcroft and Walton to produce high-velocity positive ions.[7] The interesting and even exciting development stages of those circuits have been discussed by Craggs and Meek.[4] To demonstrate the principle only a n-stage single-phase cascade circuit of the "Cockcroft–Walton type", shown in Fig. 2.3, will be presented.

HV output open-circuited: $I = 0$. The portion $0 - n' - V(t)$ is a half-wave rectifier circuit in which C'_n charges up to a voltage of $+ V_{max}$ if $V(t)$ has

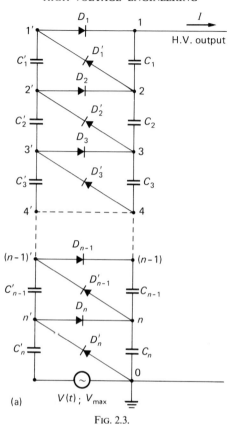

Fig. 2.3.

reached the lowest potential, $-V_{max}$. If C_n is still uncharged, the rectifier D_n conducts as soon as $V(t)$ increases. As the potential of point n' swings up to $+2V_{max}$ during the period $T = 1/f$, point n attains further on a steady potential of $+2V_{max}$, if $V(t)$ has reached the highest potential of $+V_{max}$. The part $n'-n-0$ is therefore a half-wave rectifier, in which the voltage across D'_n can be assumed to be the a.c. voltage source. The current through D_n that charged the capacitor C_n was not provided by D'_n, but from $V(t)$ and C'_n. We assumed, therefore, that C'_n was not discharged, which is not correct. As we will take this into consideration for the loaded circuit, we can also assume that the voltage across C_n is not reduced if the potential n' oscillates between zero and $+2V_{max}$. If the potential of n', however, is zero, the capacitor C'_{n-1} is also charged to the potential of n, i.e. to a voltage of $+2V_{max}$. The next

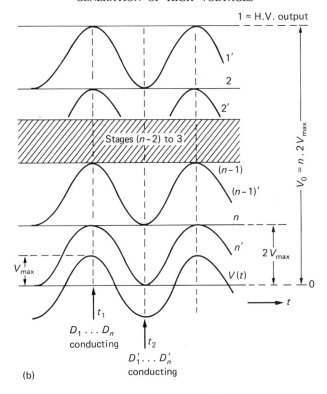

Fig. 2.3. (a) Cascade circuit according to Cockcroft–Walton or Greinacher. (b) Waveform of potentials at the nodes of cascade circuit, no load.

voltage oscillation of $V(t)$ from $-V_{max}$ to $+V_{max}$ will force the diode D_{n-1} to conduct, so that also C_{n-1} will be charged to a voltage of $+2V_{max}$.

In Fig. 2.3(b) the steady-state potentials at all nodes of the circuit are sketched for the circuit for zero load conditions. From this it can be seen that

the potentials at the nodes $1', 2' \ldots n'$ are oscillating due to the voltage oscillation of $V(t)$;

the potentials at the nodes $1, 2 \ldots n$ remain constant with reference to ground potential;

the voltages across all capacitors are of d.c. type, the magnitude of which is $2V_{max}$ across each capacitor stage, except the capacitor C'_n which is stressed with V_{max} only;

every rectifier $D_1, D_1' \dots D_n, D_n'$ is stressed with $2V_{max}$ or twice a.c. peak voltage; and

the h.v. output will reach a maximum voltage of $2nV_{max}$.

Therefore, the use of several stages arranged in this manner enables very high voltages to be obtained. The equal stress of the elements used is very convenient and promotes a modular design of such generators. The number of stages, however, is strongly limited by the current due to any load. This can only be demonstrated by calculations, even if ideal rectifiers, capacitors and an ideal a.c. voltage source are assumed.

Finally it should be mentioned that the lowest stage n of the cascade circuit (Fig. 2.3a) is the Cockcroft–Walton voltage doubler. The a.c. voltage source $V(t)$ is usually provided by a h.t. transformer, if every stage is built for high voltages, typically up to about 300 kV. This source is always symmetrically loaded, as current is withdrawn during each half-cycle (t_1 and t_2 in Fig. 2.3b). The voltage waveform does not have to be sinusoidal: every symmetrical waveform with equal positive and negative peak values will give good performance. As often high-frequency input voltages are used, this hint is worth remembering.

H.V. output loaded: $I > 0$. If the generator supplies any load current I, the output voltage will never reach the value $2nV_{max}$ shown in Fig. 2.3. There will also be a ripple on the voltage, and therefore we have to deal with two quantities: the voltage drop ΔV_0 and the peak-to-peak ripple $2\delta V$. The sketch in Fig. 2.4 shows the shape of the output voltage and the definitions of ΔV_0 and $2\delta V$. The time instants t_1 and t_2 are in agreement with Fig. 2.3b. Therefore, the peak value of V_0 is reached at t_1, if $V(t)$ was at $+ V_{max}$ and the rectifiers $D_1 \dots D_n$ just stopped to transfer charge to the "smoothing column" $C_1 \dots C_n$. After that the current I continuously discharges the column, interrupted by a sudden voltage drop shortly before t_2: this sudden voltage drop is due to the conduction period of the diodes $D_1' \dots D_n'$, during which the "oscillating column" $C_n' \dots C_1'$ is charged.

Let now a charge q be transferred to the load per cycle, which is obviously $q = I/f = IT$. This charge comes from the smoothing column, the series connection of $C_1 \dots C_n$. If no charge would be transferred during T from this stack via $D_1' \dots D_n'$ to the oscillating column, the peak-to-peak ripple would merely be

$$2\delta V = IT \sum_{i=1}^{n} (1/C_i).$$

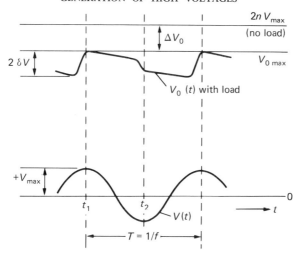

FIG. 2.4. Loaded cascade circuit, definitions of voltage drop ΔV_0 and ripple δV.

As, however, just before the time instant t_2 every diode $D'_1 \ldots D'_n$ transfers the same charge q, and each of these charges discharges all capacitors on the smoothing column between the relevant node and ground potential, the total ripple will be

$$\delta V = \frac{I}{2f}\left(\frac{1}{C_1} + \frac{2}{C_2} + \frac{3}{C_3} + \ldots \frac{n}{C_n}\right). \tag{2.7}$$

Thus in a cascade multiplier the lowest capacitors are responsible for most ripple and it would be desirable to increase the capacitance in the lower stages. This is, however, very inconvenient for HV cascades, as a voltage breakdown at the load would completely overstress the smaller capacitors within the column. Therefore, equal capacitance values are usually provided, and with $C = C_1 = C_2 = \ldots C_n$, eqn. (2.7) is

$$\delta V = \frac{I}{fC} \cdot \frac{n(n+1)}{4}. \tag{2.7a}$$

To calculate the total voltage drop ΔV_0, we first will consider the stage n. Though the capacitor C'_n at time t_1 will be charged up to the full voltage V_{max}, if ideal rectifiers and no voltage drop within the AC-source are assumed, the capacitor C_n will only be charged to a voltage

$$(V_{C_n})_{\max} = 2V_{\max} - \frac{nq}{C'_n} = 2V_{\max} - \Delta V_n$$

as C_n has lost a total charge of (nq) during a full cycle before and C'_n has to replace this lost charge. At time instant t_2, C_n transfers the charge q to C'_{n-1}, equal amounts q to $C'_{n-2}, \dots C'_2, C'_1$, and q to the load during T. Therefore C'_{n-1} can only be charged up to a maximum voltage of

$$(V_{C_{n-1}})_{\max} = \left(2V_{\max} - \frac{nq}{C'_n}\right) - \frac{nq}{C_n}$$

$$= (V_{C_n})_{\max} - \frac{nq}{C_n}.$$

As the capacitor C_{n-1} will be charged up to this voltage minus $(n-1)q/C'_{n-1}$, etc., one can easily form the general rules for the total voltage drop at the smoothing stack $C_1 \dots C_n$.

If all the capacitors within the cascade circuit are equal or

$$C_1 = C'_1 = C_2 = C'_2 = \dots C_n = C'_n = C,$$

then the voltage drops across the individual stages are

$$\Delta V_n = (q/C)\,n;$$

$$\Delta V_{n-1} = (q/C)[2n + (n-1)];$$

$$\vdots$$

$$\Delta V_1 = (q/C)[2n + 2(n-1) + 2(n-2) + \dots + 2.2 + 1]. \qquad (2.8)$$

By summation, and with $q = I/f$, we find

$$\Delta V_0 = \frac{I}{fC}\left(\frac{2n^3}{3} + \frac{n^2}{2} - \frac{n}{6}\right). \qquad (2.9)$$

Thus the lowest capacitors are most responsible for the total ΔV_0 as is the case of the ripple, eqn. (2.7). However, only a doubling of C'_n is convenient, since this capacitor has to withstand only half the voltage of the other condensers; namely $V_{\max}$. Therefore, ΔV_n decreases by an amount of $0.5\,nq/C$, which reduces ΔV of every stage by the same amount, thus n times. Hence,

$$\Delta V_0 = \frac{I}{fC}\left(\frac{2n^3}{3} - \frac{n}{6}\right). \qquad (2.10)$$

For this case and $n \geqslant 4$ we may neglect the linear term and therefore we may approximate the maximum output voltage by

$$V_{0_{max}} \simeq 2nV_{max} - \frac{I}{fC}\frac{2n^3}{3}. \tag{2.11}$$

For a given number of stages, this maximum voltage or also the mean value $V_0 = (V_{0_{max}} - \delta V)$ will decrease linearly with the load current I at constant frequency, which is obvious. For a given load, however, V_0 may rise initially with the number of stages n, but reaches an optimum value and even decays if n is too large. This—with respect to constant values of I, V_{max}, f and C—highest value can be reached with the "optimum" number of stages, obtained by differentiating eqn. (2.11) with respect to n. Then

$$n_{opt} = \sqrt{\frac{V_{max}fC}{I}}. \tag{2.12}$$

For a generator with $V_{max} = 100\,\text{kV}$, $f = 500\,\text{Hz}$, $C = 7\mu\text{F}$ and $I = 500\,\text{mA}$, $n_{opt} = 10$. It is, however, not desirable to use the optimum number of stages, as then $V_{0_{max}}$ is reduced to 2/3 of its maximum value $(2nV_{max})$. Also the voltage variations for varying loads will increase too much.

The application of this circuit for high power output, which means high products of IV_0, is also limited by eqns. (2.9) and (2.11), in which again the large influence of the product fC can be seen. An increase of supply frequency is in general more economical than increase of the capacitance values; small values of C provide also a d.c. supply with limited stored energy, which might be an essential design factor, i.e. for breakdown investigations on insulating materials. A further advantage is related to regulation systems, which are always necessary if a stable and constant output voltage V_0 is required. Regulation can be achieved by a measurement of V_0 with suitable voltage dividers (see Chapter 3, section 3.6.4) within a closed loop regulation system, which controls the a.c. supply voltage $V(t)$. For fast response, high supply frequencies and small stored energy are prerequisites.

For tall constructions in the MV range, the circuit of Fig. 2.3a does not comprise all circuit elements which are influencing the real working conditions. There are not only the impedances of the diodes and the supply transformer which have to be taken into consideration; stray capacitances between the two capacitator columns and capacitor elements to ground form a much more complex network. There are also improved circuits available by adding one or two additional "oscillating" columns which charge the same smoothing stack. This additional column can be fed by phase-shifted a.c. voltages, by which the ripple and voltage drop can further be reduced. For more details see reference 8.

Cascade generators of Cockcroft–Walton type are used and manu-factured today world-wide. More information about possible constructions can be found in the literature[9,10] or in company brochures. The d.c. voltages produced with this circuit may range from some 10 kV up to more than 2 MV, with current ratings from some 10 μA up to some 100 mA. Supply frequencies of 50/60 Hz are heavily limiting the efficiency, and therefore higher frequencies up to about 1000 Hz (produced by single-phase alternators) or some 10 kHz (produced by electronic circuits) are dominating.

Voltage Multiplier with Cascaded Transformers

The multiple charge transfer within the cascade circuit of the Cockcroft–Walton type demonstrated the limitations in d.c. power output. This disadvantage can be reduced if single- or full-wave rectifier systems, each having its own a.c. power source, are connected in series at the d.c. output

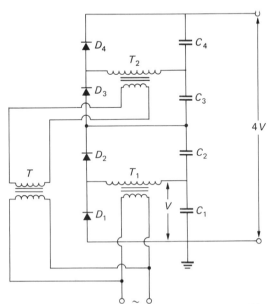

FIG. 2.5. Voltage multiplier according to Allibone et al.[11]

only. Then the a.c. potentials remain more or less at a.c. potentials. Though there are many modifications possible, the principle that will be demonstrated here is based upon a practical arrangement presented by Allibone *et al.*[11] and an improved circuit, which can be directly derived from this.

Allibone's circuit is illustrated in Fig. 2.5. Every stage comprises one h.v. transformer which feeds two half-wave rectifiers according to Fig. 2.1. As the storage capacitors of these half-wave rectifiers are series connected, even the h.v. winding of T_1 cannot be grounded. This means that the main insulation between the primary and the secondary winding of T_1 has to be insulated for a d.c. voltage of magnitude V_{max}, the peak voltage of T_1. The same is necessary for T_2, but here the h.v. winding is at a potential of $3V_{max}$. As it would be too difficult to provide the whole main insulation within this transformer, an isolating transformer T supplies T_2. The cascading of every new stage would need additional isolating transformers, which makes the

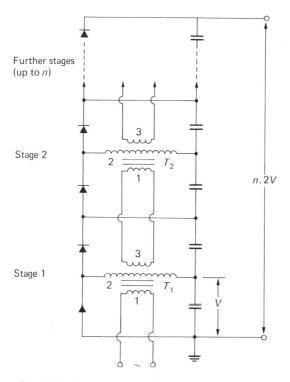

Fig. 2.6. D.C. cascade circuit with cascaded transformers.

use of more than two stages uneconomical. There is, however, an essential improvement possible, if the different stages are excited by specially designed cascaded transformers.[12]

Such an improved circuit is shown in Fig. 2.6. Every transformer per stage consists of a l.v. primary (1), h.v. secondary (2), and l.v. tertiary winding (3), the last of which excites the primary winding of the next upper stage. The necessary d.c. voltage insulation within each transformer T_1, T_2, etc., can be subdivided within the transformers. Though there are limitations as far as the number of stages is concerned, as the lower transformers have to supply the energy for the upper ones, this circuit, excited with power frequency, provides an economical d.c. power supply for h.v. testing purposes with moderate ripple factors and high power capabilities.

The "Engetron" Circuit (Deltatron)

A very sophisticated cascade transformer HVDC generator circuit was recently described by Enge in a US Patent.[13] Though such generators might be limited in the power output up to about 1 MV and some milliamperes, the very small ripple factors, high stability, fast regulation and small stored energies are essential capabilities of this circuit.

The circuit is shown in Fig. 2.7. It consists primarily of a series connection of transformers, which do not have any iron core. These transformers are coupled by series capacitors C_s which compensate for the fixed high supply frequency most of the stray inductance of the transformers. In addition to this, to every primary and secondary winding a capacitor C_p is connected in parallel, which provides an overcompensation of the magnetizing currents. The whole chain of cascaded transformers is loaded by a terminating resistor; thus the network acts similarly to a terminated line along which the a.c. voltage remains nearly constant and has a phase shift between input (high-frequency power supply) and output (termination). The transformers, therefore, are not used to increase the a.c. voltage.

It is now possible to connect to every stage indicated a usual Cockcroft–Walton cascade circuit, with only a small input voltage (some kV), producing, however, output voltages of some 10 kV per stage. The storage columns of these Cockcroft–Walton cascades are then directly series connected, providing the high d.c. output voltage for the whole cascade transformer HVDC generator unit. Typically up to about 25 stages can be used, every stage being modular constructed as indicated in Fig. 2.7 and

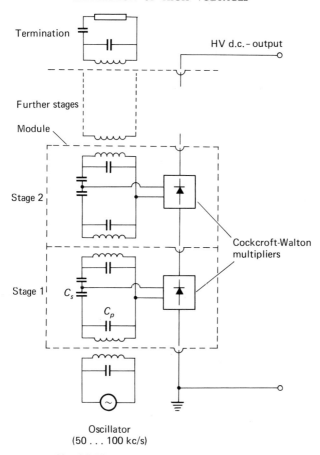

Fig. 2.7. The "Engetron" or Deltatron principle.

shown in Fig. 2.8a. As these modules are quite small, they can be stacked in a cylindrical unit which is then insulated by SF_6. A whole generator (Fig. 2.8b) is of small size and weight.

Not shown in Fig. 2.7 is the voltage regulation system, which is controlled by a parallel mixed R-C voltage divider and a high-frequency oscillator, whose frequency ranges from 50 to 100 kHz. As for these high frequencies the capacitors within the Cockcroft–Walton circuits can be very small, and the energy stored is accordingly low. Regulation due to load variations or power voltage supply variations is very fast (response time

HV

typically about 1 msec). The small ripple factor is not only provided by the storage capacitor, but also by the phase-shifted input voltages of the cascade circuits. Amongst the disadvantages is the procedure to change polarity, as all modules have to be reversed.

Summary and Concluding Remarks to 2.1.1

It has been shown that all a.c. to d.c. voltage conversion systems could be classed between the circuits of Figs. 2.1 and 2.3, if single-phase a.c. voltages are converted into d.c. voltages. A high d.c. to a.c. voltage ratio can only be gained with a high product of a.c. frequency and energy stored in the smoothing capacitors, as they have to store electrical energy within each cycle, during which the a.c. power is oscillating. If, therefore, the d.c. output should be very stable and continuous, a high product fC is necessary. A reduction of stored energy is possible if the a.c. power is not only provided at ground potential, this means if a.c. power is injected into the circuits at differential potential levels (for instance, Fig. 2.5). The savings, therefore, can

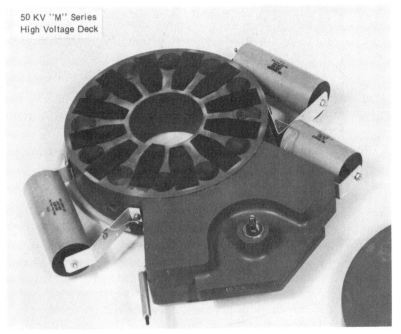

50 KV "M" Series
High Voltage Deck

(a)   Fig. 2.8.

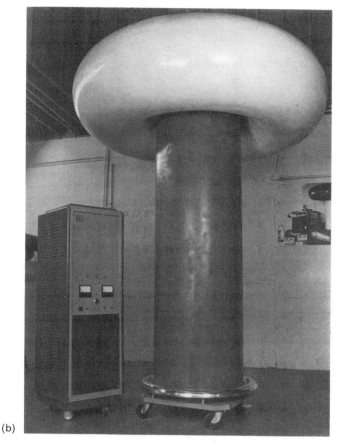

(b)

FIG. 2.8. (a) 50-kV module of an "Engetron" circuit for 2 mA. (b) Whole "Engetron" unit, 1 MV, 2 mA.

be made either on the a.c. or d.c. side. The large variety of possible circuits and technical expenditure is always strongly related to the "quality" of the d.c. power needed; this means the stability and the ripple of the output voltage.

2.1.2 Electrostatic Generators

Electrostatic generators convert mechanical energy directly into electrical energy. In contrast to electromagnetic energy conversion, however, electrical charges are moved in this generator against the force of electrical fields, thus gaining higher potential energies and consuming mechanical energy. All historical electrostatic machines, such as the Kelvin water dropper or the Wimshurst machine, are therefore forerunners of modern generators of this type. A review of earlier machines may be found in reference 14.

Besides successful developments of "dust generators" presented by Pauthenier et al.,[15] the real breakthrough in the generation of high and ultra-high d.c. voltages is linked with Van de Graaff, who in 1931 succeeded with the development of electrostatic belt-driven generators.[16] These generators are in common use today in nuclear physics research laboratories. Figure 2.9 demonstrates the principle of operation, which is described in more detail in reference 4. Charge is sprayed onto an insulating moving belt by means of corona discharge points (or direct contact) which are at some 10 kV from earth potential. The belt, the width of which may vary widely (some cm up to meters), is driven at about 15–30 m/sec by means of a motor and the charge is conveyed to the upper end where it is removed from the belt by discharging points connected to the inside of an

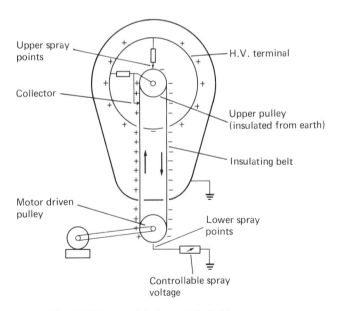

FIG. 2.9. Diagram of electrostatic belt-driven generator.

insulated metal electrode through which the belt passes. The entire equipment is usually enclosed in an earthed metal tank filled with insulating compressed gases of good performance such as air, H_2, mixtures of N_2–CO_2, Freon 12 (CCl_2F_2) or SF_6. For simple applications the metal tank can be omitted, so that the insulation is provided by atmospheric air only.

The potential of the h.v. terminal at any instant is $V = Q/C$ above earth, where Q is the charge stored and C is the capacitance of the h.v. electrode to ground. The potential of the terminal rises at a rate given by $dV/dt = I/C$, where

$$I = \hat{S}bv \qquad (2.13)$$

is the net charging current to the terminal. In this equation, $\hat{S}$ is the charge density at the belt in coulombs/m², b its width in m, and v the belt speed in m/sec. In practice, dV/dt may reach a value of 1 MV/sec and it appears that the final potential of the h.v. electrode would be infinite in the absence of any mechanism of charge loss. Equilibrium is in practice established at a potential such that the charging current equals the discharge current which includes load currents—also due to voltage dividers, leakage currents and corona losses, if present.

While the h.v. terminal electrode can easily be shaped in such a way that local discharges are eliminated from its surface, the field distribution between this electrode and earth along the fast moving belt is of greatest importance. The belt, therefore, is placed within properly shaped field grading rings, the grading of which is provided by resistors and sometimes additional corona discharge elements.

The lower spray unit, shown in Fig. 2.9, may consist of a number of needles connected to the controllable d.c. source so that the discharge between the points and the belt is maintained. The collector needle system is placed near the point where the belt enters the h.v. terminal.

A self-inducing arrangement is commonly used for spraying on the down-going belt charges of polarity opposite to that of the h.v. terminal. The rate of charging of the terminal, for a given speed of the belt, is therefore doubled. To obtain a self-charging system, the upper pulley is connected to the collector needle and is therefore maintained at a potential higher than that of the h.v. terminal. The device includes another system of points (shown as upper spray points in Fig. 2.9) which is connected to the inside of the h.v. terminal and is directed towards the pulley at the position shown. As the pulley is at a higher positive potential, the negative charges of the corona at the upper spray points are collected by the belt. This neutralizes any remaining positive charges on the belt and leaves any excess negative charges which travel down with it and are neutralized at the lower spray points.

For a rough estimation of the current I which can be provided by such generators, we may assume a homogeneous electrical field E normal to the belt running between the lower spray points and the grounded lower pulley. As $E = D/\varepsilon_0 = \hat{S}/\varepsilon_0$, D being the flux density, ε_0 the permittivity and $\hat{S}$ the charge density according to eqn. (2.13) deposited at the belt, with $\varepsilon_0 = 0.885 \times 10^{-11}$ As/Vm, the charge density cannot be larger than about 2.7×10^{-5} As/m^2 if $E = 30$ kV/cm. For a typical case the belt speed might be $v = 20$ m/sec and its width $b = 1$ m. The charging current according to eqn. (2.13) is then $I \simeq 540$ μA. Though with sandwiched belts[3] the output current might be increased as well as with self-inducing arrangements mentioned above, the actual short-circuit currents are limited to not more than a few mA with the biggest generators.

The main advantage of belt-driven electrostatic generators are the high d.c. voltages which easily can be reached, the lack of any fundamental ripple, and the precision and flexibility, though any stability of the voltage can only be achieved by suitable stabilizing devices. Then voltage fluctuations and voltage stability may be in the order down to 10^{-5}.

The shortcomings of these generators are the limited current output, as mentioned above, the limitations in belt velocity and its tendency for vibrations, which aggravates an accurate grading of the electrical fields, and the maintenance necessary due to the mechanically stressed parts.

The largest generator of this type was recently set into operation at Oak Ridge National Laboratory.[17] A view of this tandem-type heavy ion accelerator is shown in Fig. 2.10. This generator operates with 25 MV, and was tested up to internal flashovers with about 31 MV.

For h.v. testing purposes only a limited amount of generators are in use due to the limited current output. A very interesting construction, however, comprising the Van de Graaff generator as well as a coaxial test arrangement for testing of gases, is used at MIT[18] by Cooke. This generator, with an output of about 4 MV, may be controlled to provide even very low frequency a.c. voltages.

The disadvantages of the belt-driven generators led Felici to develop electrostatic machines with insulating cylindrical rotor which can sustain perfectly stable movement even at high speeds. The schematic diagram of such a machine[19] is shown in Fig. 2.11. To ensure a constant narrow air gap, the stator is also made in the form of a cylinder. If the stator is a perfect

FIG. 2.10. 25-MV electrostatic tandem accelerator (Oak Ridge National Laboratory).

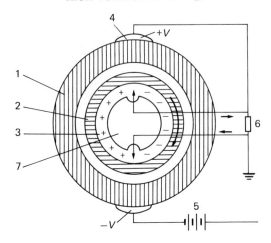

FIG. 2.11. Diagrammatic cross-section of Felici generator. (1) Cylindrical stator (resistivity 10^{11} ohm-cm). (2) Insulating rotor. (3) Ionizer. (4) Contact metallic segments. (5) Auxiliary gen. (6) Load. (7) Stationary insulating core ($-V = 30$ kV; $+V = 200$ kV).

insulator, ions are deposited on its surface which tend to weaken the field. In order to avoid such ion screening, a slight conductivity has to be provided for the stator and resistivities in the range of 10^{11}–10^{13} Ω/cm have been found satisfactory.

The overall efficiency of the machine is higher than 90% and the life expectancies are only limited by mechanical wearing of the bearings, provided the charge density on the rotor surface is kept within limits which depend upon the insulating material employed. Araldite cylinders have a practically unlimited life if the density remains sufficiently low. Unlike the rectifier circuit, the cylindrical generator delivers a smooth and continuous current without any ripple.

Sames of France have built two-pole generators of the Felici type. They give an output of 600 kV at 4 mA and are suitable for use with particle accelerator, electrostatic paint spray equipment, electrostatic precipitator, X-ray purposes and testing h.v. cables.

A cross-sectional view of the generator is shown in Fig. 2.12. The distinctive features include a cylindrical pressure vessel enclosing the generator, the rotor of which is driven at 3000 rpm by means of an induction motor. Ions from an exciting source are sprayed on to the rotor at the charging poles and are transported to the output poles with a consequent rise of potential. The transfer of charge takes place by means of thin blades

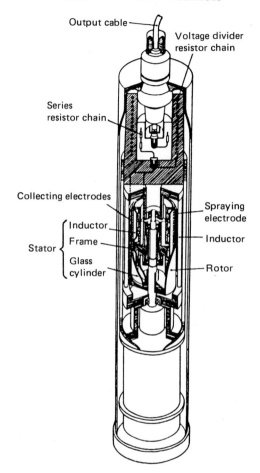

Output cable

Voltage divider
resistor chain

Series
resistor chain

Collecting electrodes

Spraying
electrode

Inductor

Inductor

Stator { Frame

Glass
cylinder

Rotor

FIG. 2.12. Sames electrostatic generator.

placed a short distance from the rotor, and in the absence of any rubbing contact the efficiency of the machine is about 90%.

The equipment is safe because of the fact that there is no stored energy in transformers or smoothing coils and capacitors. The characteristics of the 600-kV generator are such that the fluctuation in the voltage is less than 10^{-4} and the voltage drop at full load current of 4 mA is only 500 V. For a 5% variation in the main voltage, the generator voltage remains within 10^{-5}.

The main applications of these "rotating barrel" generators are in physics as well as in different areas of industrial applications and also h.v. testing. The maximum voltages are limited to less than 750 kV.

Finally, another type of electrostatic generator will only be mentioned. The vacuum-insulated "varying capacitance machine", first discussed in detail by Trump[20] and recently again investigated by Philp,[21] would provide high voltage in the range up to about 1 MV and/or high power in the range of megawatts. The high efficiency, however, could only be reached by high field gradients within the generator, which up to now can only be obtained theoretically by assuming the possible high E values in vacuum. It is, however, doubtful whether the stresses necessary can be reached within the large electrode areas present in such generators, and therefore only a reference to this type of generator might be useful.

2.2 ALTERNATING VOLTAGES

As electric power transmission with high a.c. voltages predominates in our transmission and distribution systems, the most common form of testing h.v. apparatus is related to high a.c. voltages. It is obvious then that also most research work in electrical insulation systems has to be carried out with this type of voltage.

In every laboratory HVAC supplies are therefore in common use. As far as the voltage levels are concerned, these may range from some 10 kV r.m.s. only up to more than 2 MV r.m.s. today, as the development of transmission voltages up to about 1200 kV has proceeded for many years. For routine testing, the voltage levels for power-frequency testing are always related to the highest r.m.s. phase-to-phase voltage V_m of power transmission systems (see IEC Standard, Publication 71-1). This "rated power-frequency short duration withstand voltage" V_t is different for different apparatus used within the transmission systems and also dependent upon the type of insulation coordination applied (see Chapter 7). For $V_m < 300$ kV, the ratio V_t/V_m is up to about 1.9 and may decrease with higher values of V_m. If, nevertheless, higher nominal voltages for the a.c. testing supplies are foreseen, the necessity for the determination of safety factors are most responsible for this fact.

In general, all a.c. voltage tests are made at the working frequency of the test objects. Typical exceptions are related to the testing of iron-cored windings, i.e. potential transformers, or fundamental studies on insulating materials. For iron-cored windings the frequency has to be raised to avoid saturation of the core. Depending upon the type of testing equipment used, the methods for the generation of variable-frequency voltages might be expensive.

A fundamental design factor for all a.c. testing supplies is an adequate control system for a continuous regulation of the high output voltages. In general, this will be performed by a control of the primary or l.v. input of the voltage step-up systems. It is not the aim of this chapter to deal with the details of these systems; some hints related to the different methods discussed will be sufficient.

Though power transmission systems are mostly of three-phase type, the testing voltages are usually single-phase voltages to ground. The wave-shapes must be nearly pure sinusoidal with both half-cycles closely alike, and according to the recommendations[2,3] the ratio of peak-to-r.m.s. values should be equal to $\sqrt{2}$ within $\pm 5\%$. The r.m.s. value is for a cycle of T

$$V_{(r.m.s.)} = \sqrt{\frac{1}{T} \int_0^T V^2(t)\, dt}.$$

The nominal value of the test voltage, however, is in general defined by its peak value divided by $\sqrt{2}$, i.e. $V_{max}/\sqrt{2}$. The reason for this definition can be found in the physics of breakdown phenomena in most of the insulating materials, with the breakdown mainly following the peak voltages or field strength.

Testing of h.v. apparatus or h.v. insulation always involves an application of high voltages to capacitive loads with low or very low power dissipation only. In general, power dissipation can be completely neglected if the nominal power output of the supply is determined. If C_t is the capacitance of the equipment or sample under test, and V_n the nominal r.m.s. voltage of the h.v. testing supply, the nominal KVA rating P_n may be calculated from the design formula

$$P_n = kV_n^2 \omega C_t \tag{2.14}$$

in which the factor $k \geqslant 1$ accounts for additional capacitances within the whole test circuit and some safety factor. Examples for additional capacitances are h.v. electrodes and connections between test object and voltage source, which might have large diameters and dimensions to avoid heavy discharges or even partial discharges, or measurement devices as capacitor voltage dividers or sphere gaps frequently incorporated within the test circuit. This safety factor k might range from only about 2 for very high voltages of $\geqslant 1$ MV, and may increase to higher values for lower nominal voltages, as overdimensioning is economically possible. The capacitance of test equipment C_t may change considerably, depending upon the type of equipment. Typical values are:

Simple post or suspension insulators	some 10 pF
Bushings, simple and graded	~ 100–1000 pF
Potential transformers	~ 200–500 pF
Power transformers	
< 1000 kVA	~ 1000 pF
> 1000 kVA	~ 1000–10,000 pF
H.V. power cables:	
Oil-paper impregnated	~ 250–300 pF/m
Gaseous insulated	~ 60 pF/m
Metal clad substation, SF_6 insulated	~ 1000–$> 10,000$ pF

One may calculate the nominal currents $I_n = P_n/V_n$ from eqn. (2.14) for different test voltages, different C_t values as shown above, and proper safety factors k. From such estimations it may be seen that these currents may range from some 10 mA for testing voltages of 100 kV only, up to a few amperes in the megavolt range. Though these currents are not high and the nominal power is moderate, many efforts are necessary to keep the test equipment as small as possible, as the space is limited and expensive within any h.v. laboratory. Frequently the equipment will be used also for field testing. Then the portability and transportation calls for lightweight equipment. Some facilitations are possible by the fact that most of the test voltages are only of short duration. The nominal ratings are, therefore, often related to short time periods of 15 min. Due to the relatively large time constants for the thermal temperature rise, no sophisticated cooling systems are necessary within the voltage testing supplies.

A final introductory remark is related to the necessity that all supplies can withstand sudden voltage breakdowns of the output voltage. The stress to the windings and coils accompanied by the breakdowns is usually not related to the short-circuit currents and therefore magnetic forces within the windings, as those currents are not large either; more frequently it is the stray potential distribution between the windings which will cause insulation failures. One may provide also proper damping resistors between h.v. testing supply and the test equipment to reduce the rate of the sudden voltage drop and to avoid any overvoltages within the test circuit caused by interruptions of the breakdown phenomena. Nominal values of such damping resistors between 10 and 100 kΩ will usually not influence the test conditions. These resistors, however, are expensive for high voltages and it should be checked whether the a.c. voltage supply can withstand the stresses without the damping resistors or not.

Most of the above remarks are common to the two main methods for the generation of high a.c. testing voltages: transformers and resonant circuits.

2.2.1 Testing Transformers

The power frequency single-phase transformer is the most common form of ACHV testing apparatus. Designed for operation at the same frequency as the normal working frequency of the test objects (i.e. 60 or 50 Hz), they may be used also for higher frequencies with rated voltage, or for lower frequencies, if the voltages are reduced in accordance to the frequency, to avoid saturation of the core.

From the considerations of thermal rating, the kVA output and the fundamental design of the iron core and windings there is not a very big difference between a testing and a single-phase power transformer. The differences are related mainly to a smaller flux density within the core to avoid unnecessary high magnetizing currents which would produce higher harmonics in the voltage regulator supplying the transformer, and to a very compact and well-insulated h.v. winding for the rated voltage. Therefore, a single-phase testing unit may be compared with the construction of a potential transformer used for the measurement of voltage and power in power transmission systems.

For a better understanding of advanced circuits, the fundamental design of such "single unit testing transformers" will be illustrated. Figure 2.13a shows the well-known circuit diagram. The primary winding "2" is usually rated for low voltages of ⩽ 1 kV, but might often be split up in two or more windings which could be switched in series or parallel (not shown here) to increase the regulation capabilities. The iron core "1" is fixed at earth potential as well as one terminal of each of the two windings. Simplified cross-sections of two possible constructions for the unit itself are given in Figs. 2.13b and c. In both cases the layout arrangement of core and windings are basically the same. Figure 2.13b, however, shows a grounded

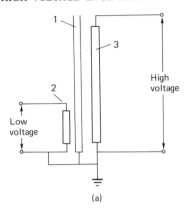

(a)

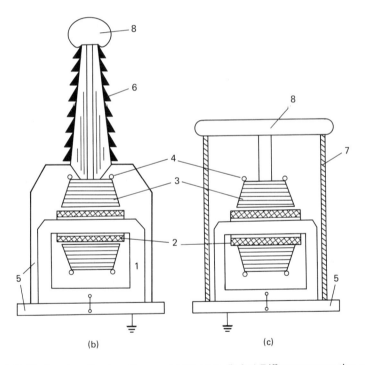

(b)   (c)

FIG. 2.13. Single unit testing transformers. (a) Diagram. (b & c) Different construction units.
(1) Iron core. (2) Primary l.v. or exciting winding. (3) Secondary h.v. winding. (4) Field grading
shield. (5) Grounded tank or base. (6) H.V. bushing. (7) Insulating shell or tank. (8) H.V.
electrode.

metal tank unit, for which a h.v. bushing "6" is necessary to bring the high voltage out of the tank "5". Instead of a bushing, a coaxial cable could also be used if this improves the connection between testing transformer and test object. In Fig. 2.13c the active part of the transformer is housed within an isolating cylinder "7" avoiding the use of the bushing. This construction reduces the height, though the heat transfer from inside to outside is aggravated. In both cases the vessels would be filled with high-quality transformer oil, as most of the windings are oil-paper insulated.

The sectional view of the windings shows the primary winding close to the iron core and surrounded by the h.v. winding "3". This coaxial arrangement reduces the magnetic stray flux and increases, therefore, the coupling of both windings. The shape of the cross-sectional view of winding no. 3 is a reference to the layout of this coil: the beginning (grounded end) of the h.v. winding is located at the side close to the core, and the end close to a sliced metal shield, which prevents too high field intensities at h.v. potential. Between both ends the single turns are arranged in layers, which are carefully insulated from each other by solid materials (kraft paper sheets for instance). Adjacent layers, therefore, form coaxial capacitors of high values, and if those capacitances are equal—produced by reduced width of the single layers with increasing diameters—the potential distribution for transient voltages can be kept constant. By this procedure, the trapezoidal shape of the cross-section is originated.

It may well be understood that the design of the h.v. winding becomes difficult, if voltages of more than some 100 kV must be produced within *one* coil. Better constructions are available by specialized techniques, mainly by cascading transformers.

The first step in this technique is to place two h.v. windings on one iron core, to join both windings in series and to connect this junction with the core.[22] For illustration, the circuit diagram is shown in Fig. 2.14 in combination with a simplified cross-section as before. The arrangement could still be treated as a single-unit transformer, the h.v. winding of which is connected at the mid-point to the core or to a metal tank, if such a tank is used as a vessel. The cross-section shows that the primary winding "2" is, however, placed now around the first part "3a" of the whole h.t. winding, whose inner layer, which is at half-potential of the full output voltage, is connected to the core. There are also two additional windings, "4a" and "4b", rated for low voltages, which act as compensating windings. These are placed close to the core and reduce the high leakage reactance between "3b" and the primary "2", or even an exciting winding "5", again a winding rated

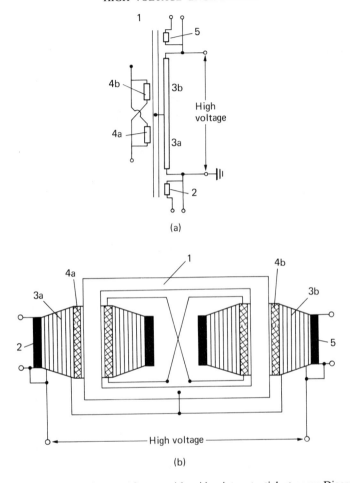

Fɪɢ. 2.14. Single unit testing transformer with mid-point potential at core: Diagram (a) and cross-section (b). (1) Iron core. (2) Primary winding. (3a & b) High-voltage windings. (4a & b) Compensating windings. (5) Exciting winding.

for low voltages as the primary winding. This exciting winding is introduced here as it will be needed for the cascading of transformers. Note that this winding is at the highest potential of the transformer. This means at the potential of h.v. output.

Though no vessel is shown in which such a unit would be immersed, it can easily be understood that for metal tank construction (see Fig. 2.13b) two h.v. bushings are now necessary. The tank itself must be insulated from earth for half-output voltage. This typical view for testing transformers can be seen in Fig. 2.15; if insulating tanks are employed, this internal layout may not necessarily be recognized from outside.

Cascaded transformers. For voltages higher than about 500 kV the cascading of transformers is a big advantage, as the weight of a whole testing set can be subdivided into single units and therefore transport and erection becomes easier. A review of earlier constructions is given in reference 4.

A prerequisite to apply this technique is an exciting winding within each transformer unit as shown in Fig. 2.14. Such a winding was not employed in the earthed core construction of Fig. 2.13, though it is common today to add this winding. The cascading principle will be illustrated with the basic scheme shown in Fig. 2.16. The l.v. supply is connected to the primary winding "1" of transformer I, designed for a h.v. output of V as are the other two transformers. The exciting winding "3" supplies the primary of the second transformer unit II; both windings are dimensioned for the same low voltage, and the potential is fixed to the h.v. V. The h.v. or secondary windings "2" of both units are series connected, so that a voltage of $2V$ is produced hereby. The addition of the stage III needs no further explanation. The tanks or vessels containing the active parts (core and windings) are indicated by dashed lines only. For a metal tank construction and the non-subdivided h.v. winding assumed in this basic scheme, the core and tank of each unit would be tapped to the l.v. terminal of each secondary winding as indicated. Then the tank of transformer I can be earthed; the tanks of transformers II and III are at high potentials, namely V and $2V$ above earth, and must be suitably insulated. Through h.t. bushings the leads from the exciting coils "3" as well as the tappings of the h.v. windings are brought up to the next transformer. If the h.v. windings of each transformer are of mid-point potential type (see Fig. 2.14), the tanks are at potentials of $0.5V$, $1.5V$ and $2.5V$ respectively, as shown in Fig. 2.15. Again, an insulating shell according to Fig. 2.13 could avoid the h.t. bushings, rendering possible the stacking of the transformer units as shown in Fig. 2.17.

The disadvantage of transformer cascading is the heavy loading of primary windings for the lower stages. In Fig. 2.16 this is indicated by the figure P, the product of current and voltage for each of the coils. For this three-stage cascade the output kVA rating would be $3P$, and therefore each of the h.t. windings "2" would carry a current of $I = P/V$. Also, only the primary winding of transformer III is loaded with P, but this power is

FIG. 2.15. Testing transformer for 1200 kV r.m.s. comprising three single unit transformers according to Fig. 2.14, with metallic tanks and bushings (High Voltage Laboratory, Technical University of Munich). [*Note*: Suspended at ceiling and connected with transformer is a selenium-type rectifier with a reverse voltage of 3.4 MV, see ref. 5.]

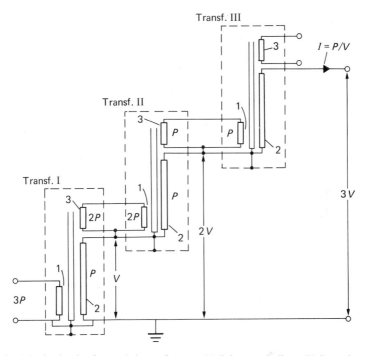

FIG. 2.16. Basic circuit of cascaded transformers. (1) Primary windings. (2) Secondary h.t. windings. (3) Tertiary exciting windings.

drawn from the exciting winding of transformer II. Therefore, the primary of this second stage is loaded with $2P$. Finally, the full power $3P$ must be provided by the primary of transformer I. Thus an adequate dimensioning of the primary and exciting coils is necessary. As for testing of insulation, the load is primarily a capacitive one, a compensation by l.v. reactors which are in parallel to the primary windings is possible. As these reactors must be switched in accordance to the variable load, however, one usually tries to avoid this additional expense. It might be necessary to also add tuned filters to improve the waveshape of the output voltage that is to reduce higher harmonics.[23]

Without any compensation, the overloading of the lower stage transformers introduces a relatively high internal impedance of the whole cascade circuit. In a simplified equivalent circuit of each transformer unit, which consists of a three-windings-type, we may define leakage or stray

Fig. 2.17. Cascaded testing transformers with insulating shell construction (courtesy IREQ).

reactances X for each winding, the primary X_p, the h.t. winding X_h and the exciting winding X_e. Neglecting losses within the windings and magnetizing currents, the calculation of the resultant reactance X_{res} of a cascade unit with n transformers having the individual reactances X_{pv}, X_{hv} and X_{ev} shows

$$X_{res} = \sum_{v=1}^{n} [X_{hv} + (n-v)^2 X_{ev} + (n+1-v)^2 X_{pv}]. \qquad (2.15)$$

(All reactances related to same voltage.)

Assuming three equal transformer units, the equation leads to a resultant reactance of

$$X_{res} = 3X_h + 5X_e + 14X_p$$

instead of only $3(X_h + X_e + X_p)$ which might be expected. Cascaded transformers are the dominating HVAC testing units in all large testing laboratories. In Fig. 2.17 the 2.4-MV cascade of the Quebec Hydro-Research Laboratory may be seen.

A final remark relates to the effect that for all transformers the output will increase with load, as this is formed by capacitors. The equivalent circuit of a transformer loaded by capacitors forms a series resonant circuit, which is shown in Fig. 2.18 and will be used to introduce the resonant circuits for testing purposes. With nominal load, the exciting frequency is well below resonance frequency, so that the voltage increase is only about proportional to the load. If the testing transformer, however, is switched to a primary voltage higher than about half the rated voltage, the output voltage will oscillate with resonance frequency, and the amplitude may easily

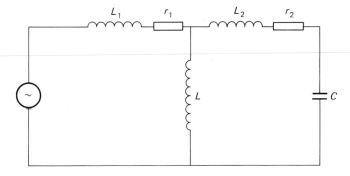

FIG. 2.18. Equivalent circuit of straight test set consisting of a transformer and test capacitance.

become higher than the rated voltage. The impedance of the voltage regulators used must also be taken into account for quantitative calculations.

2.2.2 Series Resonant Circuits

The tuned series resonant h.v. testing circuit arose as a means of overcoming the accidental and unwanted resonances to which the more conventional test sets are more prone. If we consider a conventional "straight" test set such as the first unit in Fig. 2.16 used in, say, testing a capacitance C, then its equivalent circuit will be that shown in Fig. 2.18. In this circuit $(r_1 + j\omega L_1)$ represents the impedance of the supply, the voltage regulator and the transformer primary. ωL represents the transformer shunt impedance which is usually large compared with L_1 and L_2 and can normally be neglected. $(r_2 + j\omega L_2)$ represents the impedance of the transformer secondary. $1/\omega C$ represents the capacitive impedance of the load.

If by chance $\omega(L_1 + L_2) = 1/\omega C$, accidental resonance occurs. At supply frequency the effect can be extremely dangerous, as the instantaneous voltage application can be of the order of 20 to 50 times the intended high voltage. This can occur and has given rise to some vicious explosions during cable testing. The greatest possibility of this occurring is when testing at the maximum limit of current and relatively low voltages, i.e. high capacitive load. Unfortunately the inductance of the supply regulator varies somewhat over its range, so that resonance does not necessarily occur when the voltages are at their low switch-on value, but rather suddenly at the higher voltage range.

Resonance of a harmonic can similarly occur, as harmonic currents are present due to the transformer iron core. These resonances are not quite so disastrous, but third harmonics have been observed of greater amplitude than the fundamental, and even the thirteenth harmonic can give a 5% ripple on the voltage waveform. This form of harmonic resonance causes greater voltage distortion than other effects and occurs insidiously at particular capacitance loads, usually unnoticed by conventional instrumentation.

With the series resonant set the resonance is controlled at fundamental frequency and no unwanted resonance can therefore occur.

Historically, in the period 1935–45, due to the advent of light current engineering, power engineers were increasingly aware of the potentialities of tuned circuits. It was not, however, until the late 1940s that engineers at Ferranti, England, and Standard Telefon of Kabelfabrik, Norway, combined to make this a practical proposition culminating in a 600-kV, 2400-kVA a.c. testing equipment completed in 1950, although an earlier version of a resonance transformer for supplying X-ray equipment has been described by Charlton.[24]

The cable manufacturing industry were particularly interested from the start, as amongst other features the circuit offers power factor correction of the large capacitive load—and cable lengths were steadily increasing. This early interest influenced the development of the circuit, particularly for cable testing. More general applications were appreciated as time went on.

The development of this technique will be demonstrated based upon some circuits shown in Fig. 2.19. The capacitance C_t represents the almost pure capacitive load of the test objects. In Fig. 2.19(a) a continuously variable inductance (reactor) is connected to the l.v. winding of a step-up transformer, whose secondary winding is rated for the full test voltage. By this means, the impedance of the reactor is converted to the h.v. side. If the inductance of the reactor is tuned to match the impedance of the capacitive load of constant supply frequency, the idle power of the load is completely compensated. The step-up transformer, however, has to carry the full load current, which is a disadvantage of this method. The same disadvantage applies to the circuit of Fig. 2.19(b), though no special means are necessary to cascade two or more units. The inductors are designed for high-quality factors $Q = \omega L/R$ within the limits of the inductance variation. The feed transformer therefore injects the losses of the circuits only.

These types of s.r. circuits have been produced mainly up to about ten years ago, since it was not possible to design continuously variable reactors for high voltages. As described in reference 25, a new technique with split iron cores now provides h.t. continuously variable reactors up to about 300 kV per unit. Thus the testing step-up transformers can be omitted, as indicated in Fig. 2.19(c). The inductance of these h.t. reactors may be changed by up to 10 to 20 times, offering the opportunity to tune the circuits with capacitances C_t, which vary within the same order.

The equivalent circuit diagram for all these circuits is simply a low damped s.r. circuit sketched in Fig. 2.19(d). Because the equations of such circuits are well known, detailed designs will not be discussed here. It should be emphasized that the high output voltage may best be controlled by a continuously variable a.c. supply voltage, i.e. by a voltage regulator

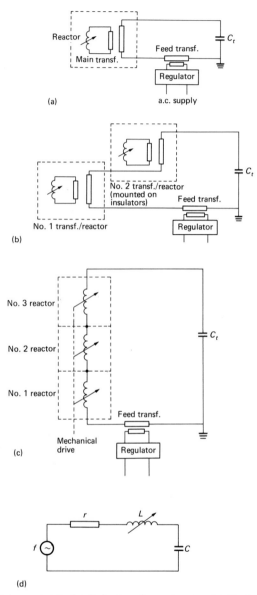

FIG. 2.19. Series resonant circuit for transformer/reactor. (a) Single transformer/reactor. (b) Two or more units in series. (c) Simplified diagram of s.r. circuit for h.t. reactor units in series. (d) Equivalent diagram of s.r. circuits.

transformer, if the circuit was tuned before. The feed transformers are rated for the nominal currents of the inductors; the voltage rating can be as low as V/Q, if V is the full output voltage and Q the worst quality factor of the whole circuit. The additional advantages of the s.r. circuits may be summarized as follows.

Additional Advantages of the Series Resonant Circuit

1. The voltage waveshape is improved not only by the elimination of unwanted resonances, but also by attenuation of harmonics already in the power supply. A practical figure for the amplification of the fundamental voltage amplitude on resonance is between 20 and 50 times. Higher harmonic voltages are divided in the series circuit with a decreasing proportion across the capacitive load. It is easily seen that harmonics in the supply become insignificant. Good waveshape helps accurate h.v. measurement and is very desirable for Schering Bridge work.

2. The power required from the supply is lower than the kVA in the main test circuit. It represents only about 5% of the main kVA with a unity power factor.

3. If a failure of the test specimen occurs, no heavy power arc will develop, as only the load capacitance will be discharged. Instead the voltage collapses immediately the load capacitance is short-circuited. This has been of great value to the cable industry where a power arc can sometimes lead to the dangerous explosion of the cable termination. It has also proved invaluable for development work as the weak part of the test object is not completely destroyed. Additionally, as the arc is self-extinguishing due to this voltage collapse, it is possible to delay the tripping of the supply circuit. This results in a recurring flashover condition with little energy, thus making it simple to observe the path of an air flashover.

4. The series or parallel operation of h.t. reactor or l.t. reactor/h.t. transformer units is simple and very efficient. Any number of units may be put in series without the high impedance problems associated with a cascaded testing transformer group [see eqn. (2.15)]. Equal voltage distributions for series connections are easily provided by a proper control of the individual reactor impedances. For heavy current testing it is possible to parallel the reactor or reactor/transformer units, even if the impedances are different, merely by controlling each associated reactance.

5. Various degrees of sophistication are possible concerning autotuning devices keeping the set in tune, if supply frequency or load capacitance varies during a long-term test, or concerning autovoltage control.

Figure 2.20 shows cascaded h.t. reactors for a s.r. circuit according to Fig. 2.19(c). From this figure a further advantage may be seen not mentioned before, namely the reduction in the size and in the weight of such units in comparison to testing transformers. For testing transformers typically, a specific weight of about 10 to 20 kg/kVA (not including the necessary regulating and control equipment) can be assumed. According to reference 26

FIG. 2.20. 2.2 MV series resonant circuit (Hitachi Research Laboratory, supplied by Hipotronix, Brewster).

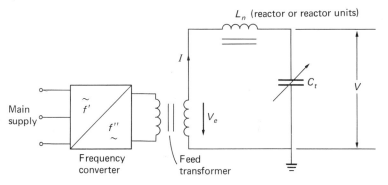

FIG. 2.21. Schematic diagram of s.r. test circuit with variable test frequency.

and Fig. 2.19(c), this weight for oil-insulated continuously variable h.v. reactors can be reduced to about 3 to 6 kg/kVA for a power frequency of 60 Hz. For field testing of cables, large rotating machines or nowadays metal-clad gas-insulated substations (GIS), a still further reduction of weight and size of the testing equipment is important. This can be reached by a very recent development[27] of a different kind of a series resonant circuit, for which chokes with constant inductances are used. As the load capacitance cannot be kept within the narrow limits, the supply frequency must thus be continuously variable to achieve resonance. This disadvantage, however, may be eliminated by the novel features, which may be briefly explained by the schematic diagram sketched in Fig. 2.21. An exciter supply, connected to the l.v. mains, excites the s.r. circuit with the variable resonance frequency; this supply is therefore designed as a controlled thyristor frequency converter. This converter supplies the losses of the testing circuit only, which are usually less than about 2% of the reactive power of C_t, as the chokes can be designed for very high-quality factors. The exciter or feed transformer is rated as shown before, and for the lowest resonance frequency which will occur. In Fig. 2.21 only one nominal inductance L_n of the h.v. reactor is indicated; this inductance, however, might be provided by any number of chokes in series and/or in parallel. C_t represents the test object and other shunt capacitances, i.e. capacitative voltage dividers or some frequency-adjusting capacitor units, if a specified testing frequency f must be achieved. Due to the resonance condition, this frequency is always

$$f = \frac{1}{2\pi\sqrt{L_n C_t}}. \qquad (2.16)$$

The nominal inductance L_n will predominantly be designed according to a nominal capacitance $C_n = C_t$, which is the highest capacitance that can be tested with the full rated voltage $V = V_n$ of the circuit, and a nominal frequency f_n, which is the lowest frequency within this rated voltage. With the above equation we thus obtain

$$L_n = \frac{1}{(2\pi)^2 f_n^2 C_n}.$$ (2.17)

A further criterion for the design of the choke is the maximum or nominal current $I = I_n$, which either overheats the coil or saturates the iron core, if any. As the losses are very small, we may neglect $R \ll \omega L_n$ within the whole frequency range; I_n may thus directly be derived from the voltage drop across L_n, which is nearly the full rated voltage V_n, or from the fact that for all frequencies or every cycle the magnetic energy of the choke is equivalent to the electric energy stored within the test specimen. Thus

$$I_n = \frac{V_n}{2\pi f_n L_n} = V_n \sqrt{\frac{C_n}{L_n}}.$$ (2.18)

These three equations are used to demonstrate the normalized operating characteristics of the circuit. For test objects with capacitance values C_t different from C_n, the resulting testing frequency f will also be different from f_n. The normalized frequency then becomes, according to eqn. (2.16),

$$\frac{f}{f_n} = \sqrt{\frac{C_n}{C_t}} = \frac{1}{\sqrt{C_t/C_n}}.$$ (2.19)

For $C_t \leqslant C_n$, the reactor L_n can be used up to the full rated voltage V_n. Though the frequency increases according to eqn. (2.19), the load current will always be lower than I_n. Ohm's Law or eqn. (2.18) can be used to derive the relationship of the normalized current for $C_t \leqslant C_n$,

$$\frac{I}{I_n} = \frac{f_n}{f} = \sqrt{\frac{C_t}{C_n}}.$$ (2.20)

For $C_t > C_n$, this circuit may still and conveniently be applied, if the testing voltage $V = V_t$ is decreased to keep the current at its nominal value I_n. As the current I is also always proportional to the testing voltage, we may extend eqn. (2.20) to

$$\frac{I}{I_n} = \frac{V_t}{V_n} \sqrt{\frac{C_t}{C_n}}.$$ (2.21)

and apply this equation to show the necessary reduction of the testing voltage for $C_t > C_n$, if we limit I to I_n:

$$\frac{V_t}{V_n} = \frac{1}{\sqrt{C_t/C_n}}.$$ (2.22)

The normalized operating conditions given by eqns. (2.19), (2.20) and (2.22) are illustrated in Fig. 2.22. Whereas for quite small test specimens the test frequency f may conveniently be limited by the addition of cheap h.t. capacitors, the relatively modest variation of this frequency for large capacitors under test will improve the flexibility of applications, i.e. for the testing of power cables with a.c. voltages. The actual limitations in testing of very large test specimens with lower voltages than V_n are given by the reduction of Q for too low frequencies, and the frequency for which the exciter transformer saturates.

A prototype reactor described in reference 28 is designed for $V_n = 200\,\text{kV}$, $I_n = 6\,\text{A}$, $f_n = 100\,\text{Hz}$. The total weight is about 300 kg only, yielding a specific weight of 0.25 kg/kVA for the nominal frequency. The reactor has a cylindrical bar iron core, which is at half-potential of the subdivided h.t. winding; this winding is coaxially placed across the core. The construction provides excellent and high Q values between 50 and 150 within a frequency range of 50 to more than 1000 Hz. Thus a very small a.c. testing supply is available which can easily be handled and conveyed. A further advantage of this circuit is obviously related to the cheap generation of frequencies higher than power frequencies, which may be used for aging tests.

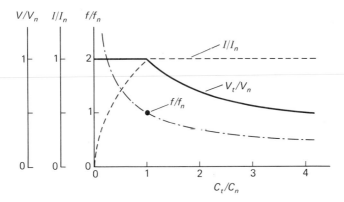

FIG. 2.22. Operating characteristics of circuit according to Fig. 2.21.

Figure 2.23 finally shows a cascaded testing set for 800 kV, 6 A, especially designed for field testing of GIS.[28]

Whereas s.r. circuits are still less in use in h.v. laboratories than testing transformers, especially designed resonant circuits have often been applied in conjunction with X-ray sets even for voltages in the MV range.[4]

FIG. 2.23. Series resonant circuit with variable testing frequency, for 800 kV r.m.s., 6A (four chokes in series).

2.3 IMPULSE VOLTAGES

Disturbances of electric power transmission and distribution systems are frequently caused by two kinds of transient voltages whose amplitudes may greatly exceed the peak values of the normal a.c. operating voltage.

The first kind are lightning overvoltages, originated by lightning strokes hitting the phase wires of overhead lines or the busbars of outdoor substations. The amplitudes are very high, usually in the order of 1000 kV or more, as every stroke may inject lightning currents up to about 100 kA and even more into the transmission line;[29] each stroke is then followed by a travelling wave, whose amplitude is often limited by the maximum insulation strength of the overhead line. The rate of voltage rise of such a travelling wave is at its origin directly proportional to the steepness of the lightning current, which may exceed 100 kA/μsec, as the voltage levels may simply be calculated by the current multiplied by the effective surge impedance of the line. Too high voltage levels are immediately chopped by the breakdown of the insulation and therefore travelling waves with steep wave fronts and even steeper wave tails may stress the insulation of power transformers or other h.v. equipment severely. Lightning protection systems, surge arresters and the different kinds of losses will damp and distort the travelling waves, and therefore lightning overvoltages with very different waveshapes are present within the transmission system.

The second kind is caused by switching phenomena. Their amplitudes are always related to the operating voltage and the shape is influenced by the impedances of the system as well as by the switching conditions. The rate of voltage rise is usually slower, but it is known today that the waveshape can also be very dangerous to different insulation systems.[30] These types of overvoltages are also effective in the l.v. distribution systems, where they are either produced by the usual sometimes current-limiting switches or where they have been transmitted from the h.v. distribution systems. Here they may often cause a breakdown of electronic equipment, as they can reach amplitudes of several kilovolts, and it should be mentioned that the testing of certain l.v. apparatus with transient voltages is a need today.[31]

Though the actual shape of both kinds of overvoltages varies strongly, it became necessary to simulate these transient voltages by relatively simple means for testing purposes. Today the various national and international standards define the impulse voltages as a unidirectional voltage which rises more or less rapidly to a peak value and then decays relatively slowly to zero. In the IEC Recommendations,[2] widely accepted today through national committees,[3] a distinction is made between lightning and switching impulses, i.e. according to the origin of the transients. Impulse voltages with front durations varying from less than one up to a few tens of microseconds are, in general, considered as lightning impulses, and Fig. 2.24 shows the shape for such a full lightning impulse voltage as well as sketched for the same voltage chopped at the tail or on the front, i.e. interrupted by a disruptive discharge. Though the definitions are clearly indicated, it should be emphasized that the virtual origin O_1 is defined where the line AB cuts the time axis. The virtual front time T_1 can only be defined for full lightning impulses and those chopped at the crest or on the tail; for front-chopped impulses the equivalent time is T_c, the time to chopping. The reason for defining the point A at 30% voltage level can be found in most oscillograms of measured impulse voltages. It is quite difficult to obtain a smooth slope within the first voltage rise, as the measuring systems as well as stray capacitances and inductances may cause oscillations. For most applications, the virtual front time T_1 is now 1.2 μsec, and the virtual time to half-value T_2 is 50 μsec. The specifications[2] permit in general a tolerance of up to $\pm 30\%$ for T_1 and $\pm 20\%$ for T_2. Such impulse voltages are referred to as a T_1/T_2 wave, and therefore the 1.2/50 wave is the accepted standard lightning impulse voltage today. Lightning impulses are therefore of very short duration, mainly if they are chopped on front. Due to inherent measurement errors (see Chapter 3, section 3.6) the values of T_1, T_c or even the time differences between the points C and D (Fig. 2.24b and c) can hardly be measured with high accuracy.

Figure 2.25 illustrates the slope of a switching impulse. Whereas the virtual time to half-value T_2 is defined similarly as before, the time to crest T_{cr} is the real time interval between the actual origin and the instant when the voltage has reached its maximum value. This definition could be criticized, as it is difficult to establish the actual crest value with high accuracy. An additional parameter is therefore the time T_d, the time at 90% of crest value. The different definitions in comparison to lightning impulses can be understood if the time scale is emphasized: the standard switching impulse has time values (including tolerances) of

$$T_{cr} = 250 \ \mu sec \pm 20\%$$

$$T_2 = 2500 \ \mu sec \pm 60\%$$

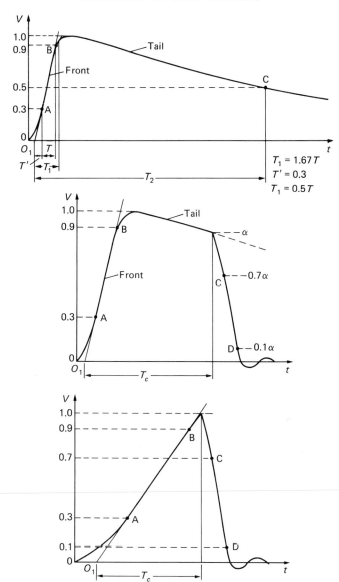

FIG. 2.24. General shape and definitions of lightning impulse voltages. (a) Full wave. (b) Wave chopped at tail. (c) Wave chopped at front. T_1 : virtual front time. T_2 : virtual time to half-value. T_c : time to chopping. O_1 : virtual origin.

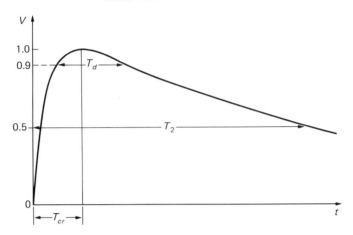

Fig. 2.25. General shape of switching impulse voltages. T_{cr}: time to crest. T_2: virtual time to half-value. T_d: time above 90%.

and is therefore described as a 250/2500 impulse. If such a waveshape is not considered sufficient or appropriate, impulses of 100/2500 and 500/2500 are recommended, and for fundamental investigations concerning the insulation strength of long air gaps or other apparatus mainly, the time to crest has to be varied between about 100 and up to 1000 μsec, as the breakdown strength of the insulation systems may be sensitive upon the voltage waveshape.[30]

2.3.1 Impulse Voltage Generator Circuits

The introduction to the full impulse voltages as defined in the previous section leads to simple circuits for the generation of the necessary waveshapes. The rapid increase and slow decay can obviously be generated by discharging circuits with two energy storages, as the waveshape may well be composed by the superposition of two exponential functions. Again the load of the generators will be primarily capacitive, as insulation systems are tested. This load will therefore contribute to the stored energy. A second source of energy could be provided by an inductance or additional capacitor. For lightning impulses mainly, a fast discharge of pure inductor is usually impossible, as h.v. chokes with high energy content can never be built without appreciable stray capacitances. Thus a suitable fast discharge circuit will always consist essentially of two capacitors.

Single-stage Generator Circuits

Two basic circuits for single-stage impulse generators are shown in Fig. 2.26. The capacitor C_1 is slowly charged from a d.c. source until the spark gap G breaks down. This spark gap acts as a voltage-limiting and voltage-sensitive switch, whose ignition time (time to voltage breakdown) is very short in comparison to T_1. As such single-stage generators may be used for charging voltages from some kV up to about 1 megavolt, the sphere gaps (see Chapter 3, section 3.1) will offer proper operating conditions. An economic limit of the charging voltage V_0 is, however, a value of about 200 to 250 kV, as too large diameters of the spheres would otherwise be required to avoid excessive inhomogeneous field distributions between the spheres. The resistors R_1, R_2 and the capacitance C_2 form the wave-shaping network. R_1 will primarily damp the circuit and control the front time T_1. R_2 will discharge the capacitors and therefore essentially control the wavetail. The capacitance C_2 represents the full load, i.e. the object under test as well as all other capacitive elements which are in parallel to the test object (measuring devices; additional load capacitor to avoid large variations of T_1/T_2, if the test objects are changed). No inductances are assumed so far, and are neglected in the first fundamental analysis, which is also necessary to understand multi-stage generators. This approximation is in general permissible, as the inductance of all elements has to be kept as low as possible.

Before starting the analysis, we should mention the most significant parameter of impulse generators. This is the maximum stored energy

$$W = \tfrac{1}{2}C_1(V_{0_{max}})^2 \qquad (2.23)$$

within the discharge capacitance C_1. As C_1 is always much larger than C_2, this figure determines mainly the cost of a generator.

For the analysis we may use the Laplace transform circuit sketched in Fig. 2.26(c), which simulates the boundary condition, that for $t \leqslant 0$ C_1 is charged to V_0 and for $t > 0$ this capacitor is directly connected to the waveshaping network. For the circuit Fig. 2.26(a) the output voltage is thus

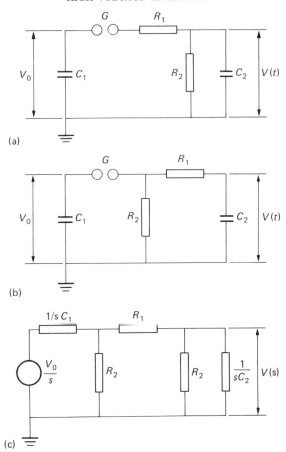

FIG. 2.26. Single-stage impulse generator circuits (a) and (b). C_1: discharge capacitance. C_2: load capacitance. R_1: front or damping resistance. R_2: discharge resistance. (c) Transform circuit.

given by the expression

$$V(s) = \frac{V_0}{s} \frac{Z_2}{Z_1 + Z_2},$$

where

$$Z_1 = \frac{1}{C_1 s} + R_1 ;$$

$$Z_2 = \frac{R_2/C_2 s}{R_2 + 1/C_2 s}.$$

By substitution we find

$$V(s) = \frac{V_0}{k} \frac{1}{s^2 + as + b} \qquad (2.24)$$

where

$$a = \left(\frac{1}{R_1 C_1} + \frac{1}{R_1 C_2} + \frac{1}{R_2 C_2} \right); \qquad (2.25)$$

$$b = \left(\frac{1}{R_1 R_2 C_1 C_2} \right);$$

$$k = R_1 C_2.$$

For circuit Fig. 2.26(b) one finds the same general expression [eqn. (2.24)], with the following constants, however,

$$a = \left(\frac{1}{R_1 C_1} + \frac{1}{R_1 C_2} + \frac{1}{R_2 C_1} \right); \qquad (2.26)$$

$$\left. \begin{array}{l} b = \left(\dfrac{1}{R_1 R_2 C_1 C_2} \right); \\[2mm] k = R_1 C_2. \end{array} \right\} \quad \text{as above}$$

For both circuits, therefore, we obtain from the transform tables the same expression in the time domain:

$$V(t) = \frac{V_0}{k} \frac{1}{(\alpha_2 - \alpha_1)} [\exp(-\alpha_1 t) - \exp(-\alpha_2 t)] \qquad (2.27)$$

where α_1 and α_2 are the roots of the equation $s^2 + as + b = 0$, or

$$\alpha_1, \alpha_2 = \frac{a}{2} \mp \sqrt{\left(\frac{a}{2} \right)^2 - b}. \qquad (2.28)$$

The output voltage $V(t)$ is therefore the superposition of two exponential functions of different signs. According to eqn. (2.28), the negative root leads to a larger time constant $1/\alpha_1$ than the positive one, which is $1/\alpha_2$. A graph of the expression [eqn. (2.27)] is shown in Fig. 2.27, and a comparison with Figs. 2.24 and 2.25 demonstrates the possibility to generate both types of impulse voltages with these circuits.

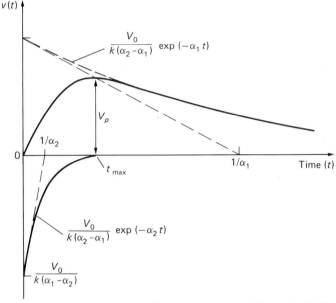

FIG. 2.27. The impulse voltage wave and its components according to circuits Fig. 2.26.

Though one might assume that both circuits are equivalent, a larger difference may occur if the voltage efficiency, η, is calculated. This efficiency is defined as

$$\eta = \frac{V_p}{V_0}; \tag{2.29}$$

V_p being the peak value of the output voltage as indicated in Fig. 2.27. Obviously this value is always smaller than 1 or 100%. It can be calculated by finding t_{max} from $\dfrac{dV(t)}{dt} = 0$; this time for the voltage $V(t)$ to rise to its peak value is given by

$$t_{max} = \frac{\ln(\alpha_2/\alpha_1)}{(\alpha_2 - \alpha_1)}. \tag{2.30}$$

Substituting this equation into eqn. (2.27), one may find

$$\eta = \frac{(\alpha_2/\alpha_1)^{-[(\alpha_1/\alpha_2 - \alpha_1)]} - (\alpha_2/\alpha_1)^{-[(\alpha_2/\alpha_2 - \alpha_1)]}}{k(\alpha_2 - \alpha_1)}. \tag{2.31}$$

For a given waveshape T_1/T_2 or T_{cr}/T_2 of the impulse voltages the values of α_1 and α_2 must be equal. The differences in efficiency η can only be due, therefore, to differences in the value of $k = R_1 C_2$ for both circuits. We may first calculate this term for the circuit Fig. 2.26(b), which has always a higher efficiency for a given ratio of C_2/C_1 as during the discharge the resistors R_1 and R_2 do not form a voltage-dividing system. The product $R_1 C_2$ is found by eqn. (2.28) by forming

$$\alpha_1 \cdot \alpha_2 = b$$
$$\alpha_1 + \alpha_2 = a$$

(2.32)

and by the substitution of a and b from eqn. (2.26). Then we obtain

$$k = R_1 C_2 = \frac{1}{2}\left(\frac{\alpha_2 + \alpha_1}{\alpha_2 \cdot \alpha_1}\right)\left[1 - \sqrt{1 - 4\frac{\alpha_2 \cdot \alpha_1}{(\alpha_2 + \alpha_1)^2}\left(1 + \frac{C_2}{C_1}\right)}\right]. \quad (2.33)$$

For $C_2 \leqslant C_1$, which is fulfilled in all practical circuits, and with $\alpha_2 \gg \alpha_1$ for all normalized waveshapes, one may simplify this equation to

$$k \simeq \frac{1 + C_2/C_1}{(\alpha_2 + \alpha_1)}. \quad (2.34)$$

The substitution of this expression in eqn. (2.31) finally results in

$$\eta = \frac{C_1}{(C_1 + C_2)} = \frac{1}{1 + (C_2/C_1)} \quad (2.35)$$

if again the inequality $\alpha_2 \gg \alpha_1$ is taken into account. The voltage efficiency for this circuit will therefore rise continuously, if (C_2/C_1) decreases to zero. Equation (2.35) indicates the reason why the discharge capacitance C_1 should be much larger than the load C_2.

More unfavourable is the circuit Fig. 2.26(a). The calculation of η may be based upon the substitution of α_1 and α_2 in eqn. (2.31) from eqn. (2.28), and a treatment of the ratio $R_1/R_2 = f(C_2/C_1)$, which increases heavily with decreasing values of C_2/C_1. With minor approximations and the inequality $\alpha_2 \gg \alpha_1$ one may find the result

$$\eta \simeq \frac{C_1}{(C_1 + C_2)}\frac{R_2}{(R_1 + R_2)} = \frac{1}{(1 + C_2/C_1)}\frac{1}{(1 + R_1/R_2)}. \quad (2.36)$$

The comparison with eqn. (2.35) shows the decrease in η due to the additional factor. As the ratio R_1/R_2 is dependent upon the waveshape, the simple dependency from (C_2/C_1) only is lost. For a 1.2/50 μsec wave and similar impulse voltages the fast increase of R_1/R_2 leads to a decrease of η for $C_2/C_1 \lesssim 0.1$; therefore, the efficiency moves through an optimum value and decreases for high C_2/C_1 values as well as for small ones. One could even show that for very small C_2/C_1 ratios this circuit will fail to work. In practice, both circuits are in use, often however in mixed and modified form. Resistive h.v. dividers have to be placed always in parallel to the test object, and their resistor value may contribute to discharge of the circuits. The front resistor R_1 is often subdivided, mainly in multistage generators treated later on. Nevertheless, the dependency of the voltage efficiency factor η is displayed in Fig. 2.28 for the normalized lightning impulse voltage 1.2/50 μsec as well as for deviating waveshapes. More information is available in the literature.[32]

Dimensioning of circuit elements. The common task is to find the resistor values for R_1 and R_2, as C_2 and C_1 are known in general. For larger generators, the discharge capacitors are always given and dimensioned for a good efficiency [see eqns. (2.35) and (2.36)] within a certain range of C_2. This total load capacitance can easily be measured if it is not known

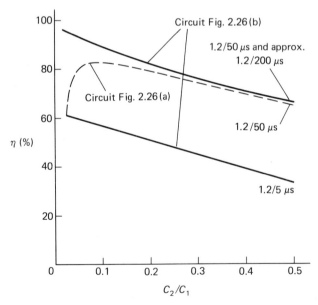

FIG. 2.28. Voltage efficient factor in dependency of the capacitance ratio C_2/C_1 for lightning impulses T_1/T_2.

in advance. The unknown resistance values can then be calculated using eqn. (2.32) and the circuit dependent values for a and b due to eqns. (2.25) and (2.26). The result will be for:

Circuit Fig. 2.26(a):

$$R_1 = \frac{1}{2C_1}\left[\left(\frac{1}{\alpha_1}+\frac{1}{\alpha_2}\right) - \sqrt{\left(\frac{1}{\alpha_1}+\frac{1}{\alpha_2}\right)^2 - \frac{4(C_1+C_2)}{\alpha_1\alpha_2 \cdot C_2}}\right]. \qquad (2.37)$$

$$R_2 = \frac{1}{2(C_1+C_2)}\left[\left(\frac{1}{\alpha_1}+\frac{1}{\alpha_2}\right) + \sqrt{\left(\frac{1}{\alpha_1}+\frac{1}{\alpha_2}\right)^2 - \frac{4(C_1+C_2)}{\alpha_1\alpha_2 C_2}}\right]. \qquad (2.38)$$

Circuit Fig. 2.26(b):

$$R_1 = \frac{1}{2C_2}\left[\left(\frac{1}{\alpha_1}+\frac{1}{\alpha_2}\right) - \sqrt{\left(\frac{1}{\alpha_1}+\frac{1}{\alpha_2}\right)^2 - \frac{4(C_1+C_2)}{\alpha_1\alpha_2 C_1}}\right]. \qquad (2.39)$$

$$\alpha_1\alpha_2 C_1$$

$$R_2 = \frac{1}{2(C_1+C_2)}\left[\left(\frac{1}{\alpha_1}+\frac{1}{\alpha_2}\right) + \sqrt{\left(\frac{1}{\alpha_1}+\frac{1}{\alpha_2}\right)^2 - \frac{4(C_1+C_2)}{\alpha_1\alpha_2 C_1}}\right]. \qquad (2.40)$$

All these equations contain the time constants $1/\alpha_1$ and $1/\alpha_2$, which depend upon the waveshape. There is, however, no simple relationship between these time constants and the times T_1, T_2 and T_{cr} as defined in the national or international recommendations, i.e. in Figs. 2.24 and 2.25. This relationship can be found by applying the definitions to the analytical expression for $V(t)$, this means to eqn. (2.27). The relationship is irrational and must be computed numerically. The following table shows the result for some selected waveshapes:

T_1/T_2 (μsec)	T_{cr}/T_2 (μsec)	$1/\alpha_1$ (μsec)	$1/\alpha_2$ (μsec)
1.2/5	—	3.48	0.80
1.2/50	—	68.2	0.405
1.2/200	—	284	0.381
250/2500	—	2877	104
—	250/2500	3155	62.5

The normalized nominal values of T_1 and T_2 are difficult to achieve in practice, as even for fixed values of C_1 the load C_2 will vary and the exact values for R_1 and R_2 according to eqns. (2.39) and (2.40) are in general not available. These resistors have to be dimensioned for the rated high voltage of the generator and are accordingly expensive. The permissible tolerances for T_1 and T_2 are therefore necessary and used to graduate the resistor values. An oscillographic measurement of the real output voltage $V(t)$ will in addition be necessary if the admissible waveshape has to be testified.

Another reason for such a measurement is related to the value of the test voltage as defined in the recommendations.[2,3] This magnitude corresponds to the crest value, as the shape of the lightning impulse is smooth. However, oscillations or an overshoot may occur at the crest of the impulse. If the frequency of such oscillations is not less than 0.5 MHz or the duration of overshoot not over 1 μsec, a mean curve should be drawn through the curve. The maximum amplitude of this curve then defines the value of the test voltage. Such a correction is only tolerated, provided their single peak amplitude is not larger than 5% of the crest value. Oscillations on the first part of the impulse (below 50% of the crest value) are tolerated, provided their single peak amplitude does not exceed 25% of the crest value. It should be emphasized that also these tolerances constitute the permitted differences between specified values and those actually recorded by measurements. Due to measuring errors the true values and the recorded ones may be somewhat different. The origin of such oscillations or the overshoot can be found in measuring errors as well as by the inductances within every branch of the circuit or the stray capacitances, which will increase with the physical dimensions of the circuit. A general rule for the necessary critical damping of single-stage or—with less accuracy—of multistage generators can easily be demonstrated by Fig. 2.29. If individual inductances L_1, L_2 are considered within the discharge circuit as indicated in Fig. 2.29(a), a quartic differential equation determines the output voltage across the load capacitance C_2. However, even such an equivalent circuit cannot be exact, as also the load capacitance C_2 will contain some inductance. Thus we may only combine the total inductance within the C_1-C_2 circuit to single inductance L, as shown in Fig. 2.29(b), and neglect the positions of the tail resistors, which have no big influence. This reduces the circuit to a simple damped series resonant circuit, and the critical resistance $R = R_1$ for the circuit to be non-oscillatory is given by the well-known equation

$$R_1 \simeq R = 2\sqrt{\frac{L}{C}} \qquad (2.47)$$

where

$$\frac{1}{C} = \frac{1}{C_1} + \frac{1}{C_2}.$$

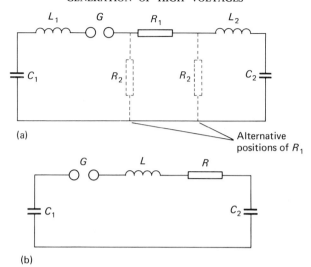

Fig. 2.29. Simplified circuit of impulse generator and load. (a) Circuit showing alternative positions of the wavetail control resistance. (b) Circuit for calculation of wavefront.

This equation is in general suitable for predicting the limiting values for the front resistor R_1. The extremely tedious analysis of circuits containing individual inductances is shown elsewhere.[33-36]

Multistage Impulse Generator Circuits

The difficulties encountered with spark gaps for the switching of very high voltages, the increase of the physical size of the circuit elements, the efforts necessary in obtaining high d.c. voltages to charge C_1 and, last but not least, the difficulties of suppressing corona discharges from the structure and leads during the charging period makes the one-stage circuit inconvenient for higher voltages.

In order to overcome these difficulties, in 1923 Marx[37] suggested an arrangement where a number of condensers are charged in parallel through high ohmic resistances and then discharged in series through spark gaps. There are many different, although always similar, multistage circuits in use. To demonstrate the principle of operation, a typical circuit is presented in Fig. 2.30 which shows the connections of a six-stage generator. The d.c.

Multistage generator

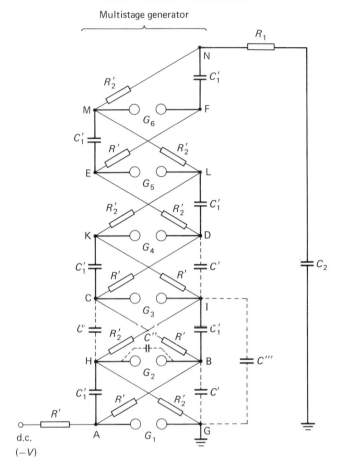

Fig. 2.30. Basic circuit of a six-stage impulse generator (Marx generator).

voltage charges the equal stage capacitors C_1' in parallel through the high value charging resistors R' as well as through the discharge (and also charging) resistances R_2', which are much smaller than the resistors R' and are comparable with R_2 in Fig. 2.26. At the end of the relatively long charging period (typically several seconds up to 1 min), the points $A, B \dots F$ will be at the potential of the d.c. source, e.g. $-V$ with respect to earth, and the points $G, H \dots N$ will remain at the earth potential, as the voltage drop during charging across the resistors R_2' is negligible. The discharge or firing of the generator is initiated by the breakdown of the lowest gap G_1, which is followed by a nearly simultaneous breakdown of all the remaining gaps. According to the traditional theory, which does not take into account the stray capacitances indicated by the dotted lines, this rapid breakdown would be caused by high overvoltages across the second and further gaps: When the first gap fires, the potential at point A changes rapidly from $-V$ to zero, and thus the point H increases its potential to $+V$. If the point B still would remain at the charging potential, $-V$, thus a voltage of $2V$ would appear across G_2. This high overvoltage will therefore cause this gap to break down and the potential at point I rises to $+2V$, creating a potential difference of $3V$ across gap G_3, if again the potential at point C would remain at the charging potential. This traditional interpretation, however, is wrong, since the potentials B and C can also follow the adjacent potentials of the points A and B, as the resistors R' are between. We may only see up to now that this circuit will give an output voltage with a polarity opposite to that of the charging voltage.

In practice, it has been noted that the gap G_2 must be set to a gap distance only slightly greater than that at which G_1 breaks down; otherwise it does not operate. According to Edwards, Husbands and Perry[33] for an adequate explanation one may assume the stray capacitances C', C'' and C''' within the circuit. The capacitances C' are formed by the electrical field between adjacent stages; C''' has a similar meaning across two stages. C'' is the capacitance of the spark gaps. If we assume now the resistors as open circuits, we may easily see that the potential at point B is more or less fixed by the relative magnitudes of the stray capacitances. Neglecting C' between the points H and C and taking into account that the discharge capacitors C'_1 are large in comparison to the stray capacitances, point B can be assumed as midpoint of a capacitor voltage divider formed by C'' and C'/C'''. Thus the voltage rise of point A from $-V$ to zero will cause the potential B to rise from $-V$ to a voltage of

$$V_B = -V + V\left(\frac{C''}{C'+C''+C'''}\right) = -V\left(\frac{C'+C'''}{C'_1+C''+C'''}\right).$$

Hence the potential difference across G_2 becomes

$$V_{G_2} = +V-(-V_B) = V\left(1+\frac{C'+C'''}{C'+C''+C'''}\right).$$

If C'' equals zero, the voltage across G_2 will reach its maximum value $2V$. This gap capacitance, however, cannot be avoided. If the stage capacitances

C' and C''' are both zero, V_{G_2} will equal V, and a sparking of G_2 would not be possible. It is apparent, therefore, that these stray capacitances enhance favourable conditions for the operation of the generator. In reality, the conditions set by the above equations are approximate only and are, of course, transient, as the stray capacitances start to discharge via the resistors. As the values of C' to C''' are normally in the order of some 10 pF only, the time constants for this discharge may be as low as 10^{-7} to 10^{-8} sec.

Thus the voltage across G_2 appears for a short time and leads to breakdown within several tens of nanoseconds. Transient overvoltages appear across the further gaps, enhanced also by the fact that the output terminal N remains at zero potential mainly, and therefore additional voltages are built up across the resistor R'_2. So the breakdown continues and finally the terminal N attains a voltage of $+6V$, or nV, if n stages are present.

The processes associated with the firing of such generators are even more sophisticated. They have been thoroughly analyzed and investigated experimentally.[33,38,39]

In practice for a consistent operation it is necessary to set the distance for the first gap G_1 only slightly below the second and further gaps for earliest breakdown. It is also necessary to have the axes of the gaps in one vertical plane so that the ultraviolet illumination from the spark in the first gap irradiates the other gaps. This ensures a supply of electrons released from the gap electrons to initiate breakdown during the short period when the gaps are subjected to the overvoltage. If the first gap is not electronically triggered, the consistency of its firing and stability of breakdown and therefore output voltage is improved by providing ultraviolet illumination for the first gap. These remarks indicate only a small part of the problems involved with the construction of spark gaps and the layout of the generator. Before some of these additional problems are treated, we shall treat more realistic Marx circuits as used for the explanations so far.

In Fig. 2.30, the wavefront control resistor R_1 is placed between the generator and the load only. Such a single "external" front resistor, however, has to withstand for a short time the full rated voltage and therefore is inconveniently long or may occupy much space. This disadvantage can be avoided if either a part of this resistance is distributed or if it is completely distributed within the generator. Such an arrangement is illustrated in Fig. 2.31, in which in addition the series connection of the capacitors C'_1 and gaps (as proposed originally by Goodlet[40]) is changed

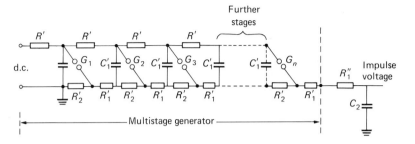

FIG. 2.31. Multistage impulse generator with distributed discharge and front resistors. R'_2: discharge resistors. R'_1: internal front resistors. R''_1: external front resistor.

to an equivalent arrangement for which the polarity of the output voltage is the same as the charging voltage. The charging resistors R' are always large compared with the distributed resistors R'_1 and R'_2, and R'_2 is made as small as is necessary to give the required wavetail. Adding the external front resistor R''_1 helps to damp oscillations otherwise excited by the inductance and capacitance of the external leads between the generator and the load, if these leads are long. It may be readily seen that this circuit can be reduced to the single-stage impulse generator circuit shown in Fig. 2.26(b). If the generator has fired, the total discharge capacitance C_1 may be calculated as

$$\frac{1}{C_1} = \sum^n \frac{1}{C'_1};$$

the effective front resistance R_1 as

$$R_1 = R''_1 + \sum^n R'_1;$$

and the effective discharge resistance R_2—neglecting the charging resistances R'—as

$$R_2 = nR'_2 = \sum^n R'_2,$$

where n is the number of stages.

For this circuit, the front resistors R'_1 do not contribute to the discharge of the main capacitors C'_1, as the current through R'_2 does not flow through R'_1 and so does not reduce the initial generator output voltage. The voltage efficiency, therefore, is high as shown before.

The consistent firing of such circuits could be explained as for the generator of Fig. 2.30. For both generator circuits, the firing is aggravated if the resistances R_2' have relatively low values. According to eqns. (2.23) and (2.40) such low values appears with generators of high energy content and/or short times to half-value, T_2. Then the time constant for discharging the stray capacitances to ground C''' (Fig. 2.30) will be too low and accordingly the overvoltages for triggering the upper stages too short. By additional means providing high resistance values within the firing period, this disadvantage can be avoided.[41]

Special Circuits for Generating Switching Impulse Voltages

The common impulse generator circuits discussed so far are well capable to produce standard switching impulses with adequate voltage efficiency η, if the circuit is well designed and the ratio C_2/C_1 is kept adequately small.

Other methods, however, have taken advantage of utilizing testing transformers to step up the amplitudes from impulse voltages also. One such circuit is shown in Fig. 2.32.[2] An initially charged capacitor C_1 is discharged into the waveshaping circuit R_1, C_2 as well as into the l.v. winding of the transformer. The elements R_1 and C_2 in dotted rectangle, or other suitable components, may be used to control the waveshape. The wavetail is not only controlled by the resistance potential divider included, but also from the main inductance of the transformer equivalent circuit. The time to crest T_{cr} is even without R_1, C_2 limited by the series inductance of the transformer, L_s, which forms a series resonant circuit in combination

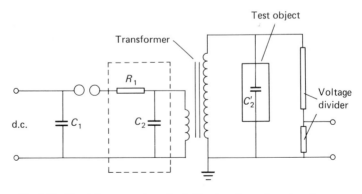

FIG. 2.32. Circuit for generation of switching impulses using a transformer.

with C_1 and the load capacitance C_2'. Neglecting any losses within the circuit, the voltage across the test object would therefore start with a $(1 - \cos \omega t)$ function, and as $T_{cr} = T/2 = \pi/f_r$, f_r being the resonance frequency, the time to crest is approximately

$$T_{cr} \simeq \pi\sqrt{L_s C}$$

where, neglecting transformer ratio,

$$C = \frac{C_1 C_2'}{C_1 + C_2'}.$$

In general, low values of T_{cr} are difficult to achieve, as L_s is quite large and also the capacitance of the h.t. winding of the transformer contributes to the load C_2'. Further problems arise with transient oscillations within the transformer windings, mainly if cascaded testing transformers are used.[42]

The physical phenomena of disruptive discharges in long air gaps as well as in other insulating systems are often related to the front of switching impulses only. Therefore, with switching surges it is not always necessary to produce double exponential waveshapes as recommended in Fig. 2.25. In fact, many investigations are sometimes made with unusual shapes of high voltages, and one can establish many circuits for mainly oscillating voltages, whose variety cannot be treated here. Only the common impulse voltage circuit with a strongly increased inductance will demonstrate this variety, as such circuits recently came into use for field testing of GIS.[43,44] The principle of such circuits is demonstrated in Fig. 2.33(a) and (b). If the front resistor R_1 in Fig. 2.26(a) is replaced by a series inductance, the circuit of Fig. 2.33(a) results, which was first described for the generation of high switching impulse voltages up to 500 kV by Bellaschi and Rademacher.[45] A typical waveshape of the output voltage is also included; it may easily be calculated, since the circuit is a damped series resonant circuit only. The advantage of such a circuit is the nearly doubling of the output voltage, if $C_2 \ll C_1$, in comparison to the charging voltage V_0 of C_1, as for $R_2 \to \infty$ the output voltage would be about equal to V_0 for the ratio C_2/C_1 assumed. Also a proper damping does not decrease the amplitude of the oscillation first very much, and therefore the first increase of the voltage may be used as the front of a switching impulse. This fundamental circuit can be applied to multistage impulse generators, in which the front resistors are replaced by h.t. chokes.[44]

A modular design of such generators offers the opportunity for easy transportation and erection on field site.

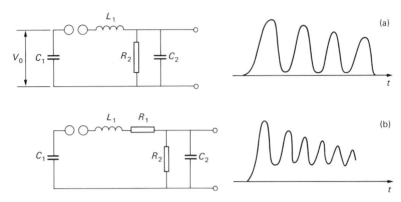

F_IG. 2.33. Circuits for the generation of oscillating switching impulses.

The second circuit of Fig. 2.33 uses an additional resistor R_1 in series to L_1, and is therefore simply a pure impulse voltage circuit with a high inductance within the discharge circuit. Therefore, unidirectional damped oscillations of the type included in the figure are produced. The resistors R_1 and R_2 subdivide the oscillating content of the discharge current. Also this circuit can be used for high voltages, as originally shown by Kojema and Tanaka.[46]

2.3.2 Operation, Design and Construction of Impulse Generators

Though the aim of this book is not concerned with detailed information about the design and construction of h.v. equipment, some additional remarks are necessary for a better understanding of the problems involved with the operation and use of impulse generators. The advice given within this chapter is mainly related to section 2.3.1 p. 56, and therefore concerns the multistage generators.

Every generator needs a d.c. power supply to charge the discharge capacitance C_1. This supply may simply consist of a h.t. transformer and rectifiers providing unidirectional currents, as the voltage smoothing is made by C_1. The d.c. supply should primarily act as a current source, so that the charging time can be controlled. The charging times should not be shorter than 5 to 10 sec, as every voltage application to an object under test may lead to prestressing effects within the insulation, influencing the withstand or breakdown strength. Much longer charging times or time intervals between successive voltage applications may be necessary, depending upon the material tested. For the rough controlled charging the d.c. supply is usually only voltage controlled by a voltage regulator at the primary of the h.t. transformer. Specialized manufacturers nowadays provide thyristor-controlled charging supplies with current-limiting output. By this method, a programmed charging of generators is possible to reach equal charging times for all levels of impulse voltages.

The layout of the construction of multistage impulse generators is largely governed by the type of capacitors involved. Oil-paper-insulated capacitors of low inductance and high capability for fast discharging are in common use; the mineral oil is often replaced by special fluids, providing higher permittivity to increase the capacitance per volume.

For other constructions predominantly capacitor units have been used, having the dielectric assembled in an insulating cylinder of porcelain or varnished paper with plane metal end-plates. This construction provided the obvious advantage that the stages of capacitors could be built up in the vertical columns, each stage being separated from the adjacent one by supports of same or similar form as the capacitor units without dielectric. Such a construction is illustrated by the generator shown in Fig. 2.34. The disadvantage relates to the difficult replacement of failing capacitor units, and therefore this originally preferred construction is not much used today. New designs prefer complete modular constructions with simple capacitor units within insulating cylinders or vessels, or within metal tanks and bushings. This design was originated by big improvements of the capacitor dielectrics, which could reduce the size of the capacitors significantly even for voltages up to 100 kV per unit or more. Such a construction is shown in Fig. 2.35 for an indoor generator of 1600 kV. Besides such indoor constructions, many of the generators for very high impulse voltages are used now under outdoor conditions for the direct testing of outdoor material and to avoid the use of too large laboratories. To eliminate the detrimental influence of weather conditions on electrical insulation as well as the mechanical influences (corrosion, etc.), most of these generators are housed in huge insulating cylinders providing for the full insulation of the output voltage and providing the opportunity to have the generator itself under air conditioning (see Fig. 2.36).

Besides the charging resistances R', all of the waveshaping resistors should be placed in such a way that they can easily be exchanged and replaced, as they must be often changed to ensure the waveshapes

FIG. 2.34. 2.4-MV impulse generator UMIST.

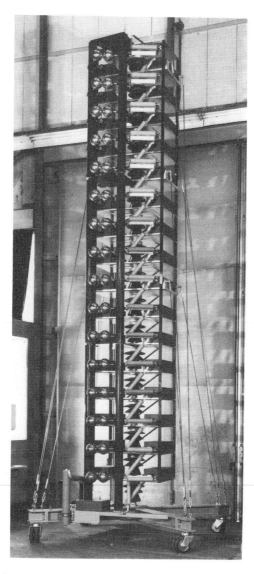

FIG. 2.35. Indoor impulse generator, 1600 kV, 80 kW, with metal tank discharge capacitors (Haefely/Switzerland).

FIG. 2.36. Outdoor impulse generator, 4000 kV, 200 kW, with air-conditioning on the main construction (Haefely/Switzerland).

necessary. The flexibility of a construction is mostly related to constructional details, which cannot be discussed here. The resistors may be composed of wire, liquids or composite resistive materials. Though the high heat capacity involved with liquid and composite (i.e. carbon) resistors would give preference to these resistor types, the instability of the resistance values is of big disadvantage. Therefore highly non-inductively wound wire resistors are best for the front and discharge resistors R_1 and R_2 of the circuits, though they are more expensive to produce. Wavefront resistors are quite satisfactory if their L/R value is less than about 0.1 μsec.

The spark gaps are usually mounted on horizontal arms and the setting of the gaps is adjusted by a remotely controlled motor in conjunction with an indicator. This remark is, of course, related to gaps working in open air only. Sometimes encapsulated and pressurized gaps are used, for which the breakdown voltage is controlled by the gas pressure. The use of proper gas mixtures gives good switching performance.[47]

Each generator should have a device to earth the capacitors when it is not in operation. Due to relaxation phenomena, d.c. operated capacitors can build up high voltages after a short-time short-circuit. This device may be an electrically operated unit which is applied to the charging point of the generator only, if the capacitors per stage are not series connected. All stage condensers then discharge through the various interstage resistors. A series protective resistance should be included in this earthing device to avoid too high discharge currents.

All leads and electrodes within the generator should be dimensioned properly to avoid too heavy corona discharges during the charging period. During the short time of discharge and therefore impulse generation, partial discharges can in general not be prevented. A complete immersion of the generators in improved insulation materials, as mineral-oil or high-pressure gases, could reduce the size effectively; such solutions, however, are only used for special purposes.[48,49]

Finally, some explanations are necessary concerning the tripping and synchronization of the operation of impulse generators. The simple method of tripping the generators by non-triggered sphere gaps, whose diameter is in general made twice as large as the largest gap distance necessary to switch the largest stage or charging voltage, suffers from the disadvantage that the exact instant of firing is not predictable. Furthermore, the presence of unavoidable dust can cause irregular operation of multistage generators due to the following reasons. Dust particles are likely to be attracted to the spheres stressed with d.c. voltages during charging, and the breakdown voltage can strongly be reduced by these particles.[50] If dust is randomly deposited only on the lowest gap (G_1 in Figs. 2.30 or 2.31), the dispersion of the d.c. breakdown voltage of this gap increases and thus the output voltage will not be stable. As the available overvoltage for the tripping of the other gaps is small and of short duration, the second and subsequent gaps cannot be set to break down at a d.c. voltage much higher than that at which the first gap discharges. The only small differences in the gap distance settings, therefore, can cause a breakdown of any gap within the generator, if dust is present. To overcome this irregular firing of generators, which even with triggered gaps may occur, a protection against dust may be provided. As separate enclosure of the gaps with any insulating material prevents any ultraviolet illumination from reaching the other gaps; only a common enclosure of all gaps is satisfactory. Early investigations demonstrating those effects have been described by Edwards et al.[33] The common enclosure of all gaps provides today a reliable method to ensure stable tripping.

A stable self-tripping by a fast mechanical closure of the first gap is a simple means to avoid self-firing due to dust particles; however, this method cannot be used to synchronize the impulse voltage with other events within a very short time interval of a microsecond or less. The early need for synchronization arose from the necessity to initiate the time sweep of oscilloscopes used for the voltage recording. Indeed, the oscilloscope has to be triggered slightly before the impulse wave reaches the deflection plates, if the wavefront is to be recorded satisfactorily. Modern oscilloscopes have built-in time delays, so that a pretrigger may not be necessary. Today, triggered firing of impulse generators would not be even required as transient recorders are available which can replace the impulse oscilloscope and which provide a continuous pretrigger system (see Chapter 3, section 3.5.3). However, as such recorders are not in common use and since controlled or triggered switching of high voltages has so many applications in different fields, a brief review will be presented.

There are many factors and properties which have to be considered if the controlled switching of voltages has to be judged. The most essential factors include:

the magnitude of the switched voltage (some kV up to MV),
the magnitude of the control voltage or signal,
the time delay between control signal and final stage of the switching,
the jitter of the time delay,

the conductivity of the switch in open and closed position,
the inductance of the switch,
the magnitude of the current switched,
the repetition or recurrence frequency, and finally,
the number of switching operations admissible.

For voltages higher than about 10 kV no solid state electronic element is capable to operate. Up to some 10 kV, different types of thyratrons may be used, especially those with heated cathode and hydrogen content. Special types of thyratrons may switch voltages up to 100 kV and currents up to 20 kA with time delays of about 10 μsec and very low jitter down to a few nanoseconds. These elements are expensive, however, and the application is aggravated by the energy supply for the heated cathode, if the cathode is at high potential. Ignitrons are restricted to voltages up to about 25 kV only. Thus, for voltages higher than 100 kV only spark gaps are nearly unlimited in application, if they are properly controlled.

The physical mechanism responsible for the very fast transition of the resistance value of a spark gap begins with the streamer breakdown of the insulating gas and finishes with the arc, which has unlimited current-carrying capabilities. The time-dependent resistance of a gap may be calculated from the well-known spark laws due to Toepler, Rompe-Weizel or Braginskii.[51] Recent investigations show that the oldest law associated with Toepler may conveniently be used for the computation of this time-dependent resistance, $R(t)$. If $i(t)$ is the current flowing in the gap, this resistance is given as

$$R(t) = \frac{k_T d}{\displaystyle\int_0^t i(t)\,dt}$$

where d is the gap distance and k_T the "Toepler spark constant". The integration may be started ($t = 0$) by a not too small current, due to the early beginning of the spark formation. The values of k_T are not real constants; they are slightly dependent upon the gas involved and the field strength within the gap before breakdown. For air, many measurements have yielded a value of $k_T \simeq 0.5 \times 10^{-4} \pm 20\%$ Vs/cm. The above relationship may be applied to a discharge circuit consisting of a discharge capacitor C in series with a resistance R and a homogeneous spark gap to calculate the current $i(t)$ and the time-dependent voltage drop across the gap. If then a time to breakdown T_b is defined as the time from the 90 to the

10% instant values of the decreasing voltage, for $C \gtrsim 2$ nF, $R \gtrsim 100 \,\Omega$ one may derive the dependency

$$T_b \simeq 13 \times 10^6 \frac{k_T}{E};$$

where T_b is in nsec; k_T in Vs/cm; E in kV/cm. Thus for short switching times high field strength E is necessary. Such high values can be achieved by pressurizing the gap, as the breakdown strength will increase about proportionally with the gas pressure (see Chapter 5, section 5.6). Also in air at atmospheric pressure switching times of about 20 nsec will be reached for voltages up to some 100 kV.

The development of triggered and therefore controlled spark gaps cannot be discussed in detail. Only the principle will be considered using the arrangement displayed in Fig. 2.37, which provides good operating characteristics. This arrangement, known as "Trigatron", consists essentially of a three-electrode gap. The main electrodes—indicated as h.v. and earthed electrodes—may consist of spheres, hemispheres or other nearly homogeneous electrode configurations. A small hole is drilled into the earthed electrode into which a metal rod projects. The annular gap between the rod and the surrounding sphere is typically about 1 mm. The metal rod or trigger electrode forms the third electrode, being essentially at the same potential as the drilled electrode, as it is connected to it through a high resistance, so that the control or tripping pulse can be applied between these two electrodes. For this special arrangement, a glass tube is fitted across the rod and is surrounded by a metal foil connected to the potential of the main electrode. The function of this tube is to promote corona discharges around

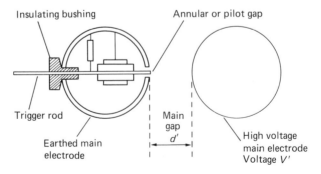

FIG. 2.37. The Trigatron spark gap.

the rod as this causes photoionization in the pilot gap, if a tripping impulse is applied to the rod. Due to this photoionization enough primary electrons are available in the annular gap which breaks down without appreciable time delay. The glass tube (or a tube of different solid insulation material, such as epoxy resin) may also fill the annular gap, so that the rod as well as the tube with its face is flush with the outside surface of the sphere. Thus a surface discharge is caused by the tripping pulse.

If a voltage V stresses the main gap, which is not too low but always lower than the peak voltage at which self-firing—i.e. the breakdown in the absence of any trigger pulse—occurs, this main gap will break down at a voltage even appreciably lower than the self-firing voltage V_s, if a tripping pulse is applied. The Trigatron requires a pulse of some kilovolts, typically $\leqslant 10$ kV, and the tripping pulse should have a steep front with steepness $\gtrsim 0.5$ kV/nsec to keep the jitter of the breakdown as small as possible. The first essential operating characteristic refers to the voltage operating limits, at which a steady operation or switching is possible. Such a characteristic is sketched in Fig. 2.38, where the operating voltage V, the voltage across the main gap, is shown in dependency of the main gap distance. The upper operation limit is identical with the self-firing voltage as defined earlier; the

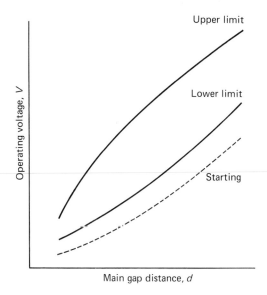

FIG. 2.38. Sketch of an operating characteristic of a Trigatron.

lower operating limit is that at which still a steady operation or breakdown is obtained with a predetermined jitter, for instance $\leqslant 100$ nsec, or time delay. Such a characteristic is clearly dependent upon the detailed construction of the Trigatron. These characteristics are also polarity sensitive, mainly if the field distribution within the gap is not very homogeneous; the polarity sensitivity refers also to the polarity of the tripping pulse, which should always be of opposite polarity of the main voltage which had to be switched.

The physical mechanism which causes the main gap to break down is fundamentally understood, though it might be quite complex in detail. Indeed, it is recognized today that two types of mechanism are active. For small spacings d and a given tripping voltage V, the breakdown may directly be initiated by the distortion and enhancement of the electrical field between trigger electrode and the opposite main electrode, leading to a direct breakdown between these two electrodes. The arc then commutates from the larger electrode to the drilled electrode for the main current. The second type of breakdown takes place for larger gap distances. The trigger pulse causes a breakdown of the annular or pilot gap, and the large amount of charge carriers of all types available after sparking will initiate the breakdown of the main gap. As a result of these two mechanisms, the time delay between the application of the tripping pulse and breakdown of the main gap is changed as it is shown in Fig. 2.39(a) and (b).[53] This time delay is displayed in relation to the ratio V/V_s for an air-insulated main gap of 9 mm, for which V_s equals about 27 kV. Figure 2.39(a) refers to the sketched Trigatron configuration providing homogeneous fields before sparking and a pilot gap system enhancing a breakdown mechanism of the first type. The more inhomogeneous configuration of Fig. 2.39(b) promotes the second type breakdown mechanism. The trigger pulse for this experiment was 15 kV, with a capacitance of 100 nF. It should be noted that the time delay may vary strongly, but for quite a large voltage range V/V_s the delay is shorter than 100 nsec for this relatively small gap distance. The jitter of the time delay, however, is extremely small.

This method of triggering can be applied with the same construction of the trigger electrode to much larger sphere gaps, with diameters up to about 1 m. Then voltages up to 800 kV may be switched with increased time delay and accordingly increasing jitter. Figure 2.40 shows a measured operation voltage characteristic as originally sketched in Fig. 2.38 for a bigger gap arrangement.

Trigatrons of this type can be applied for multiple switching of currents of

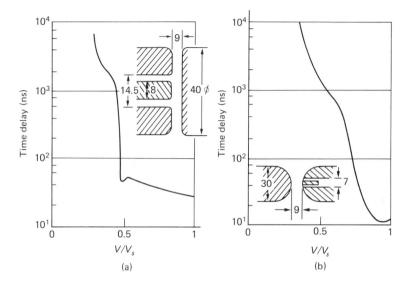

FIG. 2.39. Time delay characteristics for the open-air Trigatrons sketched, according to Petersen.[52] V_s: self-firing voltage (27 kV), V: operating voltage.

100 kA and more, if proper electrode materials are used. Tungsten may be used for the trigger rod, and molybdenum or sintered metal inserts are adequate materials for the main electrodes. High recurrence frequencies may be reached if current pulses of limited amplitudes and length are switched, if the annular gap is cooled, for instance by an airflow. For Trigatrons within impulse voltage generators, however, the recurrence frequency is very low and no cooling is necessary.

For single- or multistage impulse voltage generators these Trigatrons are most suitable. The tripping circuits used today are commercially available and provide in general two or three tripping pulses of lower amplitudes (some 100 V) which can be time shifted. These pulses are thus amplified by thyratrons, small Marx circuits or Klystrons, a special type of a gas discharge valve, in connection with impulse transformers. A very simple tripping circuit will only be shown here (Fig. 2.41), as it can be built with a few elements only. The d.c. supply charges the capacitor C_1 through a high resistance R_1 and upon closing the remotely controlled switch S a pulse is applied to the CRO trip circuit through the capacitor C_2. At the same time the capacitor C_3 is charged up and a triggering pulse is applied to the trigger

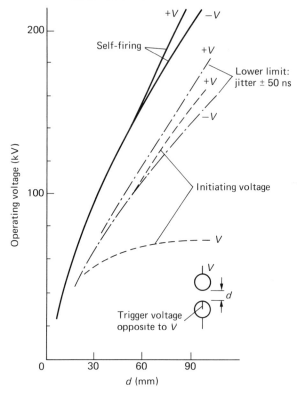

FIG. 2.40. Measured operating characteristics of an open-air Trigatron; sphere-to-sphere arrangement, 20-cm spheres, normal atmospheric air conditions. Operating voltage: Lightning impulse (courtesy Haefely & Co.).

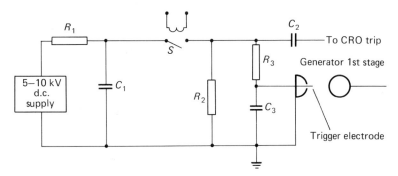

FIG. 2.41. Simple tripping circuit for impulse generators using Trigatron gap.

electrode. The tripping potential on the electrode can be adjusted by adjusting R_3 or C_3. The R_3C_3 circuit also provides a way for delaying the operation of the Trigatron and hence that of the impulse generator spark gaps. The high resistance R_2 provides a discharge circuit for the residual charges on C_3.

Another possibility for the tripping of spark gaps is provided by the application of lasers. As, however, the technical expenses are higher, reference is only made to the literature.[54,15]

REFERENCES

1. Report of the Task Force on Power System Textbooks of PEEC/IEEE; Electric Power Systems Textbooks. *Trans. IEEE.* **PAS 100** (1981), pp. 4255–4262.
2. IEC Publication 60-2 (1973). High-voltage Test Techniques, Part 2: Test Procedures.
3. IEEE Std 4—1978. IEEE Standard Techniques for High-voltage Testing, 6th Edition.
4. J. D. Craggs and J. M. Meek. *High Voltage Laboratory Technique.* Butterworth, London, 1954.
5. H. Prinz. *Feuer, Blitz und Funke.* F. Bruckmann-Verlag, Munich, 1965.
6. H. Greinacher. Erzeugung einer Gleichspannung von vielfachen Betrag einer Wechselspannung ohne Transformator. *Bull. SEV* **11** (1920), pp. 59–66.
7. J. D. Cockcroft and E. T. S. Walton. Experiments with high velocity ions. *Proc. Roy. Soc. London,* Series A, **136** (1932), pp. 619–630.
8. K. Hammer and K. Kluge. Besonderheiten bei der Entwicklung von Gleichspannungsprüfanlagen mit grossen Abgabeströmen. *Elektrie* **35** (1981), pp. 127–131.
9. H. P. J. Brekoo and A. Verhoeff. *Phil. Tech. Rev.* **23** (1962), p. 338.
10. M. Wagstaff. *Direct Current* **7** (1962), p. 304.
11. T. E. Allibone, A. Bettlestone and G. S. Innes. *Brit. J. Radiol.* **7** (1934), p. 83.
12. T. Bjerge, K. J. Koch and T. Lauritsen. *Det Kgl. Danske Videns. Selskab.* **18** (1940), p. 1.
13. H. A. Enge. Cascade transformer high voltage generator. US Patent No. 3,596,167 (July 1971).
14. N. J. Felici. *Elektrostatische Hochspannungs-Generatoren.* Verlag G. Braun, Karlsruhe, 1957.
15. M. Pauthenier and M. Moreau-Hanot. *J. de Phys. et le Radium* **8** (1937), p. 193.
16. Van Atta *et al.* The design, operation and performance of the Round Hill electrostatic generator. *Phys. Rev.* **49** (1936), p. 761.
17. Holifield Heavy Ion Research Facility. Pamphlet of Oak Ridge National Laboratory, Oak Ridge/Tenn., USA, 1981
18. MIT. Study of gas dielectrics for cable insulation. EPRI Report No. EL 220 (October 1977).
19. N. J. Felici. *Direct Current* **1** (1953), p. 122.
20. J. G. Trump. *Elect. Eng.* **66** (1947), p. 525.
21. S. F. Philps. The vacuum-insulated, varying capacitance machine. *Trans. IEEE.* **EI 12** (1977), p. 130.
22. E. T. Norris and F. W. Taylor. *J. IEE.* **69** (1931), p. 673.

23. W. Müller. Untersuchung der Spannungskurvenform von Prüftransformatoren an einem Modell. *Siemens-Zeitschrift* **35** (1961), pp. 50–57.
24. E. E. Charlton, W. F. Westendorp, L. E. Dempster and G. Hotaling. *J. Appl. Phys.* **10** (1939), p. 374.
25. R. Reid. High voltage resonant testing. IEEE PES Winter Meeting 1974, Conf. Paper C74 038-6.
26. R. Reid. New method for power frequency testing of metal clad gas insulated substations and larger rotary machines in the field. World Electrotechn. Congress, Moscow 1977, Section 1, Report 29.
27. F. Bernasconi, W. S. Zaengl and K. Vonwiller. A new HV-series resonant circuit for dielectric tests. 3rd Int. Symp. on HV Engg., Milan, Report 43.02, 1979.
28. W. S. Zaengl *et al.* Experience of a.c. voltage tests with variable frequency using a lightweight on-site s.r. device. CIGRE-Session 1982, Report 23.07.
29. R. H. Golde. *Lightning*, Vols. I and II. Academic Press, London/New York/San Francisco, 1977.
30. Les Renardieres Group. Positive discharges in long air gaps at Les Renardieres. *Electra* No. 53, July 1977.
31. F. A. Fisher and F. D. Martzloff. Transient control levels, a proposal for insulation coordination in low-voltage systems. *Trans. IEEE* **PAS 95** (1976), pp. 120–129.
32. O. Etzel and G. Helmchen. Berechnung der Elemente des Stossspannungs-Kreises fur die Stossspannungen 1,2/50, 1,2/5 und 1,2/200. *ETZ-A* **85** (1964), pp. 578–582.
33. F. S. Edwards, A. S. Husbands and F. R. Perry. *Proc. IEE* **981** (1951), p. 155.
34. A. Vondenbusch. Ein allgemeines Berechnungs-Verfahren fur Stossschaltungen mit voneinander unabhangigen Energiespeichern. Ph.D. Thesis, TH Aachen, 1968.
35. J. R. Eaton and J. P. Gebelein. *GE Rev.* **43** (1940), p. 322.
36. J. L. Thomason. *Trans. AIEE* **53** (1934), p. 169.
37. Marx, E. Deutsches Reichspatent no. 455933.
38. A. Rodewald. Ausgleichsvorgänge in der Marxschen Vervielfachungsschaltung nach der Zündung der ersten Schaltfunkenstrecke. *Bull. SEV* **60** (1969), pp. 37–44.
39. F. Heilbronner. Das Durchzünden mehrstufiger Stossgeneratoren. *ETZ-A* **92** (1971), pp. 372–376.
40. B. L. Goodlet. *J. IEE* **67** (1929), p. 1177, and British Patent No. 344 862.
41. A. Rodewald and K. Feser. The generation of lightning and switching impulse voltages in the UHV region with an improved Marx circuit. *Trans. IEEE* **PAS 93** (1974), pp. 414–420.
42. D. Kind and H. Wehinger. Transients in testing transformers due to the generation of switching voltages. *Trans. IEEE* **PAS 97** (1978), pp. 563–568.
43. W. Boeck, D. Kind and K. H. Schneider. Hochspannungsprüfungen von SF_6-Anlagen vor Ort. *ETZ-A* **94** (1973), pp. 406–412.
44. K. Feser. High voltage testing of metal-enclosed, gas-insulated substations on-site with oscillating switching impulse voltages. *Gaseous Dielectrics II*, Pergamon Press (1980), pp. 332–340 (Proc. of the 2nd Int. Symp. on Gas. Diel., Knoxville/Tenn., USA).
45. P. L. Bellaschi and L. B. Rademacher. *Trans. A. IEE* **65** (1946), p. 1047.
46. K. Kojema and S. Tanaka. *JIEE Japan* **83** (1963), p. 42.
47. J. M. Christensen *et al.* A versatile automatic 1.2 MV impulse generator. 2nd Int. Symp. on High Voltage Engg., Zurich, 1975, paper 2.1-03.
48. F. Brändlin, K. Feser and H. Sutter. Eine fahrbare Stossanlage für die Prüfung von gekapselten SF_6-isolierten Schaltanlagen. *Bull. SEV* **64** (1973), pp. 113–119.
49. F. Jamet and G. Thomer. *Flash Radiography*. Elsevier, Amsterdam, 1976.
50. T. E. Allibone and J. C. Saunderson. The influence of particulate matter on the breakdown of large sphere-gaps. Third Int. Symp. on Gaseous Diel., Knoxville/Tenn., USA, 1982. (*Gaseous Dielectrics III*, Pergamon Press, 1982, pp. 293–299.)

51. K. Möller. Ein Beitrag zur experimentellen Ueberprüfung der Funkengesetze von Toepler, Rompe-Weizel und Braginskii. *ETZ-A* **92** (1971), pp. 37–42.
52. W. Pfeiffer. Der Spannungszusammenbruch an Funkenstrecken in komprimierten Gasen. *Z. angew. Physik* **32** (1971), pp. 265–273.
53. C. Petersen. Untersuchungen über die Zündverzugszeit von Dreielektroden-Funkenstrecken. *ETZ-A* **88** (1967), pp. 480–487.
54. I. Meyer and P. Stritzke. Investigations of laser produced sparks in N_2 and He. IEE Conf. Publ. No. 143, IEE Gas Discharges (1976), pp. 390–392.
55. A. H. Guenther and J. R. Bettis. Laser-triggered spark gap switches. IEE Conf. Publ. No. 143, IEE Gas Discharges (1976), pp. 440–443.

Chapter 3

MEASUREMENT OF HIGH VOLTAGES

Measurement of high voltages—d.c., a.c. or impulse voltages—involves unusual problems that may not be familiar to specialists in the common electrical measurement techniques. These problems increase with the magnitude of the voltage, but are still easy to solve for voltages of some 10 kV only, and become difficult if hundreds of kilovolts or even megavolts have to be measured. The difficulties are mainly related to the large structures necessary to control the electrical fields, to avoid flashover and sometimes to control the heat dissipation within the circuits.

This chapter is devoted to the measurement of voltages applied for testing of h.v. equipment or in research. Voltage-measuring methods used within the electric power transmission systems are not discussed. Such methods are summarized in specialized books as, for instance, reference 2, distributed publications[3,4]* or a summary given in reference 1. A short introduction into the measuring methods related to non-destructive insulation testing is presented separately (Chapter 6), and a brief reference related to the measurement of electrical fields is included in Chapter 4, section 4.4.

The classification of the measuring methods by sub-chapters according to the type of voltages to be measured would be difficult and confusing. The physical method of quantifying a voltage may cover all kinds of voltage shapes and thus it controls the classification. The essential part of the measuring system relates also to the elements or apparatus representing the individual circuit elements. These could be treated separately, but a preferred treatment is within the chapter, in which special problems first arise. Due to space limitation no constructional details are given, but the

---

* Superscript numbers are to References at the end of the chapter.

TABLE 3.1
(*Note "+" means "in combination with"*)

Quantity \ Type of voltage	d.c. voltages	a.c. voltages	Impulse voltages
Mean value	3.3 (3.6.4 A) 3.4	not applicable	not applicable
r.m.s. value	3.2 3.6.4 A + 3.2	3.2 $\left.\begin{array}{l}3.6.4\ B\\3.6.4\ C\end{array}\right\}+3.2$	not applicable
Crest values	3.1 3.4 (special des.) Mean value + Ripple by CRO + $\left.\begin{array}{l}3.6.4\ B\\3.6.4\ C\end{array}\right\}$	3.1 3.4 (special des.) 3.5.1 3.5.2 A 3.5.3	3.1 3.6.4 (spec. des.) + $\left.\begin{array}{l}3.5.2\ B\\3.5.3\end{array}\right\}$
Voltage shape	3.4 (special des.) CRO + 3.6.4 B	3.4 (special des.) $CRO + \left\{\begin{array}{l}3.6.4\ C\\3.6.4\ B\end{array}\right.$	CRO + 3.6.4 (spec. des.)

comments referring to such problems should carefully be noted. The classification used here could introduce difficulties in selecting proper methods for the measurement of given voltages. Therefore, at this point a table is included (Table 3.1) which correlates the methods treated within the corresponding sections to the type of voltages to be measured.

3.1 PEAK VOLTAGE MEASUREMENTS BY SPARK GAPS

Simple spark gaps insulated by atmospheric air can be used to measure the amplitude of a voltage above about 10 kV. The complex mechanism of this physical effect, often employed in protecting equipment from over-voltages (protection gaps), is treated in Chapter 5. Although spark gaps for measurement purposes might be applied following given rules and recommendations only, a misuse can be avoided through an adequate study of the physical phenomena. As fast transition from the either completely insulating or still highly insulating state of a gap to the high conducting arc state is used to determine a voltage level, the disruptive discharge does not offer a direct reading of the voltage across the gap. A complete short-circuit is the result of a spark, and therefore the voltage source must be capable to allow such a short-circuit, though the currents may and sometimes must be limited by resistors in series with the gap. Strictly speaking, spark gaps can only be considered as a calibration device with a limited accuracy, but with a high reliability. Because of their high reliability and simplicity, spark gaps will probably never disappear from h.v. laboratories. Much more accurate and easier to use devices incorporating electronic circuits are generally applied for routine measurements. But these circuits are often quite sensitive to the electromagnetic effects and may therefore fail to work. A routine check and the rough calibration against sphere gaps thus eliminates the possibility of large measuring errors and awkward consequences.

The geometry of the spark gap is a decisive factor for its application. The international and also the national standards recommend only the sphere gap (section 3.1.1) for approved voltage measurements, as its reliability is best confirmed. The uniform field gaps (section 3.1.2) are merely included here to demonstrate their disadvantages and to save the beginner troublesome experiments. Rod gaps, earlier used for the measurement of impulse voltages, are treated briefly because of their obvious applications for direct voltage measurements (section 3.1.3).

3.1.1 Sphere Gaps

Two adjacent metal spheres of equal diameters whose separation distance is limited, as discussed later, form a sphere gap for the measurement of the peak value of either d.c., a.c. or both kinds of impulse voltages. The ability to respond to peak values of voltages, if the peaks are not too short in time ($\gtrsim 1$–3 μsec), is governed by a short statistical time lag, the waiting time for an electron to appear to initiate an electron avalanche and breakdown streamer, and an equally short formative time lag required for the voltage breakdown or fast current increase within the breakdown channel (see Fig. 5.42). The limitation in gap distance provides a fairly homogeneous field distribution so that no predischarge or corona appear before breakdown; the formative time lags are, therefore, also short. The permanent presence of primary or initiatory electrons within the regions of maximum field gradients to start critical avalanches within a short time lag is of great importance. The electrical field distribution within the high field regions must be fixed by the geometry of the electrode and the air density as well as its composition. Air is composed of various types of molecules which will influence the breakdown voltage. All these influences can be accounted for the the well-known break-down criteria of gases (see, for example, eqn. (5.87), Chapter 5) besides the primary electron impact, whose presence is a prerequisite.

All instructions given in the Standards or Recommendations[5,6] in detail can be related to these effects. The two standardized arrangements for the construction of the sphere gaps are shown in Figs. 3.1 and 3.2. It should be noted that also in the horizontal arrangement one sphere must be earthed.

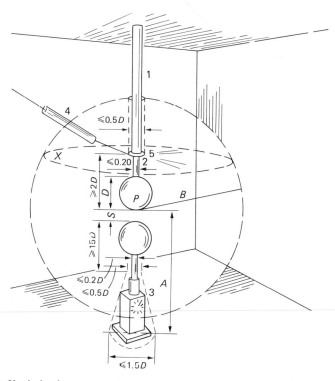

FIG. 3.1. Vertical sphere gap. 1. Insulating support. 2. Sphere shank. 3. Opening gear, showing maximum dimensions. 4. High-voltage connection with series resistor. 5. Stress distributor, showing maximum dimensions. P. Sparking point of h.v. sphere. A. Height of P above ground plane. B. Radius of space free from external structures. X. Item 4 not to pass through this plane within a distance B from P. *Note*: The figure is drawn to scale for a 100-cm sphere gap at radius spacing.

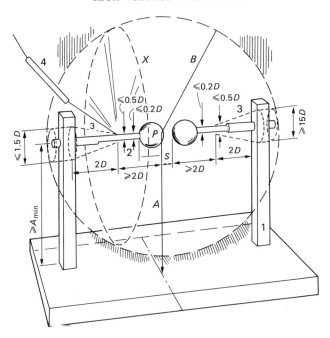

FIG. 3.2. Horizontal sphere gap. 1. Insulating support. 2. Sphere shank. 3. Operating gear, showing maximum dimensions. 4. High-voltage connection with series resistor. P. Sparking point of h.v. sphere. A. Height of P above ground plane. B. Radius of space free from external structures. X. Item 4 not to pass through this plane within a distance B from P. Note: The figure is drawn to scale for a 25-cm sphere gap at a radius spacing.

These figures contain most of the instructions necessary to define the geometry, except for values A and B which require some explanation. These two parameters define clearances such as to maintain the field distribution between the points on the two spheres that are closest to each other (sparking points) within narrow limits. The height of the sparking point P above the horizontal ground plane, which can be a conducting network in or on the floor of the laboratory, or a conducting surface on the support in which the sphere gap is placed, must be within given limits related to the sphere diameter D. To be accepted as a standard measuring device, also a minimum clearance B around the sphere must be available, within which no extraneous objects (such as walls, ceilings, transformer tanks, impulse generators) or supporting framework for the spheres are allowed. Table 3.2 gives the required clearances. Related to the accuracy of the field distri-

TABLE 3.2
Clearance around the spheres

Sphere diameter D (mm)	Minimum value of A	Maximum value of A	Minimum value of B
62.5	7D	9D	14S
125	6	8	12
250	5	7	10
500	4	6	8
750	4	6	8
1000	3.5	5	7
1500	3	4	6
2000	3	4	6

bution are also requirements for the construction of the spheres and their shanks. The most important rules are reproduced partly:

Tolerances on Size, Shape and Conditions of Spheres and Their Surface

The spheres shall be carefully made so that their surfaces are smooth and their curvature is as uniform as possible. The diameter shall nowhere differ by more than 2% from the nominal value. They should be reasonably free from surface irregularities in the region of the sparking points. This region is defined by a circle such as would be drawn on the spheres by a pair of dividers set to an opening of $0.3D$ and centred on the sparking point. The freedom from surface irregularities shall be checked by a spherometer (for more details see reference 5 or 6) or flat circular gauges, and they shall nowhere exceed 0.1 (0.2)% of the diameter D if this is less than 1000 (2000) mm.

The surfaces of the spheres in the neighbourhood of the sparking points shall be free from any trace of varnish, grease or other protective coating. They shall be clean and dry, but need not to be polished. If the spheres become excessively roughened or pitted in use, they shall be refinished or replaced. For relative air humidity exceeding 90%, moisture may condense on the surface and the measurement will then cease to be accurate.

The sphere shanks shall be reasonably in line and the shanks of the h.v. sphere shall be free from sharp edges or corners, but the diameter of the shank shall not exceed $0.2D$ over a length D. If a stress distributor is used at the end of the shank, its greatest dimension shall be in accordance with Fig. 3.1.

If these conditions are fulfilled, a sphere gap of diameter D and spacing S will spark at a peak voltage whose value will be close to the nominal values shown in Tables 3.3 and 3.4. These "calibration data", related to the atmospheric reference conditions (temperature 20°C; air pressure 101.3 kPa

TABLE 3.3 (PART 1).
Sphere gap with one sphere grounded
Peak values of disruptive discharge voltages (50% for impulse tests) are valid for:
  alternating voltages,
  negative lightning impulse voltages,
  negative switching impulse voltages,
  direct voltages of either polarity.
Atmospheric reference conditions: 20°C and 101.3 kPa

Sphere gap spacing (mm)	Voltage, kV peak		
	Sphere diameter (cm)		
	6.25	12.5	25
5	17.2	16.8	
10	31.9	31.7	
15	45.5	45.5	
20	58.5	59.0	
25	69.5	72.5	72.5
30	79.5	85.0	86
35	(87.5)	97.0	99
40	(95.0)	108	112
45	(101)	119	125
50	(107)	129	137
55	(112)	138	149
60	(116)	146	161
65		154	173
70		(161)	184
80		(174)	206
90		(185)	226
100		(195)	244
110		(203)	261
120		(212)	275
125		(214)	282
150			(314)
175			(342)
200			(366)
225			(385)
250			(400)

or 760 mmHg) and the kind and polarity of voltage applied, are a result of joint international measurements within the period of 1920 to about 1950; a summary of references is found in reference 6.

Before summarizing the research work on sphere gaps, the recommendations will be reviewed.

For a.c. and impulse voltages, the tables are considered to be accurate

TABLE 3.3 (PART 2).
Sphere gap with one sphere grounded

| | Voltage, kV peak | | | | |
| | Sphere diameter (cm) | | | | |
Sphere gap spacing (mm)	50	75	100	150	200
50	138	138	138	138	
75	202	203	203	203	203
100	263	265	266	266	266
125	320	327	330	330	330
150	373	387	390	390	390
175	420	443	443	450	450
200	460	492	510	510	510
250	530	585	615	630	630
300	(585)	665	710	745	750
350	(630)	735	800	850	855
400	(670)	(800)	875	955	975
450	(700)	(850)	945	1050	1080
500	(730)	(895)	1010	1130	1180
600		(970)	(1110)	1280	1340
700		(1025)	(1200)	1390	1480
750		(1040)	(1230)	1440	1540
800			(1260)	(1490)	1600
900			(1320)	(1580)	1720
1000			(1360)	(1660)	1840
1100				(1730)	(1940)
1200				(1800)	(2020)
1300				(1870)	(2100)
1400				(1920)	(2180)
1500				(1960)	(2250)
1600					(2320)
1700					(2370)
1800					(2410)
1900					(2460)
2000					(2490)

Note: The figures in parentheses, which are for spacing of more than 0.5D, will be within ±5% if the maximum clearances in Table 3.2 are met. On errors for direct voltages, see text.

TABLE 3.4 (PART 1).
Sphere gap with one sphere grounded
Peak values of disruptive discharge voltages (50% values) are valid
for:
  positive lightning impulses,
  positive switching impulses.
Atmospheric reference conditions: 20°C and 101.3 kPa

| Sphere gap spacing (mm) | Voltage, kV peak | | |
| | Sphere diameter (cm) | | |
	6.25	12.5	25
5	17.2	16.8	—
10	31.9	31.7	31.7
15	45.9	45.5	45.5
20	59	59	59
25	71.0	72.5	72.7
30	82.0	85.5	86
35	(91.5)	98.0	99
40	(101)	110	112
45	(108)	122	125
50	(115)	134	138
55	(122)	145	151
60	(127)	155	163
65		(164)	175
70		(173)	187
80		(189)	211
90		(203)	233
100		(215)	254
110		(229)	273
120		(234)	291
125		(239)	299
150			(337)
175			(368)
200			(395)
225			(416)
250			(433)

within $\pm 3\%$ for gap lengths up to $0.5D$. The tables are not valid for impulses
below 10 kV and gaps less than $0.05D$ due to the difficulties to adjust the gap
with sufficient accuracy. Values for spacings larger than $0.5D$ are regarded
of less accuracy and, for that reason, are shown in parentheses.

For d.c. voltages the measurement is generally subject to larger errors,
caused by dust or fibres in the air. In this case the results are considered
accurate within $\pm 5\%$ provided that the spacing is less than $0.4D$ and
excessive dust is not present.

TABLE 3.4 (PART 2).
Sphere gap with one sphere grounded

| Sphere gap spacing (mm) | Voltage, kV peak | | | | |
| | Sphere diameter (cm) | | | | |
	50	75	100	150	200
50	138	138	138	138	138
75	203	202	203	203	203
100	263	265	266	266	266
125	323	327	330	330	330
150	380	387	390	390	390
175	432	447	450	450	450
200	480	505	510	510	510
250	555	605	620	630	630
300	(620)	695	725	745	750
350	(670)	770	815	858	860
400	(715)	(835)	900	965	980
450	(745)	(890)	980	1060	1090
500	(775)	(940)	1040	1150	1190
600		(1020)	(1150)	1310	1380
700		(1070)	(1240)	(1430)	1550
750		(1090)	(1280)	(1480)	1620
800			(1310)	(1530)	1690
900			(1370)	(1630)	1820
1000			(1410)	(1720)	1930
1100				(1790)	(2030)
1200				(1860)	(2120)
1300				(1930)	(2200)
1400				(1980)	(2280)
1500				(2020)	(2350)
1600					(2410)
1700					(2470)
1800					(2510)
1900					(2550)
2000					(2590)

Note: The figures in parentheses, which are for spacing of more than 0.5D, will be within ±5% if the maximum clearances in Table 3.2 are met.

The sphere gap represents a capacitance, which may form a series resonant circuit with its leads. Heavy predischarges across a test object will excite superimposed oscillations that may cause erratic breakdown. To avoid excessive pitting of the spheres, protective series resistances may be placed between test object and sphere gap, whose value may range from 0.1 to 1 MΩ for d.c. and a.c. power frequency voltages. For higher frequencies, the voltage drop would increase and it is necessary to reduce the resistance.

For impulse voltages such protective resistors should not be used or should not exceed a value of 500 Ω (inductance less than 30 μH).

The disruptive discharge values of Tables 3.3 and 3.4 apply to measurements made without irradiation other than random ionization already present, except in

(a) The measurement of voltages below 50 kV peak, irrespective of the sphere diameters.

(b) The measurement of voltages with spheres of 125 mm diameter and less, whatever the voltage.

Therefore, for measurements under these conditions, additional irradiation is recommended and is essential if accurate and constant results are to be obtained, especially in the case of impulse voltages and small spacing (see also below). For irradiation a quartz tube mercury vapour lamp having a minimum rating of 35 W and a current of at least 1 A is best applicable. Irradiation by capsules containing radioactive materials having activities not less than 0.2 mCi and preferably of about 0.6 mCi, inserted in the h.v. sphere near the sparking points, needs precautions in handling the radioactive materials.

The application of spark gaps is time-consuming. The procedure usually consists in establishing a relation between a high voltage, as measured by the sphere gap, and the indication of a voltmeter, an oscilloscope, or other device connected in the control circuit of the equipment. Unless the contrary can be shown, this relation ceases to be valid if the circuit is altered in any respect other than a slight change of the spacing of the spheres. The voltage measured by the sphere gap is derived from the spacing. The procedure in establishing the relationship varies with the type of voltage to be measured, as follows: For the measurement of direct and alternating voltages, the voltage shall be applied with an amplitude low enough not to cause disruptive discharge during the switching transient and it is then raised sufficiently slowly for the l.v. indicator to be read accurately at the instant of disruptive discharge of the gap. Alternatively, a constant voltage may be applied across the gap and the spacing between the spheres slowly reduced until disruptive discharge occurs.

If there is dust or fibrous material in the air, numerous low and erratic disruptive discharges may occur, especially when direct voltages are being measured, and it may be necessary to carry out a large number of tests before consistent results can be obtained.

The procedure for the measurement of impulse voltages is different: In order to obtain the 50% disruptive discharge voltage, the spacing of the sphere gap or the charging voltage of the impulse generator shall be adjusted in steps corresponding to not more than 2% of the expected disruptive discharge value. Six applications of the impulse should be made at each step. The interval between applications shall not be less than 5 sec. The value giving 50% probability of disruptive discharge is preferably obtained by interpolation between at least two gap or voltage settings, one resulting in two disruptive discharges or less, and the other in four disruptive discharges or more. Another, less accurate, method is to adjust the settings until four to six disruptive discharges are obtained in a series of ten successive applications.

Since in general the actual air density during a measurement differs from the reference conditions, the disruptive voltage of the gap will be given as

$$V_d = k_d V_{d0} \tag{3.1}$$

where V_{d0} corresponds to the table values and k_d is a correction factor related to air density. The actual relative air density (RAD) is given in general terms by

$$\delta = \frac{p}{p_0} \frac{273 + t_0}{273 + t} = \frac{p}{p_0} \frac{T_0}{T} \tag{3.2}$$

where p_0 = air pressure of standard condition, p = air pressure at test conditions, $t_0 = 20°C$, t = temperature in C at test conditions.

The correction factor k_d, given in Table 3.5, is a slightly nonlinear function of RAD, a result explained by Paschen's Law (see Chapter 5, section 5.6).

TABLE 3.5
Air-density Correction Factor

Relative air density RAD	Correction factor k_d
0.70	0.72
0.75	0.77
0.80	0.82
0.85	0.86
0.90	0.91
0.95	0.95
1.00	1.00
1.05	1.05
1.10	1.09
1.15	1.13

The influence of humidity, discussed in the following clauses, is neglected in the recommendations, as its influence (an increase in breakdown voltage with increasing humidity) is unlikely to exceed 2 or 3% over the range of humidity normally encountered in laboratories.

Some of the more recent results on the different factors influencing the gap breakdown will now be discussed.

Effect of Nearby Earthed Objects

The accuracy of measurement of voltage with sphere gap is considerably affected by earthed objects around the gap. Kuffel and Husbands[7] have studied the influence of nearby earthed objects on the direct voltage breakdown of horizontal gaps. They studied the effect of surrounding the gap by a cylindrical metal cage and found that the breakdown voltage was lowered appreciably, particularly when the gap length exceeded a sphere radius.

Figure 3.3 shows the reduction in breakdown voltage for different spacings of 6.25- and 12.5-cm diameter spheres, when the radial clearance, i.e. the radius of surrounding metal cylinder (B), was varied from about 12.6D to 4D, where D = diameter of sphere. A radial clearance of 12.6D was

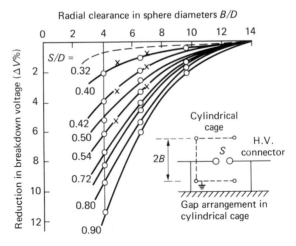

FIG. 3.3. Change in breakdown voltage of (◯) 6.25- and (×) 12.5-cm diameter sphere gaps with radial clearance.

taken as the reference point. The reduction in the breakdown voltage, with a cylindrical cage and for a given S/D fitted closely into an empirical relationship of the form

$$\Delta V = m \, \log\left(\frac{B}{D}\right) + C$$

where ΔV is the percentage reduction in the breakdown voltage from the value when the clearance was $12.6D$, and m and C are factors dependent upon S/D. This relationship is shown in Fig. 3.4 where ΔV for different values of S/D is plotted against $\log(B/D)$. The relationship is nearly linear within the range of investigation.

A similar reduction was observed when an earthed conducting plane was placed parallel to the gap axis. The reduction becomes less pronounced as the field gradient at the sparking point of the h.v. electrode is less increased. At a clearance of $9.8D$ the breakdown voltage was reduced by 0.2–0.7%, with a reference clearance to $13.4D$ and S/D ratios below 1. These results may be related to the minimum values for B recommended in Table 3.2. They confirm that the clearance should be dependent upon the gap distance S.

Fiegel and Keen[8] have studied the factors influencing the spark-over

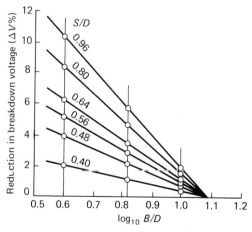

FIG. 3.4. Relationship between the change in breakdown voltage and $\log(B/D)$ for different values of S/D. $\Delta V = m \, \log_{10}(B/D) + C$.

voltage of asymmetrically connected sphere gaps. The field distribution was measured in an electrolytic tank and the effects of physical factors, e.g. shank size d, sphere diameter D, gap length S, and distance A from sparking-point to horizontal ground plane, on the field factor f (ratio of the maximum stress to average stress) were determined for vertically mounted asymmetrical sphere gaps. The field factor f for a gap length of one sphere diameter with various shank sizes, for several positions of the h.v. sphere above ground plane and $S/D = 1$ are plotted in Fig. 3.5, which shows that the effect of shank size is negligible for shank diameters within one-fifth to one-twentieth sphere diameter. Thus the regulations concerning the shank diameter can be understood.

The same authors studied the influence of proximity to ground plane on impulse flashover voltage of a 50-cm diameter sphere gap under negative polarity 1.5/40 μsec impulse voltage. Distances from the sphere gap to the impulse generator were kept at 14D and to the resistance potential divider and vertical ground plane $\geqslant 12.2D$. Figure 3.6 shows the sparkover voltage as a function of A/D for different values of the ratio S/D. The voltage values were corrected for relative air density. The voltage increases with increasing values of A/D. This characteristic would be expected, since for increase in A/D for a given S/D the field factor f decreases, as shown in Fig. 3.5, and the sparkover voltage increases. The results are compared with the values of Table 3.3, indicated as dashed lines in Fig. 3.6. They also agree with the recommendations concerning the minimum and maximum values of A/D described in Table 3.2.

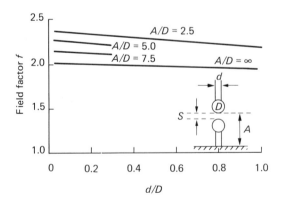

FIG. 3.5. Effect of shank diameter on field factor.

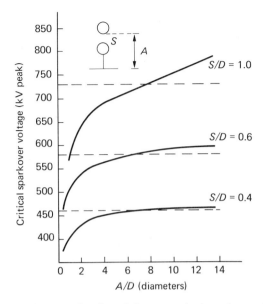

FIG. 3.6. Sparkover voltages as function of distance to horizontal ground plane—50-cm spheres.

Effect of Humidity

Kuffel[9] has studied the influence of humidity for sphere gaps varying between 20 to 250 mm in diameter and uniform field electrodes. From these results, no uniform dependency of the influence with gap length S could be observed, as this influence depends also upon the sphere diameter. The maximum rate of breakdown voltage increase with humidity was always found to be in the region 0–4 mmHg* and thereafter the change was always less. Furthermore, the relationship between breakdown voltage and humidity between 4–17 mmHg was substantially linear for spacings less than that which gave the maximum humidity effect. There was less linearity at the larger spacings. A typical result for a gap of 10 mm within 250 mm

* The air humidity is given here by the vapour pressure p_v in mmHg, which is identical to 1 Torr for a temperature of $t = 0°C$. The *absolute* humidity h_a in g/m³ can be calculated by

$$h_a = p_v \frac{288.8}{(273+t)}.$$

spheres studied with d.c. voltages as well as with a.c. power frequency voltages is shown in Fig. 3.7. The a.c. disruptive voltage is in general slightly lower than the d.c. voltage, but the difference did not exceed 0.5%.

According to these investigations the breakdown/humidity relationship display three main features:

1. The breakdown voltage increases with the partial pressure of water vapour.
2. The total voltage change for a given humidity change increases with gap length.
3. The humidity effect increases with the size of spheres and is largest for uniform field electrodes.

The first two effects may be attributed to the relative values of ionization and attachment coefficients in air of different humidities and at different voltage gradients. The increase of humidity effect with the size of spheres was explained by Kuffel[9] by taking into account the distribution of the ionization and attachment coefficients along the axis of the sphere gaps. An analysis of the distribution of these coefficients showed that the maximum

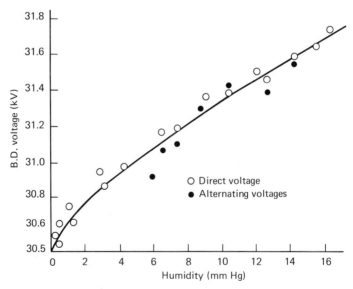

FIG. 3.7. Comparison of the influence of humidity with direct and alternating voltages for 1.0-cm gap between 25-cm diameter spheres.

effect for different sizes of sphere occurred when the minimum values of the effective ionization coefficient $(\alpha - \eta)_{min}$ (see Chapter 5, section 5.10) in the middle of the gaps were approximately the same.

Many recent investigations confirm these observations.[10–14] Within a humidity range of 4–17 g/m^2 (relative humidity range 25–95% for a temperature of 20°C), the relative increase of breakdown voltage was found to be between 0.2 to 0.35% per g/m^3, for the largest sphere diameters of 100 cm and gap lengths up to 50 cm. For very low or very high humidity conditions in laboratories this effect should therefore be taken into account.

Effect of Irradiation and of Polarity

Irradiation increases the availability of the initiating electrons and thus mainly reduces the statistical time lag of breakdown. Many experiments have shown that irradiation becomes necessary when voltages lower than 50 kV are measured or spheres of 12.5 cm diameter and less are used.

Only a few results confirming these statements can be shown here. Though the time lag is of minor importance for d.c. voltages, irradiation may lower the breakdown strength as shown by Kuffel.[15] The gap was irradiated by placing 0.5 mg of radium inside one sphere of approximate thickness of 1 mm of copper. Figure 3.8 shows the percentage lowering of breakdown voltages of various gap lengths. The effect is most marked with 2-cm diameter spheres at small spacings where a reduction in breakdown voltage of about 4.5% was obtained for a gap length of about 1 mm. The strong variations decrease and tend to disappear with larger gaps or parallel planes. Alternating voltage breakdowns were found to be less affected by irradiation as compared with direct voltages. A reduction of 1.5% in the alternating voltage breakdown was observed for a gap length of 2 cm of a 6.26-cm diameter sphere gap.

For impulse voltages it becomes more important to reduce the statistical time lag. Several workers[16–19] have studied the flashover characteristics of sphere gaps under power frequency and impulse voltages. These studies show that for shorter spacings the breakdown curves coincided, but in longer gaps the positive impulse breakdown curve rose about the negative impulse breakdown curve by an amount depending upon the sphere diameter and gap length. Results obtained by MacMillan and Starr,[16] Bellaschi and McAuley,[17] Meador[18] and Datton[19] are included in Fig.

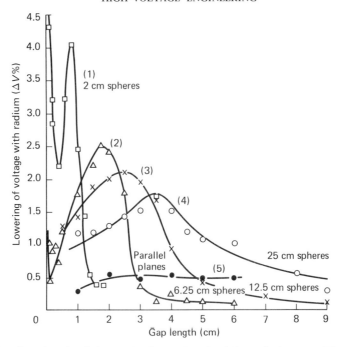

Fig. 3.8. Effect of gap irradiation on the direct voltage breakdown of sphere gaps. The curves show the percent reduction of the mean breakdown voltages of various gaps when 0.5 mg of radium was inserted in one sphere.

3.9. These investigators found that the negative impulse voltages were in agreement with the power frequency values even at larger spacings. Davis and Bowdler[20] have, however, shown that the power frequency break-down value is always lower than the corresponding negative impulse figure. In their studies of the flashover characteristics of gaps between 12.5 cm to 100 cm diameter, they have observed that at a sphere radius spacing the power frequency breakdown is about 5% lower than the negative impulse breakdown value. This difference between a.c. and even negative impulse voltage breakdown is clearly the effect of a too small irradiation, as suggested by Meek.[21] He consequently studied the effect of irradiation on impulse breakdown characteristics of sphere gaps of various sizes. He has shown that irradiation has considerable effect on the 50% flashover voltage of short as well as long gaps. The unirradiated sphere gap shows a gradual transition from 10% to 90% flashover, whereas in the case of irradiated gap the transition is sharp and a well-defined breakdown value is obtained. The

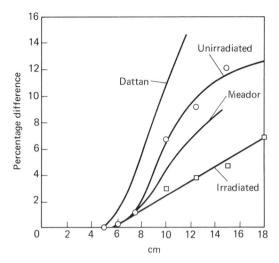

F IG. 3.9. Variation with gap length of the difference between the positive and negative impulse breakdown voltages (50% values) expressed as a percentage of the negative value for a 25-cm diameter sphere gap.

characteristic of a 25-cm diameter sphere gap is shown in Fig. 3.10. Values given by the IEC are included for comparison. The S/D ratio used is outside the recommended level.

These deviations from the table values are still small compared with very recent investigations of Kachler.[22] He used an impulse generator with encapsulated spark gaps. Encapsulation is a convenient technique to avoid erroneous firing due to dust particles, although it stops irradiation caused by the sparking gaps outside of the generator. The impulse voltages had to be increased up to 25% above the table values to cause breakdown for small sphere gaps ($D = 15$ cm) as well as for large ones ($D = 100$ cm). Thus Meek's suggestion that in many earlier investigations no attempt had been made to control the irradiation of a gap could be confirmed.

Influence of Dust Particles

Though the general influence of dust on the sparkover of gaps has been known for a long time, only recently systematic investigations have clarified this problem in detail. These investigations[23,24] will be summarized here.

See Tables 3.3 and 3.4

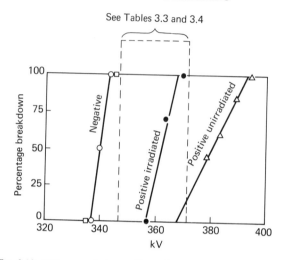

FIG. 3.10. 18.0-cm gap between 25-cm diameter spheres 1/50 wave.

The erratic breakdown in homogeneous or slightly inhomogeneous electrode configurations is to a large extent caused by floating dust particles of sufficient surface conductivity. The disruptive discharge is initiated by one individual particle. Under d.c. voltages as the particle is charged when touching an electrode, it flies to the opposite electrode due to the field forces, where the breakdown is triggered shortly before arrival. Gaps subjected to a.c. voltages are also sensitive to dust particles, though the frequency of erroneous breakdown is decreased. The movements of the particles are not influenced by the type or the pressure of the gaseous dielectric used. As an example the results obtained by Schulz[23] will be discussed. In Figs. 3.11(a) and (b) the cumulative frequency values CF of the time to breakdown, i.e. the withstand time t_w, are plotted for a 120-mm diameter sphere and 25-mm gap spacing. The gap was stressed under highly stabilized d.c. or a.c. voltages, with the voltage varying less than $\pm 0.2\%$ within 24 hr. The magnitude of the voltage applied was 3% lower than the breakdown voltage of the cleaned sphere gap. After every new voltage application, breakdown occurred after the withstand time t_w. The cumulative frequencies CF could be derived from multiple voltage applications. Figure 3.11(a) compares the d.c. and a.c. voltage results. Under d.c. voltage most of the breakdowns occurred within a very short time. Under a.c. voltage withstand times longer than some minutes were of small probability (small CF values).

Figure 3.11(b) shows the influence of moving unfiltered air as well as the influence of filtering. The air movement was achieved by a fan blowing the air perpendicular to the gap axis.

Under d.c. voltages erroneous breakdowns occurred within a few minutes even for voltages as low as 80% of the nominal disruptive discharge voltage. This explains the difficulties encountered with the application of sphere gaps for d.c. voltage measurements.

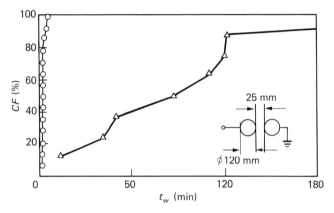

FIG. 3.11(a). Cumulative frequency CF of the withstand time t_w of a sphere gap at d.c. voltage and a.c. voltage. ◯ = d.c. voltage. △ = a.c. voltage. $u/u_{B0} = 0.97$; $u_{B0} = \hat{u}_{B0} = 71.5$ kV.

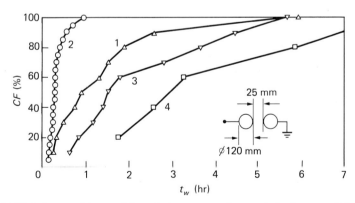

FIG. 3.11(b). Influence of dust particles and air streams on the cumulative frequency CF of the withstand times t_w of a sphere gap at a.c. voltage. 1. Unfiltered air no stream. 2. Unfiltered air stream velocity $v = 0.5$ m/sec. 3. Unfiltered air stream velocity $v = 2.0$ m/sec. 4. Filtered air stream velocity $v = 0.5$ m/sec.

3.1.2 Uniform Field Gaps

It is often believed that some disadvantages of the sphere gaps for peak voltage measurements could be avoided by using properly designed plate electrodes providing a uniform field distribution within a specified volume of air. The procedure to control the electrical field within such an arrangement by appropriately shaped electrodes is discussed in Chapter 4, section 4.2 (Rogowski or Bruce profile). It will also be shown in Chapter 5, section 5.6 that the breakdown voltage of a uniform field gap can be calculated based upon fundamental physical processes and their dependency upon the field strength. According to eqn. (5.102), the breakdown voltage V_b can be expressed also by

$$V_b = E_c(\delta S) + B\sqrt{\delta S} \tag{3.3}$$

if the gas pressure p in eqn. (5.102) is replaced by the air density δ [see eqn. (3.2)] and the gap distance is designated by S. The values E_c and B in eqn. (3.3) are also constants as the values $(E/p)_c$ and $\sqrt{K/C}$ within eqn. (5.102). They are, however, dependent upon reference conditions. An equivalent calculation as performed in Chapter 5, section 5.6 shows that

$$E_c = \left(p_0 \frac{T}{T_0}\right)\left(\frac{E}{p}\right)_c \tag{3.4}$$

and

$$B = \sqrt{\frac{Kp_0 T}{CT_0}} \tag{3.5}$$

where all values are defined by eqns. (5.102) and (3.2). Equation (3.3) would thus replace Tables 3.3 and 3.4 which are necessary for sphere gaps.

Apart from this advantage of a uniform field gap, also no polarity effect and no influence of nearby earthed objects could be expected if the dimensions are properly designed. All these advantages, however, are compensated by the need for very accurate mechanical finish of the electrodes, the extremely careful parallel alignment, and—last but not least—the problem arising by unavoidable dust, which cannot be solved for usual air conditions within a laboratory. As the highly stressed electrode areas become much larger than for sphere gaps, erratic disruptive discharges will tend to occur. Therefore, a uniform field gap insulated in atmospheric air is not applicable for voltage measurements.

3.1.3 Rod Gaps

Rod gaps have earlier been used for the measurement of impulse voltages, but because of the large scatter of the disruptive discharge voltage and the uncertainties of the strong influence of the humidity, they are no longer allowed to be used as measuring devices. A summary of these difficulties may be found in reference 4 of Chapter 2.

More recent investigations of Peschke,[14] however, have demonstrated how the simple electrode configuration rod-rod-gap may be used for the measurement of d.c. voltages, if the air density and the humidity is taken into account, and if some rules relating to the electrode arrangement are followed. This arrangement must comprise two hemispherically capped rods of about 20 mm diameter as sketched in Fig. 3.12. The earthed rod must be long enough to initiate positive breakdown streamers if the h.v. rod is the cathode. Then for both polarities the breakdown will always be initiated by positive streamers giving a very small scatter and being humidity-dependent. Apart from too low voltages ($\lesssim 120\,\text{kV}$), for which the rod-rod-gap is not sufficiently inhomogeneous, the breakdown voltage V_b

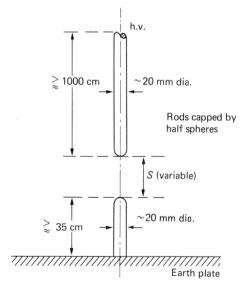

FIG. 3.12. Electrode arrangement for a rod-gap to measure high d.c. voltages.

then follows the relationship

$$V_b = \delta(A + BS)\sqrt[4]{5.1 \times 10^{-2}(h+8.65)} \quad \text{in kV} \qquad (3.6)$$

where S = gap distance in cm, δ = relative air density according to eqn. (3.2), h = absolute humidity in g/m^3.

This empirical equation is limited to $4 \leqslant h \leqslant 20$ g/m^3 and has been shown to apply in the voltage range up to 1300 kV. V_b shows a linear increase with the gap length S, and the steepness B for the gap configuration shown in Fig. 3.12 is approximately $B = 5.1$ kV/cm and is independent of polarity. The constant A displays a small polarity effect, and

$$A = 20 \text{ kV for positive polarity}$$

$$A = 15 \text{ kV for negative polarity}$$

of the h.v. electrode. The accuracy of eqn. (3.6) is better than $\pm 2\%$ and therefore higher than the accuracy provided by sphere gaps. For certain applications, the predischarge currents may load the voltage source too heavily. For usual d.c. supplies with output currents of 10 mA and more this load is acceptable.

3.2 ELECTROSTATIC VOLTMETERS

Coulomb's Law defines the electrical field as a field of forces, and since electrical fields may be produced by voltages, the measurement of voltages can be related to a force measurement. In 1884 Lord Kelvin suggested a design for an electrostatic voltmeter based upon this measuring principle. If the field is produced by the voltage V between a pair of parallel plane disc electrodes, the force F on an area A of the electrode, for which the field gradient $\mathbf{E}$ is the same across the area and perpendicular to the surface, can be calculated from the derivative of the stored electrical energy W_{el} taken in the field direction (x). Since each volume element $A\,dx$ contains the same stored energy $dW_{el} = (\varepsilon E^2 A\,dx)/2$, the attracting force $F = -dW_{el}/dx$ becomes

$$|F| = \frac{\varepsilon A E^2}{2} = \frac{\varepsilon A}{2S^2} V^2 \qquad (3.7)$$

where ε = permittivity of the insulating medium, S = gap length between the parallel plane electrodes.

The attracting force is always positive independent of the polarity of the voltage. If the voltage is not constant, the force is also time-dependent. Then the mean value of the force is used to measure the voltage, thus

$$\frac{1}{T}\int_0^T F(t)\,dt = \frac{\varepsilon A}{2S^2}\frac{1}{T}\int_0^T v^2(t)\,dt = \frac{\varepsilon A}{2S^2}(V_{r.m.s.})^2,\qquad(3.8)$$

where T is a proper integration time.

Electrostatic voltmeters are based on eqns. (3.7) or (3.8) and are arranged such that one of the electrodes or a part of it is allowed to move. By the movement, the electrical field is slightly changed which in general can be neglected. Thus, electrostatic voltmeters are r.m.s.-indicating instruments if the force integration and its display follows eqn. (3.8). Besides differences in the construction of the electrode arrangements, the various voltmeters which have been developed differ in the use of different methods of restoring forces required to balance the electrostatic attraction; these can be a suspension of the moving electrode on one arm of a balance or its suspension on a spring or the use of a pendulous or torsional suspension. The small movement is generally transmitted and amplified by a spot light and mirror system, but many other systems have also been used. If the movement of the electrode is prevented or minimized and the field distribution can exactly be calculated, the electrostatic measuring device can be used for absolute voltage measurements, since the calibration can be made in terms of the fundamental quantities of length and forces.

For a constant electrode separation S the integrated forces increase with $(V_{r.m.s.})^2$ and thus the sensitivity of the system for only small ranges of the rated voltage is small. This disadvantage is overcome, however, by varying the gap length in appropriate steps.

The paramount advantage is the extremely low loading effect, as only electrical fields have to be built up. The high-pressure gas or even high vacuum between the electrodes provide very high resistivity, and thus the active power losses are mainly due to the resistance of insulating materials used elsewhere. The voltage source loading is limited to the reactive power needed to charge the system capacitance, which can be as low as a few picofarads for l.v. voltmeters. The measurement of voltages lower than about 50 V is, however, not possible, as the forces become too small.

The measuring principle displays no upper frequency limit. The load inductance and the electrode system capacitance, however, form a series resonant circuit which must be damped, thus limiting the frequency range.

For small voltmeters the upper frequency is generally in the order of some MHz.

Many designs of electrostatic voltmeters for voltages up to 600 kV have been summarized and described in the books of Craggs and Meek (reference 4, Chapter 2), Schwab,[1] Boening,[29] Paasche,[30] Kuffel and Abdullah[26] and Bowdler.[88] To demonstrate the advantages of high-precision-type electrostatic voltmeters for very high voltages the construction of a recently developed 1000 kV standard or absolute voltmeter prescribed by House et al.[31] will be discussed here. The sectional view is shown in Fig. 3.13. A five-section capacitor and oil-insulated bushing is used to bring the extremely high voltage into the instrument metal tank, filled with pressurized SF_6. The h.v. electrode and earthed plane provide uniform electric fields within the region of a 5-cm diameter disc set in a 65-cm diameter guard plane. A weighing balance arrangement is used to allow a large damping mass [see eqn. (3.8)] and yet give adequate sensitivity for the measurement of sinusoidal voltages. The gap length can be varied between 2.5, 5 and 10 cm, and due to the maximum field stress of 100 kV/cm used the voltage ranges can be set to 250, 500 and 1000 kV. In each of these ranges the nominal maximum force on the disc is 0.8681 N (equivalent to a weight of 88.52 g) according to eqn. (3.7). The disc movements are kept as small as 1 μm by the weighing balance arrangement. The measurement accuracy is in the order of 0.1%. Further constructional details and theoretical explanations related to the stability of the measuring system are given in reference 31.

For d.c. voltage measurements in h.v. laboratories, the electrostatic voltmeters compete with resistor dividers or measuring resistors (see next chapter), as the very high input impedance is in general not necessary. For a.c. voltage measurements, the r.m.s. value is of minor importance for dielectric testing. Thus the actual use of these instruments is restricted and the number of manufacturers is therefore still decreasing.

3.3 AMMETER IN SERIES WITH HIGH IMPEDANCE AND HIGH OHMIC RESISTOR VOLTAGE DIVIDERS

Ohm's Law provides a method to reduce high voltages to measurable quantities, i.e. adequate currents or low and precisely measurable voltages. The simplest method, often used for l.v. measurements to extend a

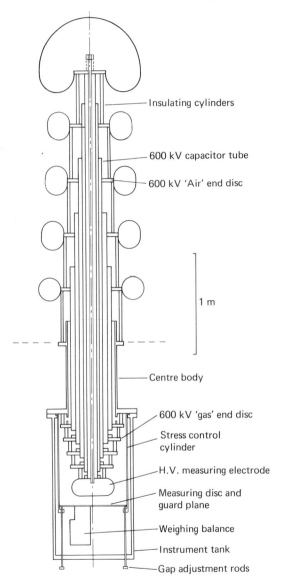

Insulating cylinders

600 kV capacitor tube

600 kV 'Air' end disc

1 m

Centre body

600 kV 'gas' end disc

Stress control
cylinder

H.V. measuring electrode

Measuring disc and
guard plane

Weighing balance

Instrument tank

Gap adjustment rods

FIG. 3.13. Sectional view of 1000-kV electrostatic voltmeter.

voltmeter range, employs an ammeter in series with a resistor R of sufficiently high value to keep the loading of the h.v. source as small as possible (Fig. 3.14(a)). Thus for a pure resistance R, the measured quantities are related to the unknown high voltage by

$$v(t) = Ri(t) \tag{3.9}$$

or

$$V = RI \tag{3.10}$$

if the voltage drop across the ammeter is neglected, which is usually allowable due to the small terminal impedance of such instruments. For d.c. voltage measurements, average current-indicating instruments such as moving coil meters are used giving the arithmetic mean value of V according to eqn. (3.10). Less usual is the measurement of r.m.s. values as the polarity of the high voltage would not be shown. Fundamentally also the time-dependency $v(t)$ according to eqn. (3.9) could be measured by, for instance, an oscilloscope. The difficulties, however, in treating the resistance R as a pure resistance are limiting this application. This problem will be

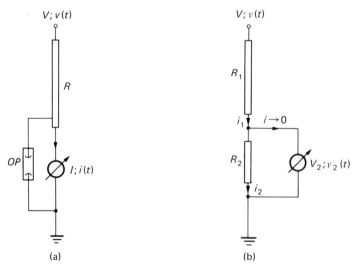

FIG. 3.14. Measurement of high d.c. and a.c. voltages by means of (a) ammeter in series with resistor R; (b) voltage divider R_1, R_2 and voltmeter of negligible current input. OP, Over-voltage protection.

discussed below. It is recommended that the instrument be protected against overvoltage with glow tube or zener diode.

The main difficulties encountered in this method are related to the stability of the resistance R. All types of resistors are temperature-dependent and often may show some voltage-dependency. Such variations are directly proportional to the voltage to be measured and impede the accuracy. Before discussing some details concerning resistor technology, an alternative method shown in Fig. 3.14(b) will be described. If the output voltage of this voltage divider is measured with instruments of negligible current consumption ($i \to 0$ or $i/i_2 \ll 1$), the high voltage is computed by

$$v(t) = v_2(t)\left(1 + \frac{R_1}{R_2}\right) \tag{3.11}$$

or

$$V = V_2\left(1 + \frac{R_1}{R_2}\right). \tag{3.12}$$

Apart from the accuracy of the output voltage measurement (V_2 or $v_2(t)$), the magnitude of the high voltage will only be influenced by the ratio R_1/R_2. As both resistors pass the same current $i_1 = i_2$, the influence of voltage and temperature coefficients of the resistors can be eliminated to a large extent, if both resistors are subjected to equal voltage stresses and if provisions are made to prevent accumulation of heat within any section of the resistor column. Thus the accuracy of the measurement can be greatly improved, though the h.v. resistor R of Fig. 3.14(a) may be the same as R_1 used in this voltage dividing system. Accurate measurement of V_2 was difficult in earlier times as only electrostatic voltmeters of limited accuracy had been available. Today electronic voltmeters with terminal impedances high enough to keep $i \ll i_2$ and giving high accuracy for d.c. voltage measurements are easy to use.

So far it appears that either method could easily be used for measurement of even very high voltages. The design of the method starts with dimensioning the h.v. resistor R or R_1 respectively. The circuit through these resistors is limited by two factors. The upper limit is set by the heat dissipation and heat transfer to the outside. A calculation assuming heat transfer by natural convection only would demonstrate upper current limits of 1 to 2 mA. Due to the loading of the h.v. source very low currents are desirable. As the resistors predominantly at the input end of the h.v.

column are at high potential and thus high field gradients have to be controlled, even with best insulating materials the leakage along the resistor column or the supporting structure controls the lower limit of the current, which cannot be smaller than about 100 μA. This magnitude would result in a resistance of 10^{10} Ω for a voltage of 1000 kV, and thus the problem of the resistor technology arises.

In practice this high ohmic resistor (R, R_1) is composed from a large number of individual elements connected in series, as no commercial types of single unit resistors for very high voltages are available. Wire-wound metal resistors made from Ni-Cr alloys or similar compositions have the lowest temperature coefficients down to less than $10^{-6}/K$ and provide adequate accuracy for the method prescribed in Fig. 3.14(a). The length of the wire required becomes, however, very considerable even for currents of 1 mA and even for the finest gauge which can be made. Individual units of about 1 MΩ each then must be small in size as only 1-kV voltage drop arises, and thus the manner of winding will enhance self-inductive and self-capacitive components. In addition the distributed stray capacitance to ground, discussed in detail in section 3.6 and briefly below, causes a strongly nonlinear voltage distribution along a resistor column and therefore overstresses the individual elements during a sudden load drop originated by voltage breakdown of a test object. Wire-wound resistors are thus not only very expensive to produce, but also quite sensitive to sudden voltage drops. Many constructions have been described in the literature and summaries can be found in references 1, 26, 29, 30 and 88.

For the voltage-dividing system, Fig. 3.14(b), common carbon, metal (oxide) film or carbon composition resistors are preferably used. They should be carefully selected due to the much larger temperature coefficients which may even be different for the same type of such resistors. The resistor value of these resistors may change also with voltage magnitude, and the voltage coefficients may be found in the manufacturer's catalogue. The self-inductance of such resistors is always negligible, though the high values of the individual film resistors is commonly reached by a helix arrangement of the film. Special h.v. resistors are helixed with wide and deep grooves to avoid flashover between adjacent windings. Too thin films are generally destroyed by fast voltage breakdown across the resistor column. This effect may well be understood if again the stray capacitances to earth are considered, or, even better, if the high field gradients at the film surfaces are encountered. If the voltage suddenly disappears, high capacitive or displacement currents are injected into the thin film material, which cannot dissipate the heat within a very short time. Thus the temperature rise within the material may be so high that some of the material even explodes. The result is an increase of the original resistance value. This effect would be calculable if the material thickness and all material constants were known. Resistor manufacturers usually do not take into account this effect as this application is not common. Carbon composition resistors, have big energy absorption capabilities. Their resistor value may, however, decrease due to short-time overloads, as the individual particles may be additionally sintered. A conditioning performed by prestressing of such resistors with short overloading voltages may decrease the effect. Thus the selection of resistors is a difficult task.

Other problems involved in a skilful design of the h.v. resistor concerns the prevention of too high field gradients within the whole arrangement and, related to this, is the effect of stray capacitances upon the frequency-dependent transfer characteristics. To demonstrate these problems the design of a 100-kV standard resistor described by Park[32] will be discussed here. This resistor, shown in Fig. 3.15, is made up of a hundred 1-MΩ wire-wound resistors connected in series and arranged to form a vertical helix. Some of these individual resistors are forming resistor elements, as they are placed within small cylindrical housings predominantly made from metal. Figure 3.16 shows a cross-section of such a resistor element; the metal

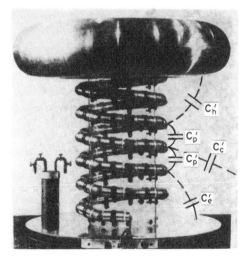

FIG. 3.15, 100-MΩ, 100-kV standard resistor according to Park.[32]

cylinders or "shields" enclose the individual resistors of small size and thus increase the diameter of the resistors. The metal shield is separated by a gap, whose insulation can withstand and insulate the voltage drop (V_1-V_2) across the element. As the absolute values of the potentials V_1, V_2 can be high, the field gradients at the surface of small wires or small individual resistor units would be too high to withstand the insulation strength of the atmospheric air used for the construction. Therefore, the larger diameter of the shields lowers the field gradients to an acceptable magnitude. A further reduction of these gradients is achieved by the helical arrangement, as now the helix might be assumed to form a cylinder of much larger diameter, across which the potential continuously decreases from the top to the bottom. These statements would be confirmed by a computation of the very complex field distribution of the three-dimensional structure. The h.v. end of the resistor is filled with a large "stress ring" which again prevents concentration of electrical field and thus corona or partial discharge formation. A corona-free design is absolutely necessary to avoid leakage currents, which would decrease the overall resistance value.

For voltages higher than about 100 kV such an air-insulated design becomes difficult. The resistor elements then need improved insulation commonly achieved by mineral oil or highly insulating gases. They have to be placed, therefore, in insulating baffles. Additional oil or gas flow provided by pumps will improve the temperature equalization.

The problem of frequency-dependent transfer characteristics is closely related to the field distribution phenomena. As charges are the origin and the end of electrostatic field lines, and such field lines will exist between points of differing potentials, the electrostatic field distribution may well be represented by "stray capacitances". Such stray capacitances have been included in Fig. 3.15 showing the 100-kV resistor, and three different kinds of capacitances are distinguished: the parallel capacitances C'_p between neighbouring resistor elements within the helix, the stray capacitances to the h.v. electrode C'_h and the stray capacitances C'_e to earth potential. Thus a

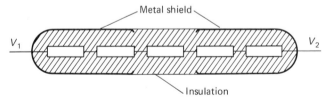

FIG. 3.16. Sketch of cross-section of a h.v. resistor element.

very complex equivalent network is formed which is shown in Fig. 3.17 by assuming five resistor elements R' only and neglecting any residual inductances of the resistors. For equal values of R', the real values of the different stray capacitances would not be equal as is assumed. Depending upon the magnitude of the individual capacitances the ratio I_1/V will therefore change with frequency. As the number of elements used in Fig. 3.17 is too small in reality, a very large number of results would appear by assuming any combinations of capacitive elements. Thus an ingenious reduction of the circuit parameters is necessary.

Though such ladder networks are treated in more detail in section 3.6, a short calculation is included at this point, originally published by Davis.[33] This calculation is based upon a "shielded resistor" network, shown in Fig. 3.18. Here it is assumed that a resistor R of equally distributed resistance values per unit length dx is enclosed by a metal shield, whose potential is P. In comparison with Fig. 3.17, the interturn capacitances C'_p are neglected. This structure leads also to only one type of stray capacitance $C = \Sigma C'$ which is uniformly distributed from the resistance to the shield. Taking a

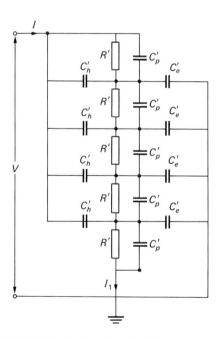

FIG. 3.17. Equivalent network of a h.v. resistor.

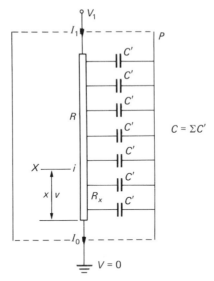

$C = \Sigma C'$

FIG. 3.18. Shielded resistor.

point X at a distance x from the earthed end, the resistance between X and the earthed end is R_x.

Let the ratio $R_x/R = K$, so that $R_x = RK$ and an element of resistance $dR_x = RdK$. The amount of capacitance associated with dR_x is then $C' = CdK$. If ϕ is the potential at X and i the current in the resistor at this point,

$$di = j\omega C(\phi - P)\,dK ; \quad d\phi = iR\,dK.$$

Solving the above equation,

$$\frac{d^2\phi}{dK^2} = R\frac{di}{dK} = j\omega CR(\phi - P),$$

and the complete solution of this equation is

$$\phi = Ae^{aK} + Be^{-aK} + P,$$

where A and B are constants and $a = \sqrt{j\omega CR}$.

The constants are obtained by putting

$$\phi = V_1, \quad \text{where } K = 1,$$

$$\phi = 0, \quad \text{where } K = 0.$$

The equation then becomes

$$\phi = \frac{e^{aK}[V_1 - P(1-e^{-a})] - e^{-aK}[V_1 - P(1-e^a)]}{e^a - e^{-a}} + P. \qquad (3.13)$$

The current i at any point is then

$$i = \frac{1}{R}\frac{d\phi}{dK}$$

$$= \frac{1}{R}\frac{a}{(e^a - e^{-a})}[e^{aK}\{V_1 - P(1-e^{-a})\} + e^{-aK}\{V_1 - P(1-e^a)\}]. \qquad (3.14)$$

The equations for the currents at the earthed end and the h.v. end can be derived by inserting the appropriate values of K. The current at the earthed end is obtained by putting $K = 0$, and is

$$I_0 = \frac{1}{R}\frac{a}{e^a - e^{-a}}[V_1 - P(1-e^{-a}) + V_1 - P(1-e^a)]$$

$$= \frac{a}{R\sinh a}[(V_1 - P + P\cosh a)].$$

By expanding the hyperbolic functions

$$I_0 = \frac{a[V_1 - P + P\{1 + (a^2/2) + (a^4/24) + \ldots\}]}{R\{a + (a^3/6) + (a^5/120) + \ldots\}}$$

$$= \frac{V_1 + (Pa^2/2) + (Pa^4/24)}{R\{1 + (a^2/6) + (a^4/120) + \ldots\}}. \qquad (3.15)$$

The current I_1 at the h.v. end is obtained by putting $K = 1$ and by similar treatment

$$I_1 = \frac{V_1 + \{(V_1 - P)(a^2/2)\} + \{(V_1 - P)(a^4/24)\}}{R\{1 + (a^2/6) + (a^4/120)\}}. \qquad (3.16)$$

The above analysis shows that the current is a function of the shield potential P and it will be of interest to express the currents for the following two special cases:

Case I: When $P = 0$, the uniformly distributed capacitance C is a stray capacitance to earth, C_e (compare with Fig. 3.17), and the current to ground becomes

$$I_0 = \frac{V_1}{R[1+(a^2/6)+(a^4/120)+\dots]}.$$

The terms containing higher powers of a than a^2 may be neglected, as $a^2 = j\omega RC$ and alternating signs as well as decreasing values of the terms do not contribute. Thus

$$I_0 \approx \frac{V_1}{R\left(1+j\dfrac{\omega RC_e}{6}\right)} = \frac{V_1}{R\left[1+\left(\dfrac{\omega RC_e}{6}\right)^2\right]}\left(1-j\frac{\omega RC_e}{6}\right). \qquad (3.17)$$

The phase angle between the input voltage V_1 and the current to earth is $-\omega RC_e/6$. Similarly, the current at the h.v. end is

$$I_1 \approx \frac{V_1(1+a^2/2)}{R(1+a^2/6)}$$

$$= \frac{V_1}{R}\frac{\left(1+\dfrac{\omega RC_e}{12}+j\dfrac{\omega RC_e}{3}\right)}{\left[1+\left(\dfrac{\omega RC_e}{6}\right)^2\right]}.$$

For not too high frequencies, we may neglect the real frequency terms, and thus

$$I_1 \approx \frac{V_1}{R}\left(1+j\frac{\omega RC_e}{3}\right). \qquad (3.18)$$

The phase angle becomes $+\omega RC_e/3$.

For a.c. voltage measurements only eqn. (3.17) is important. Apart from the phase shift the relative change of the current amplitudes with increasing frequency contains the amplitude errors. We thus may define the normalized transfer characteristic

$$H_0(j\omega) = \frac{I_0(\omega)}{I_0(\omega=0)} = \frac{1}{\left(1+j\dfrac{\omega RC_e}{6}\right)}.$$

The amplitude frequency response becomes

$$H_0(\omega) = |H_0(j\omega)| = \frac{1}{\sqrt{1+\left(\dfrac{\omega RC_e}{6}\right)^2}}. \tag{3.19}$$

This equation shows the continuous decrease of the current with frequency. The 3 db bandwidth f_B, defined by $H_0(\omega) = 1/\sqrt{2}$, is thus

$$f_B = \frac{3}{\pi RC_e} = \frac{0.95}{RC_e}. \tag{3.20}$$

For a decrease of the current amplitude by 2%, only the corresponding frequency is much lower ($\approx 0.095/RC_e$ or one-tenth of f_B). A h.v. resistor for 100 kV is assumed, with a resistance of 200 MΩ and a stray capacitance C_e of 10 pF. The eqn. (3.20) gives a bandwidth of 475 Hz, demonstrating the limited accuracy for a.c. measurements. As the resistance values cannot be reduced very much due to the heat dissipation, only a decrease of C_e can improve the frequency range.

Case II: One possible way of shielding and thus reducing the stray capacitances to ground is to raise the potential of the metal shield indicated in Fig. 3.18. When $P = V_1/2$, the expressions for I_0 and I_1 can be obtained in a similar manner as in Case I. Neglecting in eqn. (3.14) powers higher than 2, we obtain

$$I_0 \approx \frac{V_1}{R}\left(1+j\,\frac{\omega RC}{12}\right) \tag{3.21}$$

and similarly

$$I_1 \approx \frac{V_1}{R}\left(1+j\,\frac{\omega RC}{12}\right). \tag{3.22}$$

Thus the expressions for the two currents are the same. In comparison to eqn. (3.17) the change in the sign of the phase angle should be emphasized. The output current I_0 thus increases in amplitude also with frequency. Such phenomena are always associated with stray capacitances to h.v. potential C_h' as shown in Fig. 3.17. For h.v. resistors or resistor dividers as treated in this chapter, cylindrical metal shields of the type assumed cannot be applied as the external voltage withstand strength would be lowered. In Fig. 3.19 two suitable methods are therefore sketched, the efficiency of which may well be understood from the results of the above calculation. Figure 3.19(a)

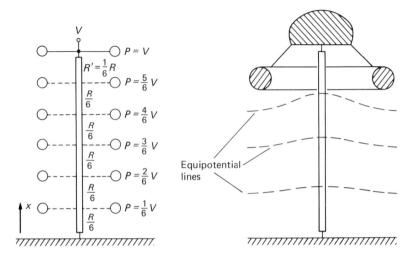

FIG. 3.19. Suitable methods for the shielding of h.v. resistors or resistor dividers. (a) Grading rings. (b) Grading top electrode.

shows stress control rings surrounding the resistor. Apart from the toroid fixed to h.v. potential, the other ring potentials would float as long as their potentials are not bound to any voltage-dividing system independent of the resistor, i.e. a resistor or parallel mixed resistor-capacitor voltage divider (see section 3.6). Apart from the additional cost, such voltage dividers are again influenced by stray capacitances and thus it is difficult to control the shield potentials with high accuracy. If the ring potentials are equivalent to the potentials provided by the current of the resistor at the corresponding plane of the toroids, the electrostatic field distribution along the resistance has no field component perpendicular to the x-direction. Thus all stray capacitances to ground C'_e or h.v. potential C'_h (Fig. 3.17) are converted to parallel capacitances C'_p, the voltage distribution of which for a.c. voltages equals exactly the voltage distribution along the resistor. With a small number of shielding electrodes equal field distribution can only be approximated.

The top stress ring of the standard resistor in Fig. 3.15 indicates an alternative method of shielding. The comparison of eqns. (3.17) and (3.21) shows opposite influences of stray capacitances to ground and to h.v. potentials. Therefore a properly shaped stress control electrode fixed to h.v. potential may also grade the potentials along the resistor, as sketched in

Fig. 3.19(b). For a linearly distributed resistor in the x-direction an ideal grading is difficult to achieve. A nonlinear resistor distribution originally proposed by Goosens and Provoost[34] for impulse resistor voltage dividers gives an elegant solution to solve the disadvantage. The calculation of the field distribution between h.v. electrode and earthed plane would demonstrate, however, the sensitivity of the distribution to surrounding objects at any potential. Thus the stray capacitance distribution will change with the surroundings, thus influencing the frequency-dependent transfer characteristics.

Summarizing the above discussions, the high ohmic resistor in series with an ammeter or the improved method of a voltage dividing system are excellent means for the measurement of high d.c. voltages and for lower amplitudes (about 100–200 kV), also a.c. voltages. A very recent development of a 300 kV d.c. measuring device of very high accuracy described by Peier and Graetsch[35] takes advantage of all principles discussed before (see Fig. 3.20): 300 equal wire-wound resistors each of about 2 MΩ are series connected, and one of these resistors is used to form the l.v. arm of a divider (ratio $\sim 300:1$). The resistors are aged by a temperature treatment. They form a helix of 50 windings and are installed in a PMMA housing containing insulating oil. The pitch of the helix varies so that the potential distribution of the resistor column equals approximately the electrostatic field potential distribution, though the divider is not provided for the precise measurement of a.c. voltages. Freedom of leakage currents due to corona was confirmed by partial discharge measurements. A very careful investigation of all sources of errors and uncertainties shows a relative uncertainty of $\pm 28 \times 10^{-6}$. This magnitude might be compared with the usual absolute accuracy, which cannot be proved due to the lack of any more accurate absolute voltmeter device for such high voltages.

3.4 GENERATING VOLTMETERS

Similar to electrostatic voltmeters the generating voltmeter, also known as rotary voltmeter or field mill, provides a loss-less measurement of d.c. and, depending upon the construction, a.c. voltages by simple means. The physical principle refers to a field strength measurement, and preliminary construction was described by Wilson,[36] who used the principle for the detection of atmospheric fields which are of small magnitude.

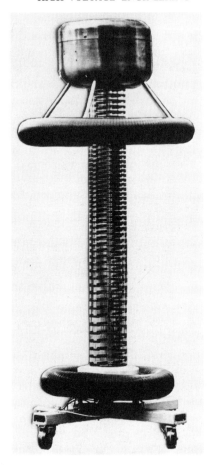

FIG. 3.20. 300-kV divider for d.c. Height 210 cm (PTB, Germany).[35]

The principle of operation is explained by Fig. 3.21. Accurately shaped h.v. electrodes excite the electrostatic field within a highly insulating medium (gas, vacuum). Every field line ending at the earthed electrode binds free charges, whose density is locally dependent upon the field gradient E acting at every elementary surface area $dA = a$. This local density is $\sigma(a) = \varepsilon E(a)$, with ε the permittivity of the dielectric. The earthed electrode is subdivided into a sensing or pick-up electrode A, a guard electrode G and a movable electrode M, all of which are at same potential. If

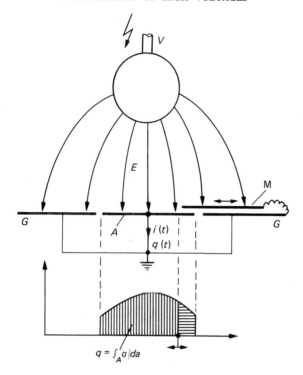

FIG. 3.21. Principle of generating voltmeters.

M is fixed and the voltage V (or field E) is changed, a current $i(t)$ would flow between A and earth. This current results from a change of the charge density σ, which is sketched as a one-dimensional distribution only. The amount of charge can be integrated by

$$q = \int_A \sigma(a)\,da,$$

where

$$A\left(= \int da \right)$$

is the area of the sensing electrode exposed to the field. If the voltage V is constant, a current $i(t)$ will flow only if M is moved, thus steadily altering the

surface field strength from full to zero values within the covered areas. Thus
the current is

$$i(t) = \frac{dq}{dt} = \frac{d}{dt} \int_{A(t)} \sigma(a)\,da = \varepsilon\,\frac{d}{dt} \int_{A(t)} E(a)\,da. \qquad (3.23)$$

The integral boundary denotes the time-varying exposed area and $\sigma(a)$ as
well as $E(a)$ are also time-dependent if the voltage is not constant.

The field lines between h.v. and sensing electrode comprise a capacitive
system. Thus the charge q can be computed by a field computation or by
calibration of the system. The integration across the time-varying area $A(t)$,
however, provides a time-varying capacitance, and if also the voltage
changes with time, $q(t) = C(t)V(t)$ and

$$i(t) = \frac{d}{dt}\,[C(t)V(t)]. \qquad (3.24)$$

Various kinds of generating voltmeters use this basic equation and the
manifold designs differ in the constructional means for providing $C(t)$ and
interpreting the current $i(t)$. One typical design will be described, sketched
in Fig. 3.22, to demonstrate the capabilities.

A synchronous motor M drives a rotating sectionized disc D, split into
two halves carefully insulated from each other and connected to a
commutator. The electrical field can penetrate to the revolving disc through
the mechanically fixed iris S, formed by a half-section of the rotating disc.
Thus the capacitance between one segment of D and an adjacent h.v.
electrode (not shown here) will vary between zero and its maximum value,
$C_{\max}$. If the two segments are short-circuited without commutator, an a.c.
current will flow due to the increase and simultaneous decrease of the
capacitances of both sections. By means of the commutator, this current
is rectified and the mean value recorded by the instrument (i.e. moving
coil meter). For a d.c. voltage of magnitude V, eqn. (3.24) is reduced to
$i(t) = VdC/dt$. With the period T_c for capacitance change and a peak to
peak change ΔC of the capacitance within $T_c/2$, the integration of eqn. (3.24)
gives

$$I = \frac{2}{T_c} \int_0^{T_c} i(t)\,dt = \frac{2V}{T_c} \int_0^{T_c} dC(t) = \frac{2V\Delta C}{T_c}.$$

For a constant speed of n rpm and $T_c = 60/n$:

$$I = \frac{n}{30}\,\Delta C V = \frac{n}{30}\,C_{\max} V. \qquad (3.25)$$

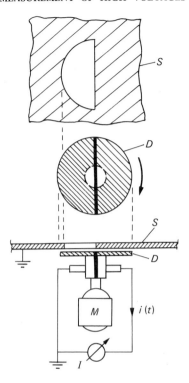

FIG. 3.22. Generating voltmeter with rotating disc.

Example:
$$n = 1800 \text{ rpm}$$
$$C_{max} = 5 \text{ pF}$$
$$V = 100 \text{ kV}$$
$$\left.\rule{0cm}{1.2cm}\right\} \quad I = 30 \ \mu A.$$

As d.c. currents are easily and accurately measured, the mechanical rectification of $i(t)$ is well justified. Commutators will introduce, however, some problems related to thermal e.m.f.s and cannot be used for small systems. Rectification and amplification of small a.c. currents is possible today with operational amplifiers. Thus a revolving sensing electrode is not suitable. Improved designs use rotating vanes, which are at guard potential, and sectionalized sensing electrodes, which do not move. A typical generating voltmeter of this type is shown in Fig. 3.23 and described by

FIG. 3.23. Field meter (Kleinwaechter, Loerrach/Germany).[37]

Kleinwaechter.[37] Some additional information is provided in references 38, 1, 30, 4 (Chapter 2).

For slowly variable d.c. voltages the design of Fig. 3.22 can still be used as long as the integrating instrument is not too inert. It can even be applied for the measurement of any instantaneous magnitude of an a.c. voltage, if the speed of the drive motor is synchronized with the frequency of the voltage to be measured. In the diagram of Fig. 3.24, the time-dependent variation of $C(t)$ is sketched together with a.c. voltage, the frequency of which, however, is twice as high as the frequency of $C(t)$. According to eqn. (3.24) the mean value of the current is now

$$I = \frac{1}{T_V} \int_{t_1}^{t_2} i(t)\,dt = f_V[C(t_2)V(t_2) - C(t_1)V(t_1)].$$

As $V(t_2)$ equals $V(t_1)$, and $\Delta C = C(t_2) - C(t_1)$, we obtain for any instantaneous value of $V(t)$

$$I = f_V \Delta C V(t) = f_V C_{\max} V(t),$$

if the phase shift between the voltage and capacitance variation is

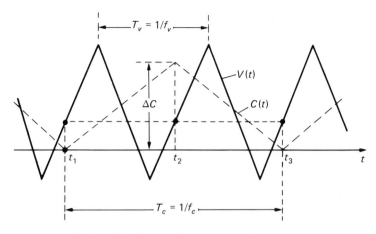

FIG. 3.24. Sketch explaining derivation of eqn. (3.26).

arbitrarily changed. With $f_V = 2f_c$, and $f_c = n/60$, we finally obtain

$$I = \frac{n}{30} C_{\max} V(t), \tag{3.26}$$

and thus the expression is the same as eqn. (3.25) giving instantaneous value of voltage. A four-pole synchronous motor with 1500 rpm is suitable for 50 Hz, and the phase angle can easily be adjusted by treating the motor relative to the iris in Fig. 3.22.

Apart from this special case, the rotating vane constructions are also capable of a.c. measurements. The a.c. current provided by eqn. (3.24) is a modulated current and must be conveniently processed. Multiple wing vanes with an accordingly high number of sensing electrodes and high drive motor speeds are necessary to provide a good modulation.

Generating voltmeters are very linear instruments and applicable over a wide range of voltages. The sensitivity may be changed by the area of the sensing electrodes (or iris) as well as by the current instrument or amplification. Their early application for the output voltage measurement of a Van de Graff's thus may well be understood. Excessive space charge accumulation within the gap between h.v. electrode and generating voltmeter, however, must be avoided. The presence of space charges will be observed if the voltage is switched off.

Vibrating electrometers are also generating voltmeters, but will only be discussed here as they are not widely used. The principle can well be understood with reference to Fig. 3.21 neglecting the moveable disc. If tl● sensing electrode would oscillate in the direction of the h.v. electrode, again a current $i(t) = dq/dt$ is excited with constant voltage V due to a variation of the capacitance $C = C(t)$. This principle was developed by Gahlke and Neubert (see reference 30, p. 77). The sensing electrode may also pick up charges when placed just behind a small aperture drilled in a metal plate. A commercial type of such an instrument is able to measure d.c. voltages down to 10 μV, or currents down to 10^{-17} A, or charges down to 10^{-15} pC, and its terminal resistance is as high as 10^{16} Ω.

3.5 THE MEASUREMENT OF PEAK VOLTAGES

Disruptive discharge phenomena within electrical insulation systems or simple insulation materials are in general caused by the instantaneous maximum field gradients stressing the materials. Alternating voltages or impulse voltages may produce these high gradients, and even for d.c. voltages with ripple, the maximum amplitude of the instantaneous voltage may initiate the breakdown. The standards for the measurement and application for test voltages therefore limit the ripple factors for d.c. testing voltages, as the peak value of d.c. voltages is usually not measured, and claim for a measurement of the peak values of a.c. and impulse voltages whenever this is adequate.

Up to this point the spark gaps (section 3.1) have been an adequate means for the measurement of the peak values of all types of voltages. The necessary calibration procedure, however, and the limited accuracy are hindering its application and call for more convenient methods. The generating voltmeter (see section 3.4) of appropriate construction would certainly satisfy the needs for a.c. power frequency voltage measurements. For voltages higher than some 100 kV, the cost of building an electrode configuration providing stable field distributions at the sensory electrodes increases rapidly. We could adequately show the disadvantages encountered with high-ohmic resistor voltage dividers (see section 3.3) applied to a.c. voltage measurements, which resulted in limitations within voltage range of 100–200 kV.

The simplest way to obtain the output peak voltage of a testing transformer is by measuring and recording the primary voltage and then multiplying the value by the transformer ratio. However, the load-dependent magnitude of the ratio as well as unavoidable waveshape variations caused by the transformer impedances which magnify or reduce the higher harmonics render such a method unacceptable. Even simpler would be to calculate the peak value of an impulse voltage from the charging voltage of the impulse voltage generator multiplied by the voltage efficiency factor η (see eqn. (2.29), Chapter 2). Here, the unknown voltage drops within the generator and the loading effects by the object under test do not allow in general the use of such methods.

The direct measurement of the high voltages across test objects and of their peak values is therefore of great importance. Many of the methods treated in this chapter require voltage dividing systems providing adequate voltage levels for the circuits used to process the peak or crest values. A detailed study and generalized theory of voltage dividing systems will be presented in section 3.6. Therefore, within this chapter the voltage divider's equivalent circuits are simplified and assumed ideal. A treatment of the construction and performance of h.v. capacitors for measuring purposes is, however, added to this chapter, as their application is closely related to the circuits described here.

The measurement of peak voltages by means of oscilloscopes is not treated in detail. Apart from the measurement of impulse crest values their application to a.c. voltages is not convenient and thus unusual. For accurate measurements a very careful adjustment and calibration of the oscilloscope would be necessary. This, however, is beyond the scope of this book.

3.5.1 The Chubb–Fortescue Methods

This simple but accurate method for the measurement of peak values of a.c. voltages was proposed by Chubb and Fortescue,[39] who as early as in 1913 became interested in the use of a sphere gap as a measuring device. The basic diagram (Fig. 3.25(a)) comprises a standard capacitor, two diodes and a current integrating ammeter (i.e. moving coil instrument) only. The displacement current $i_c(t)$ is subdivided into positive and negative components by the back-to-back connected diodes. The voltage drop across these diodes (about 1 V for Si diodes) may completely be neglected when high voltages are to be measured. The measuring instrument may be included in one of the two branches. In either case it reads a magnitude of

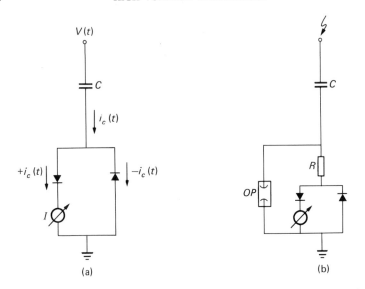

FIG. 3.25. A.C. peak voltage measurement by Chubb and Fortescue. (a) Fundamental circuit. (b) Recommended, actual circuit.

charge per cycle, or the mean value of the current $i_c(t) = C \, dV/dt$, and thus

$$I = \frac{1}{T} \int_{t_1}^{t_2} i_c(t) \, dt = \frac{C}{T} \int_{t_1}^{t_2} dV = \frac{C}{T} (V_{+\max} + |V_{-\max}|)$$

according to Fig. 3.26 which illustrates the integral boundaries and the magnitudes related to Fig. 3.25(a). The difference between the positive and negative peak values may be designated as V_{p-p}, and if both peak values are equal a condition which usually applies we may write

$$I = Cf V_{p-p} = 2Cf V_{\max}. \tag{3.27}$$

The close relation to the generating voltmeter is obvious. An increased current would be measured if the current reaches zero more than once during one half-cycle. This means the waveshape of the voltage would contain more than one maximum per half-cycle. A.c. testing voltages with such high harmonics contents are, however, not within the limits of standards and therefore only very short and rapid voltage drops caused by heavy predischarges within the test circuit could introduce errors. A filtering of the a.c. voltage by a damping resistor placed between the capacitor C and the object tested will eliminate this problem.

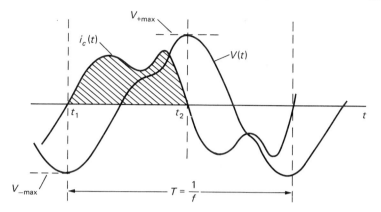

FIG. 3.26. Diagram of voltage $V(t)$ and current $i_c(t)$ from circuit Fig. 3.25(a).

The relationship in eqn. (3.27) shows the principal sources of errors. First, the frequency f must be accurately known. In many countries the power frequency often used for testing voltages is very stable and accurately known. The independent measurement of the frequency with extremely high precision (i.e. counters) is possible. The current measurement causes no problem, as these currents are in the mA range. The effective value of the capacitance should also be accurately known, and because of the different constructions available, which will be discussed in section 3.5.4, a very high precision is possible. The main source of error is often introduced by imperfect rectifiers. These have to subdivide the a.c. current $i_c(t)$ with high precision, this means the charge transferred in forward direction, which is limited by the capacitance C, must be much higher (10^4–10^5 times) than the charge in reversed voltage direction. Therefore the reverse voltage currents should be small due to the back-to-back connection of the diodes, the reverse voltages are low. However, the diodes as well as the instrument are also highly stressed by short impulse currents during voltage breakdowns. A suitable protection of the rectifying circuit is recommended as shown in Fig. 3.25(b). The resistor R introduces a required voltage drop during breakdown to ignite the overvoltage protector OP (i.e. gas discharge tube).

The influence of the frequency on the reading can be eliminated by electronically controlled gates and by sensing the rectified current by analogue-to-digital converters. By this means (see Boeck[40]) and using pressurized standard capacitors the accuracy may well reach about 0.1%.

3.5.2 Passive Rectifier Circuits and Voltage Dividers

Passive circuits are nowadays rarely used in the measurement of peak values of a.c. or impulse voltages. The rapid development of fully integrated operational amplifiers and other electric circuits during the last decade has offered many possibilities to "sample and hold" such voltages and thus displace passive circuits. Nevertheless, a short treatment will be included because of their simplicity and the adequate accuracy which they offer if properly designed. The availability of excellent Si diodes, again a result of steadily improving electronic technology, has eliminated the earlier difficulties encountered in the application of diodes to a large extent. Passive circuits can be built cheaply and they are reliable. And, last but not least, they are not sensitive to electromagnetic impact, i.e. the electromagnetic compatibility (EMC) is excellent. In contrast, the sophisticated electronic instruments are more expensive and their EMC is lower. These will be discussed in the next section. A further reason for discussing passive circuits here is their application in crest voltage measurements.

Passive circuits used for peak voltage measurements are unable to process high voltages directly and therefore they are always used in conjunction with voltage dividers which are preferably of capacitive type. It is obvious from Chapter 2 (Fig. 2.1) that the single-phase rectifier circuit with storage capacitor is the fundamental element of any analogue crest voltmeter. There are, however, many problems arising if such a simple circuit is to convert exactly the crest input voltage to a measurable quantity.

A.C. Voltages

The first adequately usable crest voltmeter circuit was described in 1930 by Davis, Bowdler and Standring. The circuit is shown in Fig. 3.27 which is used here to discuss some fundamental errors encountered in a.c. voltage measurements. A capacitor divider reduces the high voltage V to a low magnitude. If R_2 and R_d are neglected and the voltage V increases, the storage capacitor C_s is charged to the crest value of V_2 neglecting the voltage drop across the diode. Thus the voltage $V_m \approx +V_{2max}$ could be measured by an electrostatic voltmeter or other suitable instrument of very high input resistance. The capacitor C_s will not significantly discharge during a period, if the reverse current through the diode is very small and

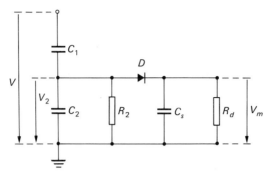

FIG. 3.27. Simple crest voltmeter for a.c. measurements, according to Davis, Bowdler and Standring.

the discharge time constant of the storage capacitor very large. If V_2 is now decreased, C_2 will hold the charge and the voltage across it and thus V_m no longer follows the crest value of V_2. Hence, a discharge resistor R_d must be introduced into the circuit. The general rules for the measuring technique require that a measured quantity be indicated within a few seconds. Thus the time constant $R_d C_s$ should be within about 0.5–1 sec. Three new errors, however, are now introduced: an experiment would readily show that the output voltage V_m decreases steadily if a constant high voltage V is switched to the circuit. This effect is caused by a continuous discharge of C_s as well as of C_2. Thus the mean potential of $V_2(t)$ will gain a negative d.c. component, which finally equals to about $+ V_{2max}$. Hence a leakage resistor R_2 must be inserted in parallel with C_2 to equalize these unipolar discharge currents. The second error refers to the voltage shape across the storage capacitor. This voltage contains a ripple discussed in Chapter 2, section 2.1. Thus the error almost independent of the type of instrument used (i.e. mean or r.m.s. value measurement) is due to discharge and recorded as the difference between peak and mean value. The error is approximately proportional to the ripple factor [see eqn. (2.2)] and thus frequency-dependent as the discharge time constant cannot be changed. For $R_d C_s = 1$ sec the discharge error amounts to $\sim 1\%$ for 50 Hz, $\sim 0.33\%$ for 150 Hz and $\sim 0.17\%$ for 300 Hz. The third source of error is related to this discharge error: during the conduction time of the diode the storage capacitor is recharged to the crest value and thus C_s is parallel to C_2. If the discharge error is e_d, this "recharge error" e_r is approximately given by

$$e_r \approx 2e_d \frac{C_s}{C_1 + C_2 + C_s}. \tag{3.28}$$

Hence C_s should be small compared to C_2, which for h.v. dividers is the largest capacitance in the circuit. There still remains a negative d.c. component of the mean potential of the voltage V_2, as the equalizing effect of R_2 is not perfect. This "potential error" e_p is again a negative term, and amounts to $e_p = -(R_2/R_d)$. Hence R_2 should be much smaller than R_d.

This leakage resistor R_2 introduces another error directly related to the now frequency-dependent ratio or attenuation factor of the voltage divider. Apart from a phase shift between V_2 and V, which is not of interest, the relative amplitudes of V_2 decrease with decreasing frequency and the calculation shows the relative error term

$$e_{vd} = - \frac{1}{2\{\omega R_2(C_1 + C_2)\}^2} \approx - \frac{1}{2(\omega R_2 C_2)^2}. \qquad (3.29)$$

Apart from a negligible influence caused by the diode's inherent junction capacitance, we see that many systematic error terms aggravate the exact crest voltage measured.

A numerical example will demonstrate the relative magnitudes of the different errors. Let $C_1 = 100$ pF, $C_2 = 100$ nF, a realistic measure for a HVAC divider with attenuation factor of 1000. For $R_d C_s = 1$ sec, the inherent error term $e_d = -1\%$ for 50 Hz. Allowing an error of one-half of this value for the recharge error e_r requires a C_s value $C_2/3$ approximately, and thus $C_s = 33$ nF. From $R_d C_s = 1$ sec the discharge resistor is calculated to be about 30 MΩ. This value is a measure for the input resistance of the voltmeter and the diode's reverse resistance necessary. Let the potential error e_p again be 0.5%. Hence $R_2 = R_d/200$ or 150 kΩ. For a frequency of 50 Hz this leakage resistor gives $e_{vd} \approx 2.25\%$. Thus the sum of errors $(e_d + e_r + e_p + e_{vd}) \approx -4.25\%$, still neglecting the voltage drop across the diode.

Hence, for passive rectifying circuits comprising capacitor voltage dividers as the voltage source, too small leakage resistors must be avoided. The possible solution to bleed the h.v. capacitor is expensive, as it requires a h.v. resistor. The addition of an equalizing branch to the l.v. arm of the voltage divider provides an attractive solution. This can be accomplished using a half-wave rectifier circuit shown in Fig. 3.27 by the addition of a second network comprising D, C_s and R_d for negative polarities. Thus the d.c. currents in both branches are opposite in polarity and equalize each other. All errors related to R_2 are cancelled. To demonstrate the principle in a further improved form, a two-way booster circuit designed by Rabus in 1950 is shown in Fig. 3.28. Two storage capacitors within every branch are

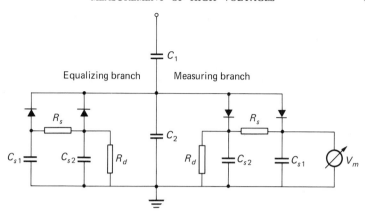

F𝕚ɢ. 3.28. Two-way booster circuit designed by Rabus.

connected by a resistor R_s and both are discharged by only one discharge resistor R_d. In this circuit, the immediate discharge of the storage capacitor C_{s1} after charging to the crest value is delayed and thus the inherent discharge error e_d can be reduced. As, however, two storage capacitors within one branch must be charged to the crest voltage, more charge is withdrawn from C_2 and hence the recharge error e_r might increase. A careful design and dimensioning of all elements within this circuit is necessary to find the optimum circuit parameters providing the lowest sum of inherent errors. For commonly used ratios and capacitance values in the voltage dividers used, the error terms can thus be kept well within about $\pm(0.5-1\%)$ even for frequencies down to 20 Hz. Detailed calculations were carried out by Zaengl.[41]

There are some other similar circuits available which will not be discussed here. The information can be found in the original publications as well as in summaries of Voelcker and Zaengl[42] or Schwab.[1]

Some additional remarks relating to the actual layout and construction of such measuring circuits will be made. The h.v. capacitor C_1 is designed for the rated voltage and is always placed within the test area. In general, the l.v. arm C_2 including the peak circuit and instrument form a measuring unit located in the control area. Hence a coaxial cable is necessary to connect the two units. The cable capacitance contributes to C_2, which is usually changed in steps to adapt the usable range of the peak measuring circuit to the variable test voltage. A change of the length of the cable necessitates recalibration of the system. The voltages across C_2 should be as high as possible, as cable shield currents excited by electromagnetic effects produce a noise voltage and superimpose it upon V_2 by the coupling impedance of the cable.[1] Every breakdown at the high voltage end is followed by a high peak current within C_1, which "sees" at the input end of the coaxial cable its surge impedance only after twice the travel time of this cable. Hence high voltages of short duration may be built up at the l.v. end of the capacitor C_1, which must be limited by proper protection devices (protection gaps or gas discharge tubes). These devices will also prevent a complete damage of the measuring circuit if the insulation of C_1 should fail. Nevertheless, short-time overvoltages across C_2 appear during a disruptive discharge, if the capacitors forming C_2 are not carefully arranged to prevent excessive inductive voltage drops. Thus it is most desirable to place part of the capacitor directly under C_1, and part in the measuring cabinet.

Impulse Voltages

The measurement of crest values of impulse voltages with short times to crest (lightning impulses) by passive elements only was impossible for a long time. About thirty years ago the availability of vacuum diodes with relatively low internal resistance and of vacuum tubes to build active d.c. amplifiers offered the opportunity to design circuits for peak impulse voltage measurement but of relatively low accuracy.

Impulse voltages are single events and the crest value of an impulse is theoretically available only during an infinitely short time. The actual crest value may less stringently be defined as a crest region in which the voltage amplitude is higher than 99.5%. For a standard 1.2/50 μsec wave the available time is then about 1.1 μsec. Consider now the simple crest voltmeter circuit of Fig. 2.37 discussed earlier, omitting the discharge resistor R_d as well as R_2. The diode D will then conduct for a positive voltage impulse applied to the voltage divider, and the storage capacitor must be charged during the rising front only. But instantaneous charging is only possible if the diode has no forward (dynamic) resistance. The actual forward resistance R_D gives rise to a changing time constant $R_D C_s$ and it will be shown in more detail in section 3.6 that a "response time", which is equal to the time constant $R_D C_s$ for such an RC circuit, of about 0.2 μsec would be necessary to record the crest value with good accuracy. For a low C_s value of 1000 pF the required $R_D = 200 \Omega$. As also the diode's junction capacitance must be very small in comparison to C_s, diodes with adequate

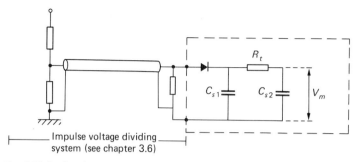

Impulse voltage dividing
system (see chapter 3.6)

FIG. 3.29. Peak voltmeter (within dashed line) with continuous charge exchange.

values must be properly selected. The more difficult problem, however, is the time required to read the voltage across C_s. The voltage should not decrease significantly, i.e. $\leqslant 1\%$ for at least about 10 sec. Hence the discharge time constant of C_s must be longer than 10^3 sec, and thus the interaction between the diode's reverse resistance and the input resistance of the instrument necessary to measure the voltage across C_s should provide a resultant leakage resistance of 10^{12} Ω. A measurement of this voltage with electrostatic voltmeters or electronic electrometers is essential, but the condition for the diode's reverse resistance can hardly be met. To avoid this problem, a charge exchange circuit shown in Fig. 3.29 was proposed. If the capacitor C_{s1} originally charged to crest value transfers most of its charge to a much larger second storage capacitor C_{s2} within a short time, i.e. much shorter than 1 sec, C_{s1} cannot lose much of the charge through the finite reverse resistance of the diode and the discharge time constant after the charge transfer is greatly increased because C_{s1} and C_{s2} are paralleled. The transfer resistance R_t must always be lower than the reverse resistance of the diode. As $C_{s2} \gg C_{s1}$, the output voltage V_m is decreased very much and therefore an electrostatic voltmeter becomes inapplicable as the voltages are too low, d.c. amplifiers must therefore be used. Also other peak reading devices must always be combined with active electronic circuits, some of which are described elsewhere.[1] In practical use operational amplifiers as well as digital electronic devices are used.

3.5.3 Active or Amplifying Circuits

Due to the demand within other technical fields, analogue or digital instruments are widely commercially available. The main problem

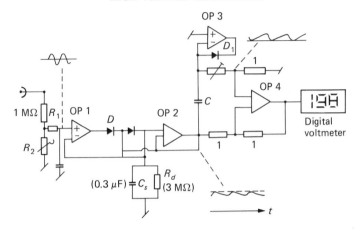

FIG. 3.30. Simplified circuit of a crest voltmeter for a.c. voltages with discharge error compensation (courtesy Haefely & Co.).

encountered with these instruments when applied in h.v. laboratories is related, however, to their electromagnetic compatibility resulting from transient disturbances following breakdown phenomena.

The aims of amplifying circuits may be summarized as follows: a high and linear input impedance (1–2 MΩ) is necessary to avoid excessive loading of the h.v. dividers of any kind. Thus the error terms e_r, e_p and e_{vd} discussed in section 3.5.2 can be minimized. In circuits used for continuous measurement of a.c. peak voltages, the reduction of the discharge error is much more difficult. In analogue circuits this may be achieved by a continuous compensation of the ripple area. To demonstrate the principle only, a simplified circuit is sketched in Fig. 3.30 related to an actual circuit of a specialized manufacturer. A voltage attenuator for low voltages (<1 kV) reduces and adapts the input voltages to be processed by the first operational amplifier $OP1$. An RC filter dimensioned for a damping of too high frequency components reduces short overvoltages, which are not relevant to peak voltage measurements. $OP1$ charges the storage capacitor C_s, which is discharged through the discharge resistor R_d with a time constant of 1 sec. The voltage drop across the two series connected diodes D is cancelled by $OP1$ acting as a voltage follower. Thus the second voltage follower $OP2$ still amplifies the ripple produced by the passive rectifying circuit. Its feedback to the connection point of the diodes D, however, avoids leakage of C_s by the reversed biased diodes. The ripple is detected by the capacitively coupled operational amplifier *OP3*, which rectifies the voltage by the diode D_1 whose forward conduction voltage is strongly linearized by the amplifier. By this means, the ripple voltage appears across an adjustable voltage divider. The inversion of the output voltage of *OP2* and summation with the ripple voltage performed by *OP4* thus eliminates the ripple and therefore the discharge error to a large extent. The output voltage may be measured by an analogue or digital voltmeter.

The principle of such a circuit (without ripple compensation) can also be used for peak impulse voltage measurements. The discharge of the storage capacitor through R_d is then avoided and replaced by a reset switch. Very high-quality operational amplifiers with high slew rates are necessary, and the long storage time is usually achieved by two or three rectifying circuits with amplification in series. More details may be found in the literature.[43-45;89]

The increasing availability of specialized fully integrated analogue and digital circuits will contribute to the development of a large variety of peak holding circuits. A recent publication by Schulz[46] describes a mixed circuit for a very precise a.c. peak measurement with a statistical uncertainty of $<2.8 \times 10^{-4}$ which includes a capacitor voltage divider for 200 kV, composed of a pressurized gas capacitor and mica capacitors for the l.v. arm. The peak detecting circuit consists essentially of a special sample-and-hold amplifier (a.c. to d.c. converter) and a very precise digital voltmeter, with both being controlled by a microprocessor. The main aim of this control is to avoid any discharge error as mentioned earlier. Such complex and expensive measuring units are built for calibration purposes only and not for laboratory applications. For impulse voltage measurements, the transient recorders comprising fast parallel ADCs will increasingly be used. The description of the principle of transient recorders may be found elsewhere[47] and a recent publication by Malewski and Dechamplain[48] demonstrates the necessity of additional shielding of such commercial equipment. Transient recorders will probably replace, to some extent, the usual CRO technique in the near future for impulse voltage measurements.

3.5.4 High-voltage Capacitors for Measuring Circuits

The important influence of the effective capacitance of any h.v. capacitors used in the Chubb–Fortescue circuit of section 3.5.1, as well as in most of the peak reading circuits for a.c. voltages, makes it necessary to present a short treatment of capacitor units widely used in testing and research laboratories.

In comparison to h.v. capacitors used within h.v. transmission and distribution systems for load or series compensation as well as for other components necessary within h.v. apparatus (i.e. voltage grading capacitors for switchgear, etc.), the requirements for measuring capacitors are different. First, the effective capacitor values are quite low and they range between some 10 and 100 pF only. These low values are sufficient to provide the energy needed for the measurement and to provide low load for the voltage source. The second requirement is related to the accuracy and stability of the C values relative to temperature, humidity or other atmospheric conditions, external fields and voltage range, including all effects associated with this magnitude, i.e. partial discharges or nonlinearity.

A h.v. capacitor may consist of a single capacitance unit defined as a basically two-electrode arrangement or of a chain of capacitor units rated for relative "low" voltages (kV range) electrically connected in series. The technology as well as the electrical behaviour is quite different for the two cases and therefore a separate discussion is appropriate.

Single Capacitance Units

Ultra high vacuum would provide the ideal dielectric between metal plates forming an arrangement with known and fixed field distribution. Ultra high vacuum has excellent electrical strength though limited by electrode effects. The difficulties and associated costs, however, to place such electrodes in large vessels or tanks providing ultra high vacuum conditions without maintenance are the reasons that vacuum is not used for very high voltages.

According to Paschen's Law high electric strength can also be achieved with gases at high pressure. Atmospheric pressure may be treated as the lower limit of a high pressure and, dependent upon the type of gas used, the upper limit is set again by predominantly electrode surface effects which place an economic limit given by the decreasing relative dielectric strength of the gas (in kV/cm bar) and the increasing cost of pressure vessels. Gases are dielectrics with predominantly electronic polarization only, providing a very low relative permittivity which is not influenced by technical frequencies and only by the particle density. Hence a gaseous dielectric is adequate for the construction of h.v. capacitors.

Thus the problem reduces to finding electrode arrangements which provide unchangeable field distributions between two electrodes forming the capacitance. As a certain maximum field strength will limit the insulation strengths of any gas, a homogeneous field distribution would obviously seem to be most convenient. The cross-sectional view of the 1-MV electrostatic voltmeter in Fig. 3.13 demonstrates such an arrangement placed in a metal tank. The earthed stress control as well as the guard ring placed around the measurement disc provide the necessary shielding or field stress control effect between the h.v. electrode and the disc, both forming a h.v. capacitor. The large bushing necessary to connect the h.v. electrode with the applied voltage and to control the external flash-over indicate the expenditures necessary to adapt small plane electrode systems, made possible by the use of highly pressurized and excellent insulating gases, with the limited electrical strength of atmospheric air. It is also difficult to control exactly the gap distance, if temperature differences and the consequent material movements are considered. Nevertheless, there have been many constructions presented for electrostatic voltmeters (the problem of field control at the measuring electrode is directly correlated to a capacitance control) and preliminary atmospheric air capacitors taking advantage of the homogeneous electrode arrangements.

The coaxial cylindrical electrode configuration provides the second opportunity to achieve a fairly good field distribution, if the difference between the two radii of the electrodes is not too large. In Chapter 4, section 4.2.2 the two-dimensional coaxial field is treated and it is shown that the radii can be optimized to keep the diameter of the outer electrode as small as possible for a given voltage and a limited field strength at the inner electrode. Thus, the radial dimensions do not become very large if the system is pressurized. As the capacitance C per unit axial length l is $C/l = 2\pi\varepsilon/\ln(r_2/r_1)$, where r_1 and r_2 are the radii of the inner and outer cylinder respectively, even with the optimum ratio $r_2/r_1 = e$ this capacitance is about 56 pF/m and thus large enough to achieve adequate capacitance values (30–100 pF) with limited length of the electrodes. A further advantage relates to the possible variation of the capacitance if the inner electrode is not completely centralized. The central position is a position of minimum value of capacitance as shown by a computation of the capacitance varying with eccentricity according to the relevant formula,[38]

$$\frac{C}{l} = \frac{2\pi\varepsilon}{\cosh^{-1}\left(\dfrac{r_1^2 + r_2^2 - D}{2r_1 r_2}\right)},\tag{3.30}$$

where D is the distance between the axes of both cylinders. The expression shows that a small eccentricity does not contribute much to a change in capacitance. This is the main reason why most of the "standard capacitors" used today comprise this coaxial cylinder system. Originally suggested by Schering and Vieweg in 1928,[1] a cross-section of such a compressed gas capacitor is shown in Fig. 3.31. The main h.v. electrode *1* encloses the l.v.

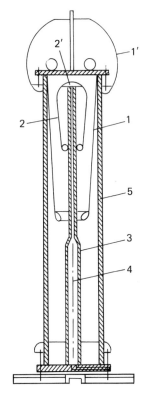

FIG. 3.31. Cross-section of a compressed gas capacitor (standard capacitor). 1. Internal h.v. electrode. 1′. External h.v. electrode. 2. Low-voltage electrode with guarding. 2′, 3. Supporting tube. 4. Coaxial connection to l.v. sensing electrode. 5. Insulating cylinder.

electrode with guard ring 2 completely and thus shields the electrode from the influence of all external fields. The pressure vessel 5 is of a dielectric material and contributes to minimize the height. The supporting tube 3 is at earth potential. One main insulation problem involved in this construction relates to the tangential field distribution outside the dielectric vessel, as the limited electrical strength of atmospheric air must withstand the strong field concentration in the vicinity of the lower end of the h.v. electrode. Even a rough plot of the equipotential lines surrounding the electrode system may show this field concentration, which is sketched in Fig. 3.32, a result obtained by Keller.[49] The maximum stress which occurs at the end of the h.t. electrode remains approximately the same, and is independent of the length of the dielectric cylinder. The reduction of this external field by simple means is not possible; even the simplest solution to increase the diameter of the vessel and to distribute the equipotential lines within the cylinder is difficult due to the necessary increase in mechanical strength of the vessel construction.

Compressed gas capacitors provide, if well designed and constructed, a h.v. capacitance of highest possible stability; they are, however, expensive.

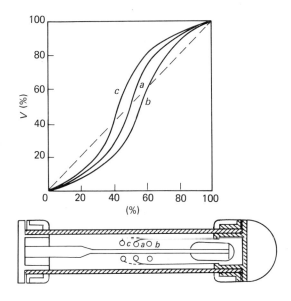

FIG. 3.32. Potential distribution along a compressed capacitor for various lengths of h.t. electrode.

Due to their outstanding performance with regard to the precision of the capacitance value and very low tan δ values they are predominantly used as standard capacitor within h.v. bridges for C tan δ measurements (see Chapter 6). Variations in the construction are, of course, possible.[50–52] These have been built for a.c. voltages up to 1500 kV. CO_2, N_2 or SF_6 are convenient gases for insulation. Sulphur hexafluoride provides the highest electric strength and thus only pressures up to about 0.4 MPa (in comparison to 1 to 1.5 MPa with other gases) are necessary. The relative influence of the pressure-dependent permittivity upon capacitance value may be calculated taking into account the increase of the relative permittivity ε_r with gas density, given by

$$\varepsilon_r = 1 + \alpha \frac{273}{100} \frac{p}{T}; \quad \begin{matrix} p \text{ in kPa} \\ T \text{ in K} \end{matrix} \qquad (3.31)$$

where

$$\alpha \approx 0.00232 \quad \text{for } SF_6,$$

$$\alpha \approx 0.00055 \quad \text{for } N_2,$$

$$\alpha \approx 0.00076 \quad \text{for } CO_2.$$

As the actual gas density in a vessel may be influenced by the construction also, the actual variation with p and T will be specified by the manufacturer. Dissipation factors tan δ are in general well below 10^{-5} for power frequency.

Figure 3.33 shows physical picture of a standard capacitor for a rated voltage of 1000 kV.

"Stacked" Capacitor Units

This second type of a capacitor construction consists of a large number of single capacitor elements in series. Single units of conventional capacitors with predominantly oil-kraftpaper insulation or any type of solid dielectric capacitors cannot be built for voltages higher than about 10 kV, and hence this series connection is necessary. As the necessary total capacitance must be low, these capacitor units are piled up and thus a stretched stack of large height/diameter ratio is formed.

Whatever the construction of an individual unit, there are always charges located at some parts of the electrodes which do not contribute to the actual series capacitance. These electrodes are at a potential which is essentially given by the capacitor elements which form a voltage-dividing system. The "foreign" charges are thus related to stray capacitances in the same way as discussed in section 3.3.

A realistic equivalent circuit of stacked capacitor units each comprising a

FIG. 3.33. Standard (compressed gas) capacitor for 1000 kV r.m.s. (Micafil, Switzerland).

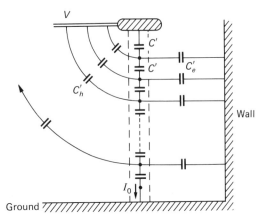

FIG. 3.34. Stray capacitances influencing the equivalent capacitance of h.v. capacitors.

capacitance C' is shown in Fig. 3.34. For large capacitors within laboratories the stray capacitances to earth may strongly be influenced by the walls, which often are electromagnetically shielded; this is assumed in this sketch. The h.v. lead including top electrode of the whole capacitor may contribute to small stray capacitances to h.v. potential V. A calculation of the current I_0 flowing to ground from the last earthed capacitor could be carried out essentially in the same way as the computation performed in section 3.3, eqns. (3.13)–(3.18). Assuming similar approximations within the expressions for the current I_0 we achieve by expansion of the hyperbolic functions the following result:

$$I_0 = V\omega C \frac{1 + \dfrac{C_h}{4C}}{1 + \dfrac{C_e}{6C} + \dfrac{C_h}{12C}} = V\omega C_{eq} \qquad (3.32)$$

where $C = C'/n$; $C_e = nC'_e$; $C_h = nC'_h$; and n a large (infinite) number of capacitor elements C'. The capacitance $C = C'/n$ is obviously the resultant capacitance of the chain computed from the usual series circuit, i.e. $1/C = 1/C_1 + 1/C_2 + \dots 1/C_n$. Equation (3.32) demonstrates that the "equivalent" or effective capacitance C_{eq} of a stacked capacitor cannot be calculated from individual elements, as the stray capacitances are not exactly known. A l.v. capacitor within a voltage divider (Fig. 3.27 or 3.28) or a divider within the Chubb–Fortescue circuit (Fig. 3.25) will only "see" the current I_0.

Many recent measurements performed with huge stacked capacitor units[53] confirmed the fundamental applicability of eqn. (3.32). It was also shown that the influence of the stray capacitance to the h.v. side, C_h' can be neglected. Nevertheless, it is necessary to rate the series capacitors so that the term $C_e/6C$ does not exceed some percentage. Thus we may simplify eqn. (3.32) to

$$C_{eq} \approx C\left(1 - \frac{C_e}{6C}\right). \tag{3.33}$$

This effect of decreasing capacitance can experimentally be easily checked by a correct measurement of C_{eq} with a h.v. bridge (Schering or transformer ratio arm bridge, see Chapter 6). In such bridge circuits, the unknown capacitor is placed at its working condition. If the high voltage is applied, the l.v. end of this unknown capacitor remains essentially at earth potential, as the bridge potential at the null indicator is very low; hence, the potential distribution across the test object remains unchanged. A measurement of C_{eq} with a usual two-terminal capacitance bridge cannot be made and would indicate wrong results.

The dimensioning of stacked capacitor units for the measurement of high voltages must take this effect into consideration. C_e can approximately be calculated by the assumption that the stacked capacitors are of cylindrical shape, thus forming a metallized vertical cylinder placed upon a horizontal plane, as sketched in Fig. 3.35. The well-known formula for this arrange-

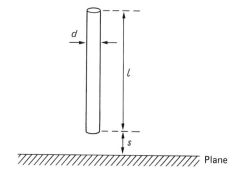

Fig. 3.35. Cylindrical conductor above plane [see eqn. (3.34)].

ment[54] is

$$C_e = \frac{2\pi \varepsilon l}{\ln\left[\dfrac{2l}{d}\sqrt{\dfrac{4s+l}{4s+3l}}\right]}$$ (3.34)

and for $s \ll l$:

$$C_e \approx \frac{2\pi \varepsilon l}{\ln\dfrac{1.15l}{d}}.$$ (3.35)

Since even more accurate approximations will not contribute much to the result as shown by Zaengl[54] and Luehrmann,[55] one may evaluate eqn. (3.35) only, and one can easily see that the absolute values C_e/l range within about 10 to 15 pF/m. If stacked capacitors are made with constant capacitance values independent of the height l of the unit, the influence of the stray capacitance to ground will thus increase according to eqn. (3.33). The error term in this equation may be as large as 5% to reach variations of C_{eq} smaller than 1%, as only the possible variations of the stray capacitance can contribute. This condition leads to

$$\frac{C_e}{6C} = \frac{C_e/l}{6C/l} \lesssim 5\%.$$

With $C_e/l = 10$–15 pF/m we obtain

$$C/l \approx C_{eq}/l \simeq 30\text{–}50 \text{ pF/m}.$$ (3.36)

If this condition is not fulfilled, capacitors within measuring circuits should be fixed and placed within a laboratory and no movable structures or equipment disturbing the potential distribution of the capacitor should be in the vicinity.

Depending upon the dielectric material used for the construction of the capacitor units, the capacitance may change with temperature and frequency. An additional frequency dependency may arise from too large residual inductances. In general, these inductances can be neglected for frequencies up to 0.1–1 MHz. Their influence on the transfer characteristics of voltage dividers is treated in the next section.

3.6 VOLTAGE DIVIDING SYSTEMS AND IMPULSE VOLTAGE MEASUREMENTS

The measurement of impulse voltages even of short duration presents no difficulties, if the amplitudes are low or are in the kilovolt range only. The tremendous developments during recent years related to the technique of common CROs or fast ADC circuits provide instruments with very high bandwidth and the possibility also to display short-duration single phenomena. Though the usual input voltage range of these instruments is low, h.v. probes or attenuators for voltages up to some 10 kV are commercially available.

The problems arise with much higher voltages and it is well known that impulse voltages with magnitudes up to some megavolts are used for testing and research today. The voltage dividers necessary to accommodate these voltages are specialized apparatus, and there are only a few manufacturers throughout the world who are ready to produce such dividers with adequate accuracy. Self-provided construction is often adequate if the problems are known. But also the application of such voltage dividers needs a fundamental understanding of the interactions present in voltage-dividing systems. Hence an attempt is made to introduce the reader by theory as well as with some hints on constructional details on this probably most difficult field of h.v. measuring techniques.

We will start with a generalized voltage generation and dividing system and briefly discuss the layout (section 3.6.1). Depending upon the voltage shape to be measured, the requirements related to the whole measuring system must be well defined (section 3.6.2). A generalized analytical calculation of the transfer properties of the whole measuring circuit involves the complex interactions between the different parts of the circuit (section 3.6.3). The theory of the "isolated" voltage dividers as an essential part of the circuit demonstrates the different types of these instruments and their possible applications (section 3.6.4). For fast transient voltages the interactions between the dividers and their adherent circuits are discussed and methods for the evaluation of the transfer properties are presented (section 3.6.5). Finally, advice on a proper design of the l.v. arm of the voltage dividers is given (section 3.6.6).

3.6.1 Generalized Voltage Generation and Measuring Circuit

Figure 3.36 illustrates a common and also adequate layout of any voltage testing circuit within a h.v. testing area. The voltage generator *1* is connected to a test object *3* by a lead *2*. These three elements form a voltage generating system. The lead *2* to the test object may comprise any

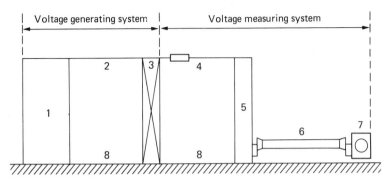

Fɪɢ. 3.36. Basic voltage testing system. 1. Voltage supply. 2. Lead to test object. 3. Test object. 4. Lead to voltage divider. 5. Voltage divider. 6. Signal or measuring cable. 7. Recording instrument. 8. Ground return.

impedance or resistance to damp oscillations, if necessary, or to limit the short-circuit currents if the test object fails. The measuring system starts at the terminals of the test object and comprises a connecting lead *4* to the voltage divider *5*, and a secondary instrument *7*, whose signal or measuring cable *6* is placed between its input terminals and the bottom or l.v. part of the divider. The appropriate ground return *8* should assure l.v. drops for even highly transient phenomena and keep the ground potential to earth as close as possible.

This layout is sometimes altered and there can be acceptable reasons for such a change. For d.c. voltages and small currents drawn by the test object, the voltage divider can be incorporated within the voltage supply, if the lead *2* has no or only a protecting resistance, the voltage drop across which can be neglected. Essentially the same statements are applicable to low-frequency a.c. voltages, but a possible influence of the lead inductance should be checked. In practice, also for impulse voltage testing circuits the voltage divider may form part of the impulse generator. The simple reasons can easily be understood from the impulse generator circuits (see Chapter 2, Fig. 2.26). There, the waveshaping load capacitance C_2 is often combined with a l.v. capacitor connected in series, thus forming an adequate voltage divider. An undamped connection to the object under test then leads to the erroneous assumption, that negligible voltage drop can occur across the lead. This assumption may be correct for smoothly rising impulse voltages and quite short leads. Connecting leads with length of many metres, however, are often used and thus this assumption may become unacceptable. It must be remembered that the test object is a capacitor and thus the circuit formed by the lead and test object is resonating. These oscillations are likely to be excited by any steep voltage rise from the generator output, but will only partly be detected by the voltage divider. Completely wrong is the assumption that a voltage divider built in within the generator is measuring the correct voltage across the test object following a voltage collapse or disruptive discharge. The whole generator including voltage divider will be discharged by this short-circuit at the test object and thus the voltage divider is loaded by the voltage drop across the lead 2. This lead forms to first approximation an inductance, and hence the oscillatory discharge currents produce heavy voltage oscillations which are then measured by the capacitor divider. These voltages are often referred to as overvoltages across the test object, but this statement is incorrect. For the measurement of predominantly lightning impulses, therefore, the layout of the circuit according to Fig. 3.36 must be used if an accurate measurement of full and chopped voltages is desired.

There is a further reason for placing the voltage dividers away from any energized objects. High-voltage dividers consist of "open" networks and cannot be shielded against external fields. All objects in the vicinity of the divider which may acquire transient potentials during a test will disturb the field distribution and thus the divider performance. The lead from the voltage divider to the test object 4 is therefore an integral part of the measuring system. The influence of this lead will theoretically be treated in section 3.6.3. There it will be established that a damping resistor at the input end of this lead contributes to improved transfer characteristics of the system.

In order to avoid heavy electromagnetic interactions between the secondary instrument and h.v. test area as well as safety hazards, the length of the signal cable 6 must be adequately chosen. Very short cables can only be used if remote controlled recording instruments withstanding the electromagnetic impacts are available; such a specialized impulse voltage oscilloscope is described in reference 56. For any type of voltage to be measured, the signal cable should be of a coaxial type. The shield or outer conductor picks up the electrostatic fields and thus prevents the penetration of this field to the inner conductor. Though even transient magnetic fields will penetrate into the cable, no appreciable voltage (noise) is induced due to the symmetrical arrangement. Ordinary coaxial cables with braided shields may well be used for d.c. and a.c. voltages. For impulse voltage measurements, these cables must provide very low losses to reduce distortion of the voltage pulses to be transmitted. As it is impossible to avoid cable shield currents not related to the transmitted signal, these currents can heavily distort these signals if the coupling impedance of the cable is not very low. In the frequency domain, this impedance $Z_c(\omega)$ is defined by

$$Z_c(\omega) = \frac{V_n/l}{I_d},$$ (3.37)

where I_d is the disturbing current flowing in the shield, and V_n/l the voltage drop at the inner surface of the shield per unit length l of the cable. More information about the origin of disturbing cable shield currents may be found in references 1 or 57 and in other recent publications.[58,59] For a pure d.c. current within the shield, the coupling impedance is given by the voltage drop due to the d.c. resistance of the shield. If the frequency of these currents increases, the impedance will continuously decrease if the shield is of rigid cross-section, as the eddy currents will attenuate the current density at the inner surface of the cylindrical shield. Hence rigid or corrugated shields, i.e. flexwell cables, are best suited for noise reduction. For braided shields, the coupling impedance is in general not a stable quantity, as the current distribution within the shield is likely to be influenced by resistive contacts within the braid. As a general rule, Z_c will decrease with frequency only within a limited frequency region, and then will heavily increase. Double-shielded cables with predominantly two insulated braided shields will improve the behaviour.

In Fig. 3.36 there is finally the ground return 8. For h.v. test circuits disruptive discharge must always be taken into account. Large and heavily oscillating short-circuit currents are developed and hence every ground return with simple leads only cannot keep the voltage drops small. The impedance, therefore, must be reduced. Large metal sheets of highly conducting material such as copper or aluminium are best. Many recently built h.v. laboratories provide such ground returns in combination with a Faraday cage for a complete shielding of the laboratory. Expanded metal sheets give similar performance. At least metal tapes of large width should be used to reduce the impedance. A parallel connection of tapes within flat areas will further decrease the inductance and thus approximate the efficiency of huge metal sheets.

Information concerning the layout of testing and measuring circuits is also provided by a special application guide as a part of IEC Publication.[60]

The measuring system thus comprises four main components with quite different electrical behaviour. The simulation of these components will depend upon the necessary frequency range to measure the voltage across the test object with high accuracy. An evaluation of this frequency range must thus precede this simulation.

3.6.2 Demands upon Transfer Characteristics of the Measuring System

The voltage measuring system defined in Fig. 3.36 is a four-terminal network and can thus be represented as shown in Fig. 3.37. V_i indicates the voltage across the test object (3 in Fig. 3.36), and the output voltage V_o appears at the recording instrument, i.e. at the screen of a CRO.

The input voltages V_i are either continuous steady-state voltages for d.c. and a.c. generating systems, or single events for impulse voltages. In both cases, the instantaneous amplitudes will change with time, even for d.c. voltages with a periodic ripple.

For a sinusoidal input voltage $v_i(t) = V_{mi} \sin(\omega t + \phi_i)$ the magnitude V_{mo} and phase angle ϕ_o of the output voltage $v_o(t) = V_{mo} \sin(\omega t + \phi_o)$ can be determined either by calculation with known network parameters or by measurements, although such measurements are difficult to perform for very high ratios of V_{mi}/V_{mo}. The frequency response of the system then can be subdivided into an amplitude (frequency) response $H(\omega) = V_{mo}/V_{mi}$ and a phase (frequency) response $\phi(\omega) = \phi_o(\omega) - \phi_i(\omega)$. It is well known that both quantities are also displayed by assuming complex amplitudes $\mathbf{V}_i = V_{mi} \exp(j\phi_i)$ and $\mathbf{V}_o = V_{mo} \exp(j\phi_o)$, and the system transfer or network response function

$$\mathbf{H}(j\omega) = \frac{\mathbf{V}_o}{\mathbf{V}_i} = |\mathbf{H}(j\omega)| \exp\{j[\phi_o(\omega) - \phi_i(\omega)]\} \qquad (3.38)$$

where $|\mathbf{H}(j\omega)| = H(\omega)$ as defined above.

FIG. 3.37. Representation of the measuring system as a four-terminal network.

Neither d.c. voltages with ripple nor a.c. testing voltages are pure sinusoidal, but periodic in nature. The input voltages may then be described by a—in general—limited number of complex amplitudes $\mathbf{V}_{ik}$ obtained by the application of Fourier series:

$$\mathbf{V}_{ik} = \frac{1}{T} \int_{-T/2}^{T/2} v_i(t) \exp(-jk\omega t)\, dt$$

$$= |\mathbf{V}_{ik}| \exp(j\phi_{ik}), \tag{3.39}$$

where $\omega = 2\pi/T$, T is the time period and k are discrete numbers. The periodic input quantity is thus analyzed into sinusoidal frequency components, and the complex amplitudes are displayed by the amplitude line spectrum $|\mathbf{V}_{ik}|$ and the angular frequency line spectrum ϕ_{ik}. For every component with the frequency $\omega_k = k\omega$, the network response may easily be found with eqn. (3.38), and the responses can be summed up using the principle of superposition. Applying again the complex form of the Fourier series, this summation gives:

$$v_o(t) = \sum_{k=-\infty}^{\infty} \mathbf{V}_{ik} \mathbf{H}(j\omega_k) \exp(jk\omega t). \tag{3.40}$$

A direct comparison between $v_o(t)$ and $v_i(t)$ can thus be made and the errors evaluated.

For the single events of impulse voltages, only an infinite number of sinusoidal voltages is able to represent the input voltage $v_i(t)$. This continuous frequency spectrum is defined by the Fourier integral or Fourier transform of $v_i(t)$

$$\mathbf{V}_i(j\omega) = \int_{\tau=-\infty}^{\infty} v_i(t) \exp(-j\omega\tau)\, d\tau \tag{3.41}$$

and contains amplitude and phase spectra. The linearity and homogeneity of the time invariant systems assumed enables us again to calculate the time response of the system by a convolution of the continuous frequency spectrum with the network response function and the transition from frequency to time domain by means of the inverse Fourier transform:

$$v_o(t) = \frac{1}{2\pi} \int_{\omega=-\infty}^{\infty} \mathbf{V}_i(j\omega)\mathbf{H}(j\omega) \exp(j\omega t)\, d\omega. \tag{3.42}$$

In practice, the real input quantity $v_i(t)$ is not known, as only $v_o(t)$ can be measured. This output voltage, however, has suffered from the loss of information contained in $\mathbf{H}(j\omega)$. No appreciable transmission errors could occur, if at least the amplitude frequency response $H(\omega) = |\mathbf{H}(j\omega)|$ would be constant within a frequency range, in which the line or continuous frequency spectra, $\mathbf{V}_{ik}$ or $\mathbf{V}_i(j\omega)$, cannot be neglected. Thus the computation of the spectra of an estimated input quantity is a very efficient tool to judge the necessary frequency range or bandwidth of our measuring system and its individual components.

The highest demands upon the measuring system transfer functions are clearly imposed by impulse voltages. The analysis of the impulse voltage generating circuits (see Chapter 2, section 2.3.1) displayed a waveshape of the generator output voltage, which is a double exponential function. Neglecting the possible interactions between the voltage measuring and generating systems, we thus may assume an input voltage for the measuring system, given by $v_i(t) = A[\exp(-t/\tau_1) - \exp(-t/\tau_2)]$, where A is a constant value and τ_1, τ_2 the time constants according to eqn. (2.27). This voltage can be chopped at any instantaneous time T_c as defined in Fig. 2.24 caused by a disruptive discharge of the test object, but the voltage collapse is extremely rapid. The input voltage is then given by

$$v_i(t) = \begin{cases} 0 & \text{for } t < 0; t > T_c \\ A[\exp(-t/\tau_1) - \exp(-t/\tau_2)] & \text{for } 0 \leqslant t \leqslant T_c. \end{cases} \quad (3.43)$$

Applying this voltage and its boundary conditions to eqn. (3.41) gives $\mathbf{V}_i(j\omega)$. The calculation implies no fundamental difficulties, the result, however, is lengthy and is obtained as

$$\mathbf{V}_i(j\omega) = A(Re + j\,Im) \quad (3.44)$$

where

$$Re = \frac{\tau_1}{1+(\omega\tau_1)^2} \{1 + [\omega\tau_1 \sin(\omega T_c) - \cos(\omega T_c)] \exp(-T_c/\tau_1)\} - \dots$$

$$\dots - \frac{\tau_2}{1+(\omega\tau_2)^2} \{1 + [\omega\tau_2 \sin(\omega T_c) - \cos(\omega T_c)] \exp(-T_c/\tau_2)\};$$

$$Im = \frac{\tau_1}{1+(\omega\tau_1)^2} \{\omega\tau_1 - [\omega\tau_1 \cos(\omega T_c) + \sin(\omega T_c)] \exp(-T_c/\tau_1)\} - \dots$$

$$\dots - \frac{\tau_2}{1+(\omega\tau_2)^2} \{\omega\tau_2 - [\omega\tau_2 \cos(\omega T_c) + \sin(\omega T_c)] \exp(-T_c/\tau_2)\}.$$

For the special case of a non chopped voltage $(T_c \to \infty)$, the Fourier transform of the input voltage is merely

$$\mathbf{V}_i(j\omega) = A\left[\left(\frac{\tau_1}{1+(\omega\tau_1)^2} - \frac{\tau_2}{1+(\omega\tau_2)^2}\right) - j\left(\frac{\omega\tau_1^2}{1+(\omega\tau_1)^2} - \frac{\omega\tau_2^2}{1+(\omega\tau_2)^2}\right)\right].$$
(3.45)

The numerical evaluation of eqns. (3.44) and (3.45) is shown in Fig. 3.38 for a full lightning impulse 1.2/50 μsec ($\tau_1 = 68.2$ μsec : $\tau_2 = 0.405$ μsec) and different instants of chopping, T_c. A normalization was made by $\mathbf{v}_i(j\omega) = \mathbf{V}_i(j\omega)/V_i(\omega = 0)$ and only the relative amplitudes $|\mathbf{v}_i(j\omega)| = v_i(\omega)$ are displayed. From the result the following conclusions can be made:

The content of harmonics for a full lightning impulse $(T_c \to \infty)$ becomes very small in a frequency range of about 0.5–1 MHz; hence an amplitude response of our measuring circuit, which is really flat up to this frequency range, would obviously not provide significant errors. Depending upon the decay of the amplitude response with frequency, the bandwidth (-3 dB point) has to be much higher, i.e. about 5–10 MHz.

The chopping of the voltage introduces a heavy increase of the harmonics content. For $T_c = 4$ μsec, i.e. a chopping at the impulse tail, an accurate measurement of the crest voltage may still be provided by the above-mentioned amplitude response, though appreciable errors might appear during the instant of chopping. The voltages chopped within the front

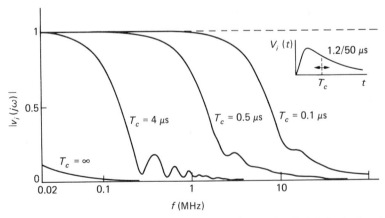

FIG. 3.38. Normalized amplitude frequency spectra (Fourier transform) of a lightning impulse voltage 1.2/50 μsec, wave full and chopped.

($T_c = 0.5$–0.1 μsec), however, will require a very wide bandwidth f_B and for constant error times the bandwidth must obviously increase with decreasing chopping time. Desirable values of f_B for $T_c = 0.5$ μsec only would be wider than 100 MHz, but such large values cannot be achieved with measuring systems for very high voltages.

This frequency domain method described so far for determining a transfer characteristic quantity to estimate measuring errors is cumbersome in application and even difficult to use, as two quantities, $H(\omega)$ and $\phi(\omega)$, are necessary to measure the system transfer function. For h.v. measuring systems, the evaluation of a system by means of an "experimental unit step response"[60] was introduced and its validity checked by many investigations. This time-domain method is based upon the fact that the Fourier transform [eqn. (3.41)] of a single-step function is proportional to $1/j\omega$ and thus all frequencies are contained. Let us, therefore, represent the input voltage of our measuring system by such a step function:

$$v_i(t) = \begin{cases} 0 & \text{for } t < 0 \\ V_{mi} & \text{for } t > 0. \end{cases} \tag{3.46}$$

The output voltage of the measuring system, $v_o(t)$, is then much smaller in amplitude, it may also be time-delayed with reference to the voltage input, and it will be distorted mainly at its front. This "unit step response" is denoted by the term $G(t)$ and is sketched in Fig. 3.39a. The time $t = 0$ is defined by eqn. (3.46), the time delay described by τ_{de}, and for a good measuring system the final value $V_{mi}(1/N)$ will be reached in a short time. The magnitude N indicates the steady-state voltage ratio between input and output voltage.

In section 3.6.3, $G(t)$ will be calculated based upon equivalent circuits. This quantity is also easy to measure by means of CROs. With a unit step, the output voltage response to any arbitrary input voltage can be calculated from the superposition theorem or Duhamel's integral:

$$v_o(t) = v_i(t)G(+0) + \int_0^t v_i(\tau)G'(t-\tau)\,d\tau$$

$$= G(t)v_i(+0) + \int_0^t v_i'(t-\tau)G(\tau)\,d\tau. \tag{3.47}$$

where $G'(t-\tau)$ or $v_i'(t-\tau)$ is the derivative of $G(t)$ or $v_i(t)$ with respect to τ. This integral can be solved numerically by digital computers, if analytic expressions are not available.[90]

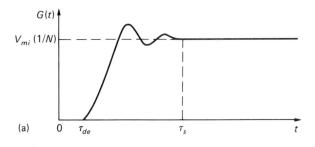

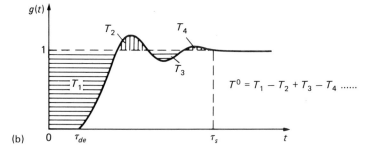

FIG. 3.39. Unit step response and definition of the response time T^0. (a) Unit step response as output voltage. (b) Normalized unit step response.

The chopping of a lightning impulse voltage at the front ($T_c \lesseqgtr 1$ μsec in Fig. 3.38) is often used for h.v. testing and the demands upon the measuring circuits become severe. The chopping on front provides a nearly linearly rising voltage up to T_c. Let us assume an ideally linearly rising voltage,

$$v_i(t) = St \tag{3.48}$$

where S is the steepness. With eqn. (3.47), the output voltage becomes

$$v_o(t) = S \int_0^t G(\tau)\, d\tau = \frac{S}{N} \int_0^t g(\tau) \cdot d\tau \tag{3.49}$$

where $g(t)$ is the normalized quantity of the unit step output voltage $G(t)$, whose final value becomes thus 1. Then the term $Nv_o(t)$ represents the high voltage comparable to $v_i(t)$ of eqn. (3.48), and we may introduce this term into eqn. (3.49) and expand this equation to

$$Nv_o(t) = S\left[t - \int_0^t [1 - g(\tau)]\, d\tau \right]. \tag{3.50}$$

This expression relates the output to the input voltage as long as St increases. The integral term will settle to a final value after a time τ_s indicated in Fig. 3.39. This final value is an interesting quantity, it shows that differences in amplitudes between input St and magnified output voltage $Nv_o(t)$ remain constant. Hence we may write

$$v_i(t) - Nv_o(t) = S \int_0^{t > \tau_s} [1 - g(\tau)]\, d\tau = S \int_0^\infty [1 - g(\tau)]\, d\tau = ST^0 \quad (3.51)$$

where

$$T^0 = \int_0^\infty [1 - g(\tau)]\, d\tau \quad (3.52)$$

is the "response time" of the measuring system. This quantity gives the time which can be found by the integration and summation of time areas as shown in Fig. 3.39b. T^0 includes a real time delay τ_{de} of the output voltage, which is in general not measured, if the time instant of the appearance of the unit step input is not recorded. The IEC Recommendations[60] therefore neglect this time delay. The justification for neglecting this delay are shown in Fig. 3.40: There the linearly rising input voltage is suddenly chopped, and the output voltage multiplied by N is approximately sketched for the unit step response of Fig. 3.39. Equation (3.50) can be applied up to the instant of chopping, T_c; for later times, eqn. (3.47) must be rearranged, and it can easily be seen that a superposition of three terms (response to St;

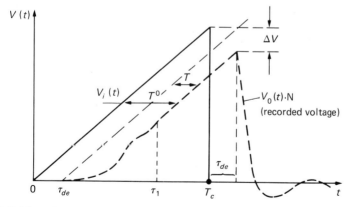

FIG. 3.40. Measuring error ΔV for linearly rising voltages chopped at T_c. Definition of response time T^0 and T.

negative unit step response with amplitude ST_c; negative response to St for $t > T_c$) will govern this output voltage. As the sudden change in the output voltage is also delayed, the amplitude error ΔV is obviously given by

$$\Delta V = v_i(T_c) - Nv_0(T_c + \tau_{de}) = S(T^0 - \tau_{de}) = ST$$

if $T_c > \tau_s$. Thus the simple relationship

$$T = T^0 - \tau_{de} \tag{3.53}$$

exists, where T is equal to a response time similar to T_0, but integrated from Fig. 3.39 by

$$T = \int_{\tau_{de}}^{\infty} [1 - g(\tau)]\, dt. \tag{3.53a}$$

The relative amplitude error δ for a chopped linearly rising voltage thus becomes

$$\delta = \frac{\Delta V}{ST_c} = \frac{T}{T_c}. \tag{3.54}$$

For $T = 50\ \mu sec$, and $T_c = 0.5\ \mu sec$, this error is 10%.

Clearly these simple qualification criteria for a measuring system have some drawbacks. First, eqn. (3.54) can only be used if the assumptions (linearly rising voltage, $\tau_s < T_c$) are fulfilled. Linearly rising high voltages, however, are difficult to generate and it is even more difficult to confirm this linearity by measurements, as the measured values are not accurate.[53] Due to its definition, the response time T or T^0 can even be negative. Low or negative values are likely to be achieved by excessive ringing or large overshoot of the step response. Although the settling time τ_s will then be usually too long to be applied to a measuring system for short linearly rising voltages, the sensitivity of the system to nonlinearly rising voltages becomes troublesome. This could easily be demonstrated by a systematical evaluation of eqn. (3.47). Only one example is shown in Fig. 3.41, and the example does not need further explanations.

The actual integration of a measured unit step response to obtain the response time must be carried out carefully and it is very essential that the final value of $g(t) \cong 1$ is accurately fixed within an oscillogram. In section 3.6.5 it is also shown that the actual unit step response cannot be measured for the real layout of the h.v. measuring circuit. In spite of these disadvantages, the concept of response times cannot be disregarded. The biggest advantage is related to its computation: It will be demonstrated in

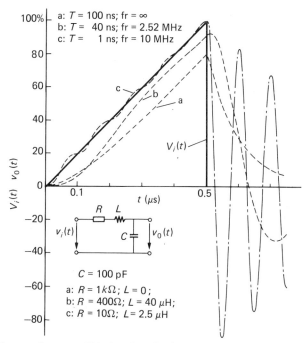

FIG. 3.41. Computed response $V_o(t)$ of a R-L-C circuit with given parameters to a linearly rising input voltage $V_i(t)$ chopped at $T_c = 0.5$ μsec.

the next section that T^0 or T can be calculated analytically even for very sophisticated networks without the knowledge of $g(t)$. Hence, the value of this quantity giving a measure related to the transfer properties of a measuring system must be acknowledged, though additional response parameters are necessary to correlate step responses with other type of measuring errors.[90,91]

3.6.3 Fundamentals for the Computation of the Measuring System

The computation of a four-terminal network as shown in Fig. 3.37 can be performed by the application of the general network theory. The representation of the actual measuring system (Fig. 3.36) by a four-terminal network imposes, however, certain restrictions. As demonstrated later, the theory of travelling waves or distributed parameters is used to evaluate the behaviour of the system during transients, and thus it is assumed that the electromagnetic phenomena are quasistationary in the two directions perpendicular to the direction of wave propagation. These conditions are limiting the accuracy of the calculations when the dimensions of the measuring systems are too large. The limitations are obviously directly correlated with the definition of a voltage as independent quantity from space within an electromagnetic field, but the dimensions of our h.v. systems are in the range of metres, and thus the quasistationary nature of the electromagnetic phenomena is severely restricted. For example, the travelling time of a wave at velocity of light is 20 nsec between two points 6 m apart. If impulses chopped on the front at $T_c = 200$ nsec are considered, the time is only ten times longer than the field propagation time.

With these restrictions in mind, we nevertheless may start a generalized computation of our four-terminal network. The Laplace transform will now be used throughout the treatment, with the complex frequency $s = \sigma + j\omega$ being the Laplace operator. Input and output parameters can be described by the matrix equation

$$\begin{bmatrix} V_i(s) \\ I_i(s) \end{bmatrix} = \begin{bmatrix} A_{11}(s); A_{12}(s) \\ A_{21}(s); A_{22}(s) \end{bmatrix} \cdot \begin{bmatrix} V_o(s) \\ I_o(s) \end{bmatrix} = [A] \begin{bmatrix} V_o(s) \\ I_o(s) \end{bmatrix} \qquad (3.55)$$

where $[A]$ is the network matrix of the system defined by this equation.

The measuring system will load the generating system and thus the input impedance of the measuring system is sometimes necessary. As the output current I_o for a voltage dividing system of h.v. ratio cannot influence the input, the condition $I_o = 0$ can always be assumed. From eqn. (3.55) then the input impedance is

$$Z_i(s) = \frac{V_i(s)}{I_i(s)} = \frac{A_{11}(s)}{A_{21}(s)}. \qquad (3.56)$$

The most important quantity is the voltage transfer function. For $I_o = 0$, this function becomes

$$H(s) = \frac{V_o(s)}{V_i(s)} = \frac{1}{A_{11}(s)}. \qquad (3.57)$$

It contains the ratio N of the voltage dividing system. This ratio is a constant quantity for low frequencies only and hence we may derive this ratio by

$$N = \lim_{s \to 0} \begin{bmatrix} V_i(s) \\ V_o(s) \end{bmatrix} = \lim_{s \to 0} [A_{11}(s)] = A_{11}(0). \qquad (3.58)$$

The voltage transfer function, eqn. (3.57), is conveniently normalized by N. Denoting the normalization by $h(s)$, we obtain

$$h(s) = NH(s) = \frac{A_{11}(0)}{A_{11}(s)}. \tag{3.59}$$

The unit step voltage $G(t)$ as described and defined in section 3.6.2, can be found by applying the Laplace inversion integral to the transfer function multiplied by $(1/s)$, the Laplace transform of a unit step. Thus

$$G(t) = L^{-1}\left[\frac{1}{s}H(s)\right] = L^{-1}\left[\frac{1}{sA_{11}(s)}\right]. \tag{3.60}$$

From eqn. (3.59), the normalized unit step response is

$$g(t) = NG(t). \tag{3.61}$$

For very complex transfer functions which will appear for our networks containing mixed distributed parameter circuits, the applicability of the Laplace transform is restricted, as it is too difficult to find solutions in the time-domain [eqn. (3.60)]. Then the response time T^0 cannot be computed by eqn. (3.52). Based upon a well-known final value theorem of the Laplace transform, which is

$$\lim_{t \to 0} f(t) = \lim_{s \to 0} [sF(s)]$$

we may compute the response time from the following equation, which can be derived by applying this final value theorem to eqn. (3.51):

$$T^0 = \lim_{s \to 0}\left[\frac{1 - h(s)}{s}\right].$$

As $\lim_{s \to 0} h(s) \triangleq 0$ by definition, the rule of Bernoulli-l'Hôpital leads to

$$T^0 = \lim_{s \to 0}\left[-\frac{dh(s)}{ds}\right] = \lim_{s \to 0}[-h'(s)]. \tag{3.62}$$

The final value theorem contains some restraints, i.e. $f(t)$ and df/dt must be Laplace transformable and the product $sF(s)$ must have all its singularities in the left half of the s-plane. Equation (3.62) thus may fail sometimes.

The response T can be computed from eqn. (3.53), if τ_{de} is known. It may be difficult, however, to predict an actual time delay based upon $h(s)$ only. The comparison of experimental and thus actual time delays with computed results may suffer from this disadvantage; for more information about this very specialized question, the reader is referred to the literature.[53]

These general results can now be applied to more detailed measuring circuits. Numerous equivalent circuits could be presented. We will, however, follow a representation, developed by Asner,[61] Creed *et al.*[62] and Zaengl.[63] In principle it deals with an adequate simulation of the lead to the voltage divider. It was impossible for a long time to detect the influence of this lead, as no means have been available to measure the actual unit step response of the systems. CROs of high sensitivity and high bandwidth are necessary to measure $G(t)$, but such oscilloscopes did not appear before about 1955. Thus neither the performance of the voltage dividers used could really be checked nor the performance of the whole measuring circuit. Many details within the construction of a voltage divider, however, can completely destroy the fundamentally good layout based upon theoretical investigations.

A more detailed representation of our simple four-terminal network, Fig. 3.37, is shown in Fig. 3.42. Three four-terminal networks are combined, forming a "three component system". System *1* represents a damping impedance Z_d at the input end of the lead 2, connecting this impedance with the voltage dividing system 3, which terminates the lead. Due to their complex structure and relatively high input impedance, the voltage dividers cannot properly match the leads' surge impedance Z_L. The damping impedance Z_d is therefore placed at the input end of the lead, as the travelling wave theory may easily show that only at this place a successful damping of oscillations is possible. The lead 2 is thus treated as a lossless transmission line and is characterized by its surge impedance Z_L and its

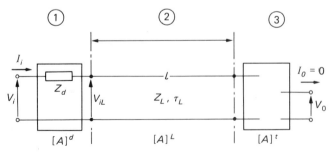

FIG. 3.42. The "three-component system" comprised by a (1) damping, (2) transmission and (3) terminating system.

travel time τ_L, which implies that the capacitance per unit length is constant. Leads to the voltage dividers consist of metal tubes or metal wires, the diameter of which should be such as to avoid any heavy predischarges. That waves are really travelling with velocity of light was readily shown in many investigations (i.e. references 62, 63, 53). The simple representation of the lead by Z_L and τ_L only was also confirmed by many investigations, although this representation is approximate.

Not represented in the circuit of Fig. 3.42 is the signal cable and the recording instrument. It will be shown in section 3.6.6 that a lossless signal cable (see item 6 in Fig. 3.36) can be connected to the different kinds of dividers without appreciably influencing the unit step response. In this arrangement they form a part of the divider's l.v. arm. As also the recording instruments (item 7, Fig. 3.36) have high input impedances and wide bandwidth, their possible influence on the response is small and can thus be neglected.

Up to now the terminating or voltage dividing system 3 had not been specified in detail, as its network depends upon the type of divider used. For the computation of the transfer properties the relevant matrix representation according to eqn. (3.55) is used. Thus the matrix $[A]$ of the whole measuring system is

$$[A] = [A]^d [A]^L [A]^t.$$

The matrix $[A]$ can partly be solved by inserting the specific matrix elements for $[A]^d$ and $[A]^L$ defined with the circuit elements of Fig. 3.42. The details of the computation are lengthy and are omitted here. The following results, however, are of greatest interest.

The normalized voltage transfer function, $h(s) = N V_o(s)/V_i(s)$, is best described by introducing reflection coefficients for travelling waves, which either are reflected from the terminating system (K_t) or from the damping system (K_d). They are defined by

$$K_t(s) = \frac{\dfrac{A_{11}^t(s)}{A_{21}^t(s)} - Z_L}{\dfrac{A_{11}^t(s)}{A_{21}^t(s)} + Z_L} = \frac{Z_t(s) - Z_L}{Z_t(s) + Z_L} \tag{3.63}$$

$$K_d(s) = \frac{\dfrac{A_{12}^d(s)}{A_{11}^d(s)} - Z_L}{\dfrac{A_{12}^d(s)}{A_{11}^d(s)} + Z_L} = \frac{Z_d(s) - Z_L}{Z_d(s) + Z_L}. \tag{3.64}$$

With these coefficients, the transfer function is:

$$h(s) = e^{-\tau_L s} \frac{Z_d(0) + Z_L}{Z_d(s) + Z_L} \frac{1 + K_t(s)}{1 + K_t(0)}$$

$$\times \frac{1 - K_t(0)K_d(0)}{1 - K_t(s)K_d(s)\exp(-2\tau_L s)} \frac{A_{11}^t(0)}{A_{11}^t(s)}. \quad (3.65)$$

The inherent time delay caused by the travel time of the lead, τ_L, can well be seen from the first factor; the last factor represents the normalized transfer function of the voltage dividing system. The normalized unit step response could be calculated using eqn. (3.60). A glance at the transfer function may indicate difficulties encountered with its transformation into the time domain, especially if the transfer function of the terminating system is very complex in its structure. A very simple example, however, will demonstrate the reflection phenomena introduced by the lead. Let the damping system be a pure resistor, i.e. $Z_d(s) = R_d$, and the terminating system be simulated by a pure resistor divider without any frequency-dependent impedances, i.e. the divider may merely be represented by its input resistance R_t. Thus $K_t(s) = (R_t - Z_L)/(R_t + Z_L) = K_t$, and $K_d(s) = (R_d - Z_L)/(R_d + Z_L) = K_d$, and both are real numbers only. According to eqn. (3.59), the normalized transfer function of a pure resistor divider will be equivalent to 1. Equations (3.65) and (3.61) provide the normalized unit step response

$$g(t) = L^{-1} \left\{ \frac{\exp(-\tau_L s)}{s} \frac{1 - K_t K_d}{1 - K_t K_d \exp(-2\tau_L s)} \right\}.$$

The well-known evaluation of this expression is based upon the expansion of the last factor by a geometric row:

$$g(t) = L^{-1} \left\{ \frac{\exp(-\tau_L s)}{s} (1 - K_t K_d)[1 + (K_t K_d) e^{-2\tau_L s} + \ldots \right.$$

$$\left. \ldots + (K_t K_d)^2 e^{-4\tau_L s} + (K_t K_d)^3 e^{-6\tau_L s} + \ldots] \right\}. \quad (3.66)$$

The infinite number of factors thus represents the possible number of reflections. Within the time intervals $(1 + 2n) \leqslant t/\tau_L < (3 + 2n)$, where $n = 0, 1, 2 \ldots$, the amplitudes of $g(t)$, however, are constant. In Fig. 3.43, eqn. (3.66) is evaluated for the most probable case, that when $R_t \gg Z_L$, i.e. $K_t = +1$, and R_d is smaller or larger than Z_L. For $R_d = Z_L$, $K_d = 0$ and any reflection phenomena disappear. This is in fact the reason, why the

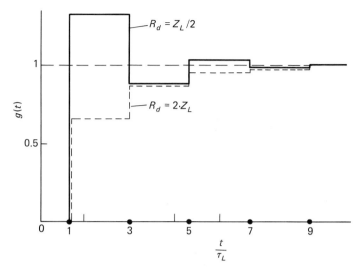

FIG. 3.43. Unit step response according to eqn. (3.66).

damping resistor is placed at the input end of the lead. This very simplified example shows also that the response time will be influenced by the damping resistor. The magnitude of this influence is related to the length of the lead by τ_L.

An exact evaluation of the response time is based upon eqn. (3.62), substituted into eqn. (3.65). The result is:

$$T^0 = T_t + \tau_L \left[\frac{Z_t(0)\dfrac{Z_d(0)}{Z_L} + Z_L}{Z_t(0) + Z_d(0)} \right] + \frac{Z_d(0)}{Z_L}$$
$$\times \left[T_{kt} \frac{Z_t(0) + Z_L}{Z_t(0) + Z_d(0)} - T_{kd} \frac{Z_d(0) + Z_L}{Z_t(0) + Z_d(0)} \right] \quad (3.67)$$

where

$$T_t = \frac{A_{11}^{t'}(0)}{A_{11}^{t}(0)} \quad (3.68)$$

is the response time of the terminator,

$$T_{kt} = \frac{K_t'(0)}{1 + K_t(0)} \quad (3.69)$$

is the reflection response time of the terminator,

$$T_{kd} = \frac{K'_d(0)}{1 + K_d(0)}$$ (3.70)

is the reflection response time of damping system,

$$Z_t(0) = \frac{A^t_{11}(0)}{A^t_{21}(0)}$$ (3.71)

is the d.c. input resistance of the terminator,

$$Z_d(0) = \frac{A^d_{12}(0)}{A^d_{11}(0)}$$ (3.72)

is the d.c. resistance of the damping system.

The influence of the dividers' lead again is illustrated by eqn. (3.67). The complexity of this result is further discussed in section 3.6.5. In general, the voltage dividing system, mainly represented by its response time T_t, will essentially control the transfer characteristics of the whole system. Thus it is justified to treat the terminating system in advance and isolated from the lead to achieve a general understanding of all h.v. dividing systems and their adequate application.

3.6.4 Voltage Dividers

Voltage dividers for d.c., a.c. or impulse voltages may consist of resistors or capacitors or convenient combinations of these elements. Inductors are not used as actual voltage dividing circuit elements, as pure inductances of proper magnitudes without excessive capacitive components cannot be built. The elements are usually installed within insulating vessels of cylindrical shape with the ground and h.v. terminals at both ends. The height of a voltage divider depends upon the flashover voltage and this follows from the rated maximum voltage applied; this flashover voltage is also influenced by the potential distribution and thus is influenced by the design of the h.v. electrode, the top electrode. For voltages in the megavolt region, the height of the dividers becomes large, as one may assume the following relative clearances between top electrode and ground:

2.5 to 3 m/MV for d.c. voltages;
2 to 2.5 m/MV for lightning impulse voltages;

more than 5 m/MV$_{(r.m.s.)}$ for a.c. voltages
more than 4 m/MV for switching impulse voltages.

The limitations and difficulties in grading the potential distributions along series connected resistors or capacitors was discussed in the sections 3.3 and 3.5.4. The most difficult problems in a simulation of the actual network of voltage dividers is in the inadequate representation of the stray capacitances (see Figs. 3.17, 3.18, 3.34). Whereas the location and the dimensions of the active parts, i.e. resistor or capacitor units, within a voltage divider are exactly known, the same statements are impossible to achieve for stray capacitances. It would also be too difficult to present equivalent circuits with distributed parameters, which are necessary to account for the physical size of the units, by assuming a too high number of individual elements of unequal values. Apart from the fundamental difficulties in performing analytical computations of such circuits, the results are then individually related to the high number of parameters.

It has been acknowledged by many investigators that a recurrent or distributed parameter network with equally distributed parameters is probably the best compromise to simulate the actual transfer characteristics by equivalent circuits. Such a distributed parameter network for a generalized voltage divider is shown in Fig. 3.44. Our "terminating system" $[A]^t$ of Fig. 3.42 is now formed by a large number (n) of elements or sections, and the n impedances Z'_l in series are providing the voltage reduction. An equal number of impedances Z'_q to earth are distributed along this column. The input voltage V is thus greatly reduced to the low output voltage V_2. The total impedances are then defined by

$$Z_l = \Sigma Z'_l = n Z'_l; \quad Z_q = \left(\Sigma \frac{1}{Z'_q} \right)^{-1} = \frac{Z'_q}{n}. \tag{3.73}$$

The number n is by this definition equivalent to the voltage ratio V/V_2 of the divider; it may differ from N as defined before, as the impedance Z_d of the lead (Fig. 3.42) may change the ratio of the whole voltage measuring system.

The matrix representation of such a network, which is equivalent to a transmission line network, is well known. Applying eqn. (3.57) and eqn. (3.59) to this network, one easily may find the normalized transfer function (index t = terminator), which is

$$h_t(s) = \frac{n V_2}{V} = \frac{n \sinh \frac{1}{n} \sqrt{Z_l(s)/Z_q(s)}}{\sinh \sqrt{Z_l(s)/Z_q(s)}}. \tag{3.74}$$

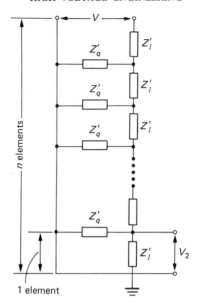

FIG. 3.44. Distribution parameter equivalent circuit of voltage dividers.

The normalized unit step response is

$$g_t(t) = L^{-1}\left[\frac{1}{s}h_t(s)\right].$$

Both quantities can be computed and analyzed for different equivalent circuits, for which the impedances Z'_l and Z'_q are specified. Z'_q, however, will always be represented by stray capacitances C'_e to earth, as no voltage dividing system is known which would comprise any other passive circuit elements at these locations. This stray capacitance is thus assumed to be equally distributed.

Resistor Voltage Dividers

The best representation of such dividers has to assume inductive components L' of the actual resistor R' as well as capacitive elements C'_p in parallel to the resistors (see Fig. 3.45). Inductances are inherent with every flow of current due to the magnetic field, and the parallel capacitors C'_p may

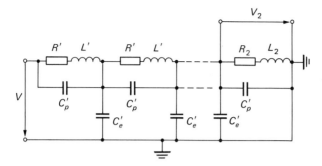

FIG. 3.45. Equivalent circuit for resistor voltage dividers. $R = nR'$; $L = nL'$; $C_e = nC_e'$; $C_p = C_p'/n$; $R_2 = R'$; $L_2 = L'$; $R_1 = (n-1)R'$.

be formed by the construction of the resistors. The neglecting of any inductance in series to these stray capacitances indicates the simulation of electrical fields within insulation medias of low permittivity only; the individual values are thus of any small magnitude by the distributed parameter representation.

The normalized transfer function is easily found from eqn. (3.74), and is

$$h_t(s) = n \frac{\sinh \dfrac{1}{n} \sqrt{\dfrac{(R+sL)sC_e}{1+(R+sL)sC_p}}}{\sinh \sqrt{\dfrac{(R+sL)sC_e}{1+(R+sL)sC_p}}}. \tag{3.75}$$

The computation of $g_t(t)$ for this and all the other circuits presented thereafter can be made with minor approximations justifiable for $n \gg 1$. The details can be found in the literature,[64,65] only the result is presented:

$$g_t(t) = 1 + 2e^{-at} \sum_{k=1}^{\infty} (-1)^k \frac{\cosh(b_k t) + \dfrac{a}{b_k} \sinh(b_k t)}{1 + \dfrac{C_p}{C_e} k^2 \pi^2}; \tag{3.76}$$

where

$$a = R/2L;$$

$$b_k = \sqrt{a^2 - \frac{k^2 \pi^2}{LC_e[1 + (C_p/C_e)k^2\pi^2]}};$$

$$k = 1, 2, 3 \ldots \infty.$$

Both quantities can be used to demonstrate the limits of applications if representative values for the circuit constants are taken into consideration.

First, it is clear that resistor dividers are ideal for d.c. voltage measurements. The transfer function $h_t(s)$ for high R values and accordingly small values of L/R increases steadily with a decrease of the frequency. For $s \to 0$, $h_t(s) \cong 1$ and therefore

$$V_2 = \frac{V}{n} = V\frac{R_2}{R_1 + R_2}$$

(see Fig. 3.45 for definition of R_1 and R_2). The advantage of this relationship and its effect upon the accuracy and stability of the divider ratio was discussed in section 3.3. The ability to measure a.c. voltages as well as ripple inherent in d.c. voltages depends upon the decrease of $h_t(s)$ with frequency. Since for all constructions of high ohmic resistor dividers the L/R values are lower than about 0.1 μsec, and also $C_p \ll C_e$, the controlling factor of the transfer function is given by the product RC_e. We thus can neglect L and C_p in eqn. (3.75) as well as in eqn. (3.76) and therefore:

$$h_t(s) \approx n\frac{\sinh\frac{1}{n}\sqrt{sRC_e}}{\sinh\sqrt{sRC_e}} \tag{3.77}$$

$$g_t(t) = 1 + 2\sum_{k=1}^{\infty}(-1)^k \exp\left(-\frac{k^2\pi^2}{RC_e}t\right) \tag{3.78}$$

where

$$k = 1, 2, 3 \ldots \infty.$$

Equation (3.77) can be used to calculate the bandwidth f_B from the amplitude frequency response $|g_t(s)|$, if $|g_t(s)| = 1/\sqrt{2}$. The evaluation shows the simple relationship

$$f_B = \frac{1.46}{RC_e}. \tag{3.79}$$

Similarly, the response time T^0 can be computed applying eqn. (3.52) to eqn. (3.78). The result gives

$$T^0 = \frac{RC_e}{6} \approx T. \tag{3.80}$$

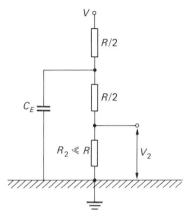

FIG. 3.46. Common equivalent circuit representing approximately the distributed parameter circuit, Fig. 3.45, with $L = C_p = 0$. $C_E = (2/3)C_e$ for equal response times [eqn. (3.81)]. $C_E = 0.44\,C_e$ for equal bandwidth [eqn. (3.82)].

Though the unit step response starts continuously, since for $t = 0$; $dg_t/dt = 0$, a very pronounced time delay τ_{de} cannot be defined. Thus $T^0 \approx T$. f_B and T^0 could be used to define much simpler equivalent circuits for the distributed parameter network. Figure 3.46 shows this very common equivalent circuit. For $R_2 \ll R_1$ the easy to calculate step response is

$$g_t(t) = 1 - \exp(-t/\tau);$$

where $\tau = RC_E/4$. Since for this truly exponential rise the response time equals to τ, the not distributed capacitance to ground C_E in this equivalent circuit is

$$T^0 = \frac{RC_e}{6} = \frac{RC_E}{4}; \quad C_E = \frac{2}{3}C_e, \tag{3.81}$$

if equal response times are used for comparison. Comparing, however, the bandwidth of both systems, which is equivalent to $f_B = 1/2\pi\tau$ for the simplified circuit, we obtain

$$\frac{4}{2\pi RC_E} = \frac{1.46}{RC_e}; \quad C_E = 0.44\,C_e. \tag{3.82}$$

The reasons for these discrepancies can easily be detected if the real unit step response according to eqn. (3.78) is compared with a true exponential rise provided by the simplified equivalent circuit (Fig. 3.46). This com-

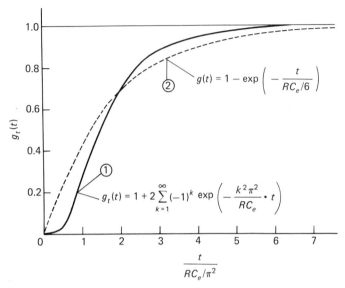

FIG. 3.47. Comparison of the unit step responses with equal response time. (1) For equivalent circuit Fig. 3.45 with $L = C_p = 0$ [eqn. (3.78)]. (2) For equivalent circuit Fig. 3.46 with $C_k = (2/3)C_e$.

parison is shown in Fig. 3.47 for equal response times. The delayed, but faster, increase of $g_t(t)$ for the distributed circuit is the main reason for the discrepancies.

In section 3.5.4 it was shown that the stray capacitances C'_e may approximately be calculated from the dimensions of any structure. In section 3.3 we have also given some guidance for the dimensioning of the resistor values for d.c. or a.c. dividers. Combining both these rules, we may summarize that

$$\frac{C_e}{[\text{pF}]} \approx (10\text{–}15)\frac{H}{[\text{m}]}; \quad \frac{R}{[\text{G}\Omega]} \approx (1\text{–}2)\frac{V}{[\text{MV}]};$$

where H equals to the height of a divider, and V is rated high voltage. We may introduce these magnitudes into eqn. (3.79) and find the following simple relationship:

$$f_B \approx \frac{50\ldots150}{HV} \quad \text{with} \quad \begin{cases} f_B \text{ in Hz} \\ H \text{ in m} \\ V \text{ in MV} \end{cases} . \tag{3.83}$$

Assuming a d.c. voltage divider for $V = 1$ MV, which will be about 3 m in height, eqn. (3.82) shows a bandwidth of not more than 50 Hz. It is, therefore, impossible to measure d.c. ripple voltages with high value resistor divider for voltages higher than some 100 kV. Equation (3.83) shows also the limitations for the application of simple resistor voltage dividers without preventive measures: An accurate measurement of power frequency voltages needs f_B values $\gtrsim 1$ kHz, resulting in a product HV of about 100 kV m. This product limits the application of the above to voltages not exceeding 100–200 kV.

The measurement of impulse voltages demands a much higher bandwidth as discussed in section 3.6.2. The decrease of C_e by very carefully adapted shielding or potential grading methods is limited, though a reduction by a factor of about 5–10 seems possible. But this is not enough. There is only one practicable solution, i.e. to reduce the value of R by some orders of magnitude. Let us assume that we have to build a resistor divider with $T \approx T^0 = 50$ nsec, still introducing an amplitude error δ of 10% for linearly rising voltages chopped at $T_c = 0.5$ μsec [see eqn. (3.54)]. Thus the product RC_e becomes 300 nsec according to eqn. (3.80). Let the resistance be about 2 m in height, providing lightning impulse withstand strength of about 1000 kV. Without excessively large top electrodes for forced shielding, C'_e is about 10 pF/m and thus $R \approx 300 \times 10^{-9}/20 \times 10^{-12} =$ 15 kΩ. This is indeed the order of magnitude which can be used for voltage dividers applicable for the measurement of lightning impulse voltages. This low value of a resistance will load the impulse generators, but this resistive load is tolerable if the discharge resistors within the generator are adapted. A large increase of the rated voltage is, however, not possible. The reduction of C_e by huge shielding electrodes becomes impractical as the dimensions must increase with the divider's height. Thus the response time with the resistance value unchanged increases proportional to C_e or $C'_e H$. Response times larger than 200 μsec for the measurement of 1.2/50 lightning impulses chopped on the crest or the tail are, however, not accepted by the standards.[6] A further problem is created by the heat dissipation within the resistors. For constant R values and increasing voltage, the energy dissipated in the resistive materials increases proportionally with V^2, and during the short time of voltage application not much heat can be transferred to the surrounding insulation material, the energy must be stored within the resistor. A calculation of the temperature increase within the wire-wound metal resistors would indicate the difficulties to achieve low-inductive resistor units applicable to this h.v. stress. These are the main reasons why resistor voltage dividers for voltages higher than 1.5–2 MV and resistance values of 10–20 kΩ cannot be built.

There are, however, some possibilities to improve the unit step response of such dividers, which will only be treated briefly.

Reduction of resistance value. If only front-chopped impulse voltages of short duration ($\lesssim 1$ μsec) have to be measured, a further reduction of R is possible if the impulse generator has high stored energy and the wave-shaping front resistors (R_1 in Fig. 2.26) are of low value. The heat dissipation problem is solved only by the chopping. It is essential, however, to reduce the inductive time constant L/R of the resistors as far as possible. For assessment, we have to refer to the equivalent circuit, shown in Fig. 3.45, and the relevant transfer properties. The numerical evaluation of eqn. (3.76), an example of which is given in Fig. 3.48, shows the appearance of

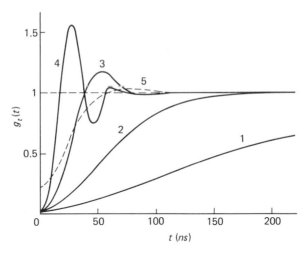

FIG. 3.48. Calculated unit step response for resistor dividers. Equivalent circuit according to Fig. 3.45.

L/R = 10 nsec;	C_e = 40 pF;	C_p = 1 pF	R_{crit}
(1) R = 30 kΩ			15.5 kΩ
(2) R = 10 kΩ			8.9 kΩ
(3) R = 3 kΩ			4.85 kΩ
(4) R = 1 kΩ			2.8 kΩ
L/R = 10 nsec;	C_e = 12 pF;	C_p = 1 pF	
(5) R = 10 kΩ			13.4 kΩ

oscillations in the unit step response with too low resistance values, though L/R was kept constant as well as C_e and C_p. The reasons for this instability can easily be explained using eqn. (3.76). Although the damping factor $\exp(-at)$ of the infinite series remains constant, the hyperbolic functions will change to trigonometric ones, depending upon the series number k. The most efficient term within the series is the first one ($k = 1$). For this term, this transition takes place if b_k becomes complex. Hence,

$$R_{crit} \approx R \leqslant 2\pi \sqrt{\frac{L}{C_e} \frac{1}{1+\pi^2 C_p/C_e}}. \tag{3.84}$$

This "critical" resistance is included in the table of Fig. 3.48, and the comparison with the computed responses confirms the validity of the above equation.

Typical examples for such low resistor voltage dividers are shown by Rohlfs et al.[66] or Pellinen et al.[67]

Reduction of C_e. The possibility of reducing the stray capacitance to earth by metal electrodes connected to h.v. potential was theoretically treated in section 3.3. The practical application of field-controlling top electrodes was introduced by Bellaschi,[68] it is a widely used and effective method. The combination of a field-controlling h.v. electrode with a nonlinear distribution of the resistance values per unit length was also explained earlier.[34] The inherent disadvantages of all field-controlling methods are twofold: First, the unit step response is very sensitive to the surrounding objects, as a strong relative change of C_e is likely to be produced by small changes of the external potential distribution. The second disadvantage is related to the interaction between the lead and the divider. Large shielding electrodes introduce a relatively large external parallel capacitance across the divider, which is not equal to C_p in our equivalent circuit. This capacitance loads the lead and enhances travelling wave oscillations, which can only be damped by the impedance Z_d of the lead. Additional explanations are given in the next section.

C_e can also be reduced by a decrease of the dimensions of the resistor. Harada et al.[69] proposed a 1-MV divider with $R = 9.3$ kΩ, the resistor of which was only 46 cm in axial length, but placed in a much longer insulating vessel. In this design difficulties arise with the heat dissipation within this small resistor and with the field gradient control in the neighbourhood of the resistor. For further details the reader should refer to the original paper.

Compensation methods. Our equivalent circuits assume an equal distribution of the voltage dividing elements in the resistor column. Also the l.v.
arm is assumed to be equal to a resistor unit of the h.v. arm. This is, of
course, not true, as the connection of the signal cable with the l.v. arm needs
a special construction (see section 3.6.6, Fig. 3.61). For resistor dividers, the
voltage unit step response is about equal to the step response of the current
through the l.v. arm. In this way also the current increases in a manner that
is similar in shape as is given by the voltage unit step response. As long as R_2
(Fig. 3.45) is not larger than the surge impedance of the signal cable, one
may simply increase the inductance L_2 to increase the resistance of the
output voltage. The low value of the surge impedance, which is in parallel
with R_2, limits the efficiency of this method. In practice, the actual value of
L_2 is predominantly determined by the construction of the l.v. arm. The
actual unit step response may, therefore, be quite different from the
computed one. Poor construction may even introduce oscillations, if no
adequate values of C'_p and L_2 (Fig. 3.45) are present and the resistance R_2 is
badly constructed.

Other compensating networks at the input end of the signal cable have
been proposed[70] which can be evaluated using the well-known methods of
network synthesis.[1] The efficiency of such networks is, however, limited.

Parallel-mixed Resistor-capacitor Dividers

If in the equivalent circuit for resistor dividers of Fig. 3.45 the stray
capacitances C'_p are increased, i.e. if real capacitor units are placed in
parallel to the resistor R', a parallel-mixed resistor-capacitor divider is
formed. This parallel arrangement of resistors and capacitors is a well-
known technique used for attenuators within electronic measuring instruments, i.e. CROs, and is often referred to as a compensated resistor voltage
divider. The idea to use this circuit for h.v. dividers was introduced by
Elsner in 1939,[71] with the goal of reducing the effect of the stray
capacitances to earth, C'_e. The efficiency of the C'_p capacitors can actually be
seen by comparing unit step responses of Fig. 3.47, curve 1, with those in the
Fig. 3.48. Neglecting any C_p values within the simplified R-C latter network
causes the USR (unit step response) to start continuously with time. Even
the small C_p value of 1 pF in Fig. 3.48 excites a small step in the USR, and
the value of this step $g_t(+0)$ is obviously depending upon the capacitance

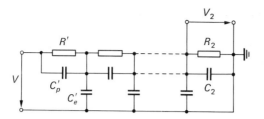

FIG. 3.49. Simplified equivalent circuit for parallel-mixed resistor-capacitor dividers. $R = nR'$;
$C_p = C'_p/n$; $C_e = nC'_e$; $R_2 = R'$; $C_2 = C'_p$.

ratio C_p/C_e (compare the curves 1 to 4 with 5). The increase in the ratio of C_p/C_e increases this step and thus the question arises whether it is possible to increase this first step to the final value or not.

It can be accomplished theoretically only if we assume that the representation of actual capacitor units placed in parallel to the resistors in the equivalent circuit of Fig. 3.45 would be correct. It is, however, not correct if this equivalent circuit is used to compute high-frequency phenomena or unit step responses in the nanosecond or even microsecond range. The reason for this is simple. The inherent inductance L of every capacitor C causes a series resonance frequency $f_r = 1/2\pi\sqrt{LC}$, which is quite low for capacitance values capable to compensate h.v. dividers (for instance: $f_r = 10$ MHz for $L = 1$ μH; $C = 200$ pF).

The actual USR of parallel-mixed resistor-capacitor dividers is therefore similar to pure capacitor voltage dividers, which will be treated later. Apart from the fact that this type of divider is still in use for the measurement of impulse voltages, with R values in the 10–100 kΩ range and C_p values in the order of some 100 pF, we shall simulate the transfer properties by a simplified equivalent circuit only, which will not cover the high-frequency range. This equivalent circuit is shown in Fig. 3.49. The computation of the normalized transfer function and unit step response yields for equal elements in the h.v. and l.v. curves, i.e. $R_2 C_2 = R'C'_p$:

$$h_t(s) = n \frac{\sinh \dfrac{1}{n} \sqrt{\dfrac{sRC_e}{1+sRC_p}}}{\sinh \sqrt{\dfrac{sRC_e}{1+sRC_p}}} \tag{3.85}$$

$$g_t(t) = 1 + 2 \sum_{k=1}^{\infty} (-1)^k \frac{\exp(-a_k t)}{1 + k^2 \pi^2 C_p/C_e} \tag{3.86}$$

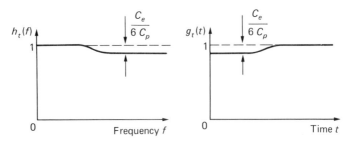

FIG. 3.50. Schematic diagrams for the normalized amplitude frequency response (a) and unit step response (b) for voltage dividers according to Fig. 3.49.

where

$$a_k = \frac{k^2\pi^2}{RC_e(1+k^2\pi^2 C_p/C_e)};$$

$$k = 1,2,3\ldots.$$

The peculiar effect of this circuit is detected by the calculation of the limiting values for very high and very low frequencies, or very short and very long times:

$$\lim_{s\to 0}\,[h_t(s)] = 1; \quad \lim_{t\to\infty}\,[g_t(t)] = 1.$$

$$\lim_{s\to\infty}\,[h_t(s)] \simeq 1 - \frac{C_e}{6C_P}; \quad \lim_{t\to 0}\,[g_t(t)] \simeq 1 - \frac{C_e}{6C_P}.$$

A sketch of the normalized amplitude frequency response and USR in Fig. 3.50 demonstrates the response of this dividing system to different voltage ratios. The difference of these ratios is formed by the relation $C_e/6C_p$, and very high values of C_p would be necessary to reduce this difference to very small values. It is obvious that these differences in ratio will be easier reduced by a reduction of C_2 within the l.v. arm to increase the voltage drop across C_2 for high frequencies, for which the divider responds by its capacitance ratio. A calculation, published by Harada et al.,[72] shows the condition

$$R_2 C_2 = R_1 C_{p1}\left\{\sqrt{\frac{C_e}{C_{p1}}}\;\frac{1}{\sinh\sqrt{\dfrac{C_e}{C_{p1}}}}\right\} \approx R_1 C_{p1}\left(1 - \frac{C_e}{6C_p}\right) \quad (3.87)$$

where

$$C_{p1} = \frac{C_p'}{(n-1)} \approx \frac{C_p'}{n} = C_p;$$

$$R_1 = (n-1)R' \approx nR' = R.$$

Whereas according to Harada the discontinuity of the slope within the USR vanishes by this procedure, an exact calculation of the amplitude frequency response would demonstrate that there still remains a small discontinuity within this curve. In summary then, it is *not* recommended to compensate low value resistor dividers for high voltages with parallel capacitor units, as the equivalent circuit of Fig. 3.49 is inadequate to treat short time phenomena. A compensation of high ohmic dividers commonly used for the measurement of d.c. or a.c. voltages, however, is very attractive to increase the performance in the intermediate frequency range (100 Hz up to some 100 kHz, depending upon the size of the divider). A still further improvement is possible if the resonance phenomena within the capacitor column are damped. This damping procedure is shown below.

Capacitor Voltage Dividers

It was shown in section 3.5.4 that pure capacitor voltage dividers could be made by either using single h.v. capacitance units, i.e. a compressed gas capacitor, in series with a l.v. capacitor, or to apply many stacked and series connected capacitor units to form a h.v. capacitance. The absence of any stray capacitance to earth with compressed gas capacitors provides a very well-defined h.v. capacitance, small in value and small in dimensions, and by this even a pure capacitor voltage divider with excellent high-frequency performance can be built if the l.v. arm or capacitor is constructively integrated in the layout of such a capacitor. This means that this capacitor must be very close to the h.v. capacitance, and this can be provided for instance by inserting a symmetrical arrangement of l.v. capacitors between the l.v. sensory electrode *2* and the guard ring *2'* or supporting tube *3* (see Fig. 3.31). Though such a construction was proposed by Schwab,[73] similar systems may well be formed by other coaxial arrangements,[74] the applicability to very high voltages is mainly restricted by the high cost of such constructions and the difficulties involved with the replacement and exchange of l.v. arms to change the voltage ratio.

A treatment of capacitor voltage dividers with stacked capacitor units is thus justified. The distributed parameter network is able to simulate the transfer properties. Figure 3.51 shows such a network, which may encounter all possible circuit elements. The actual stacked capacitors are now simulated by the capacitance units C', and L' takes in account the inherent inductance. The series resistance R' may be used to simulate either only small losses within the capacitor units C', or even real resistors in series with these units. The small values of stray capacitances in parallel to the stacked columns C'_p and to ground C'_e complete the equivalent circuit.

A glance at the unit step response, which is represented as

$$g_t(t) = 1 - \frac{C_e}{6(C+C_p)} + 2\exp(-at)\sum_{k=1}^{\infty}(-1)^k \frac{\cosh(b_k t) + \dfrac{a}{b_k}\sinh(b_k t)}{AB},$$

where
$$A = \left(1 + \frac{C_p}{C} + \frac{C_e}{Ck^2\pi^2}\right), \quad a = \frac{R}{2L}, \tag{3.88}$$

$$B = \left(1 + \frac{C_p k^2\pi^2}{C_e}\right), \quad b_k = \sqrt{a^2 - \frac{k^2\pi^2 \cdot A}{LC_e B}},$$

shows a close similarity to the USR of resistor dividers, eqn. (3.76). Both equations are actually the same, if the value C in eqn. (3.88) approaches infinite values. With the finite values of C, which are representing capacitor voltage divider, the main difference is at first related to the negative term $C_e/6(C+C_p) \simeq C_e/6C$, which is independent of the time and thus also the frequency. This term was also found in the treatment of the "equiv-

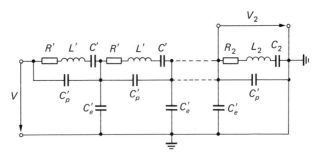

Fig. 3.51. Equivalent circuit for capacitor voltage dividers. $R = nR'$; $L = nL'$; $C_e = nC'_e$; $C = C'/n$; $C_p = C'_p/n$; $R_2 = R'$; $L_2 = L'$; $C_2 = C'$.

alent capacitance", see eqn. (3.33). It appears again as a result of our procedure of the normalization of the USR. All explanations referring to the proper dimensioning of stacked capacitors, therefore, apply also to this result, which demonstrates the possible variations of the ratio n with C_e.

The time dependency of the USR for "pure" capacitor dividers, i.e. with $R = 0$ in the equivalent circuit, is obviously very complex. In eqn. (3.88), with $R = 0$, the damping term $\exp(-at)$ will be equal to 1, and all hyperbolic functions are converted to trigonometric ones. The numerical evaluation of this equation for this case is heavily aggravated due to the infinite number of sinusoidal terms. It is also not realistic to assume no resistance, as the dissipation factor and the electrodes of the capacitors will cause some damping. For a series equivalent, this dissipation factor is $\tan \delta = \omega R'C' = \omega RC$. The relaxation phenomena within the dielectric materials control this dissipation factor for high frequencies. For most of the materials used, $\tan \delta$ is nearly independent of frequency, and thus no constant value of R may really take this effect into account. It has been confirmed approximately by measurements[75] that we may assume an adequate resistance value to evaluate eqn. (3.88) as was done in Fig. 3.52. The oscillations can be partly related to the travel time $\tau = \sqrt{LC_e}$, as a unit step voltage applied to the input end of such a ladder network can travel

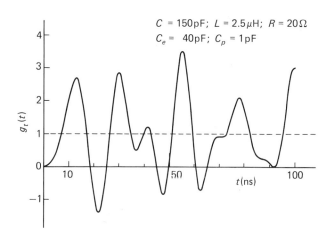

Fig. 3.52. Calculated unit step response for a capacitor voltage divider; equivalent circuit see Fig. 3.51. $R = 20\ \Omega$; $L = 2.5\ \mu H$; $C = 150$ pF; $C_e = 40$ pF; $C_p = 1$ pF.

along the column. If the voltage amplitude is not reduced to a zero value when the earthed l.v. part is reached, it will be reflected exciting oscillations across the last column element, the l.v. part.

Pure capacitor voltage dividers are therefore sensitive to input voltages with short rise times and the output voltage may oscillate with non-oscillating input voltages. Such a capacitance divider within a whole measuring circuit, i.e. with leads connected to its input, will form a series resonant circuit and thus the whole measuring circuit will oscillate. Thus it is obvious that pure capacitor dividers are not adequate to measure impulse voltages with a steep front (front chopped lightning impulse voltages) or any highly transient phenomena (voltage during chopping). Switching impulse voltages or even full lightning impulse voltages, however, can be properly recorded, if the transient phenomena during the front of the impulse have disappeared.

The similarity of the unit step response equations for resistor voltage dividers to those treated in this part stimulated the possible improvement of pure capacitor dividers by inserting real resistor units in series with the capacitors.[75] If the value of these resistors is not high, but just sufficient to damp the oscillations, it is likely to achieve a good transient performance. A similar equation to eqn. (3.84) could be derived by calculating the transition from hyperbolic to trigonometric functions for the argument b_k and $k = 1$ in eqn. (3.88), which provides again a critical resistance. An evaluation of the USR according to eqn. (3.88) is shown in Fig. 3.53, assuming adequate values for a capacitor voltage divider for a voltage of about 1 MV (height ≈ 3 m). The influence of the magnitude of the resistance R is obvious. A very well-damped response is reached by resistance value of

$$R \approx 4 \sqrt{\frac{L}{C_e}} \tag{3.89}$$

though the larger overshoot observed with lower values can still be accepted. The short response time is in accordance with the theory. T^0 or T can be calculated by the transfer function as well as from eqn. (3.88). It is equivalent to eqn. (3.80), and thus $T^0 = RC_e/6$. The small resistors necessary to damp the oscillations are not able to introduce too high response times, and thus a combination of a low value resistor divider with a capacitor divider is available. The input impedance of these dividers increases with lowering the frequencies, and hence the loading effect of the voltage generating system is limited. Their application for a.c., switching or

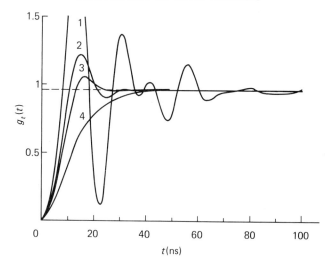

FIG. 3.53. Computed unit step response $G_i(t)$ for damped capacitive dividers according to equivalent circuit. Fig. 3.51.

$C = 150 \text{ pF};$ $\quad L = 2.5 \,\mu\text{H};$ $\quad C_e = 40 \text{ pF};$ $\quad C_p = 1 \text{ pF}$

(1) $R = 250 \,\Omega$	
(2) $R = 750 \,\Omega$	$4\sqrt{\dfrac{L}{C_e}} = 1000 \,\Omega$
(3) $R = 1000 \,\Omega$	
(4) $R = 2000 \,\Omega$	

lightning impulse voltages without restrictions is, therefore, possible. If a parallel branch of high ohmic resistors is added, also d.c. voltages can be measured as shown before.

These "damped capacitor dividers" are not limited in the voltage range, as a stacking of capacitor units is not limited as well as the insertion of distributed resistors. These resistors are not heavily loaded, as only transient input voltages cause currents. A "general purpose" voltage divider is therefore available, and they are in general use today.[72,83] Figure 3.54 shows such a voltage divider for a lightning impulse voltage of some MV. The electrodes are not provided to shield the divider, i.e. to reduce C_e, but only to prevent heavy discharges and thus to increase the flashover voltage. A high performance of the transfer characteristics can only be reached with a careful design and proper compensation of the l.v. arm, which is also formed by a series connection of resistors with capacitor units.

FIG. 3.54. Damped capacitor voltage divider for 4.5-MV impulse voltage, outdoor. In the
background: impulse generator 5.6 MV, 450 kJ (Courtesy Haefely, Basel/Switzerland).

3.6.5 Interaction between Voltage Divider and Measuring Circuit

The analytical treatment of our measuring system presented so far is still unsatisfactory. Whereas the USR of the voltage dividers could readily be calculated, similar results are missing for the entire circuit. It was also not shown how the generalized expression for the response time and its interaction with the circuit elements, eqn. (3.67), can be applied in practice; this equation would certainly be useless if the actual measurements of unit step responses do not confirm its validity.

As was mentioned in section 3.6.3, that the analytical solution for the USR of the whole measuring system, represented by a three-component system Fig. 3.42, is difficult if the transfer function must be transformed into the time domain. Numerical solutions by advanced programming, however, are possible, and many computer programs are available. The results presented here are calculated with the transient network program published by Dommel.[76] The lossless transmission line (see 2, Fig. 3.42) is simulated in this program by the exact solution of the partial differential equations of a line and thus does not introduce any errors. The simulation of the terminating system, i.e. the voltage dividers, needs a subdivision of the distributed parameter networks into a finite number of sections. If the number of elements n (for n see Fig. 3.44) is larger than 5, the results are close to the infinite number solution.

Only a few results are presented. Numerical computations need numerical values for the surge impedance of the lead Z_L to the divider. For the common set-up of a voltage testing system (Fig. 3.35), this lead is more or less horizontal above the ground return, which is assumed to be an extended plane. Many experiments[53] demonstrated that the travel time τ_L is controlled by the velocity of light c_0. As $Z_L = \sqrt{L_L/C_L}$ and $\tau_L = \sqrt{L_L C_L}$ $= l/c_0$, with L_L being the total inductance and C_L the total capacitance of this lead, $Z_L = l/c_0 C_L$, with l being the length of the lead. The capacitance of the lead can be computed assuming that a finite cylindrical lead of diameter d is at height H above a plane, which is earthed. The well-known capacitance formula

$$C_L = \frac{2\pi\varepsilon_0 l}{A};$$

where

$$A = \ln\left[\frac{2l}{d}\sqrt{\frac{\sqrt{1+(2H/l)^2}-1}{\sqrt{1+(2H/l)^2}+1}}\right] = \ln\left(\frac{4H}{d}\right) - \ln\frac{1}{2}(1+\sqrt{1+2(H/l)^2})$$

may well be used, though this lead is placed between the test object and the voltage divider. As $c_0 = (\varepsilon_0 \mu_0)^{-0.5}$, where ε_0 = permittivity of free space, μ_0 = permeability of free space, the surge impedance becomes

$$(Z_L)_{\text{hor}} = \frac{1}{2\pi} \sqrt{\frac{\mu_0}{\varepsilon_0}} \quad A = 60\, A(l, d, H)[\Omega] \tag{3.90}$$

for this *horizontal* lead. Later it will be shown that also a vertical lead will be necessary to measure the experimental USR of the system. Thus we need Z_L for a vertical lead also. According to Fig. 3.35 and eqn. (3.34), this capacitance is known. With the same assumptions as made above, we obtain

$$(Z_L)_{\text{vert}} = \frac{1}{2\pi} \sqrt{\frac{\mu_0}{\varepsilon_0}} \ln\left[\frac{2l}{d} \sqrt{\frac{4s+l}{4s+3l}}\right] \approx 60 \ln\left(\frac{1.15l}{d}\right)[\Omega] \quad \text{for } s \ll l. \tag{3.91}$$

The differences in the surge impedances are not large if the usual dimensions are taken into account.

In Fig. 3.55 a very simple equivalent circuit represents a 20-kΩ resistor divider with a lead length of 3 m (τ_t = 10 nsec). The divider is idealized by the omission of any stray capacitances or inductances, but a parallel capacitance of $C_t = 50$ pF across the whole divider represents a top electrode which may shield the divider. A pure resistor R_d provides ideal damping conditions for travelling waves. For $R_d = 0$, no noticeable damping effect is observed within the exposed time scale, as the high resistance of the divider provides a weak damping only. Though the oscillations are nonsinusoidal, the fundamental frequency can clearly be seen. This frequency is obviously close to the resonance frequency f_r, generated by the lead inductance L_L and the divider's capacitance C_t. As $L_L = Z_L \tau_L$, this inductance is 3 μH, giving f_r = 13 MHz. This example can also be applied to show the typical USR for pure capacitor or parallel-mixed resistor-capacitor voltage dividers, as C_t can well be assumed to form these types of dividers. Higher values of C_t will decrease the frequency of the oscillations. Acceptable responses are only provided by a damped lead. To prevent any overshoot, R_d must equal Z_L. The increase in the front time and increase of the response time T^0 or $T = T^0 - \tau_L$ is obviously produced by the time constant $R_d C_t$, which equals 15 nsec for $R_d = Z_L$ and the special values assumed. Very large capacitor dividers with stacked capacitor units comprise much higher capacitance values, and in such cases the large

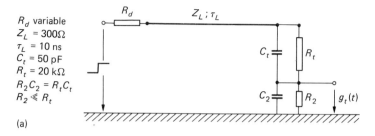

R_d variable
$Z_L = 300\,\Omega$
$\tau_L = 10$ ns
$C_t = 50$ pF
$R_t = 20$ kΩ
$R_2 C_2 = R_t C_t$
$R_2 \ll R_t$

(a)

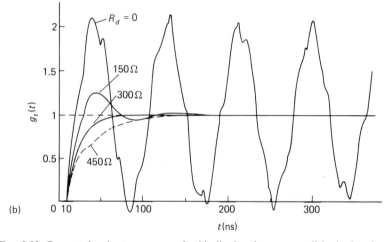

(b)

t(ns)

FIG. 3.55. Computed unit step response for idealized resistor or parallel-mixed resistor-capacitor divider with lead. (a) Equivalent circuit. (b) Computed USR.

response time of such measuring systems is produced by the necessary damping of the lead.

We may easily compute T^0 or the actual response time $T = T^0 - \tau_L$ from eqns. (3.67) to (3.72). It is clear that $T_t = 0$ (ideal dividers) and $T_{kd} = 0$ (no frequency dependency of $Z_d(s) = R_d$). With the only frequency-dependent term for the input impedance of the divider $Z_t(s) = R_t/(1 + sR_tC_t)$, we may easily find that $T_{kt} = R_tC_t/(1 + Z_L/R_t)$. The final result may be best represented in the form

$$T = T^0 - \tau_L = \frac{1}{(1 + R_d/R_t)}\left[R_dC_t - \tau_L\left(1 - \frac{Z_L}{R_t}\right)\left(1 - \frac{R_d}{Z_L}\right)\right]. \quad (3.92)$$

Some remarkable findings may be observed:

For $R_d = Z_L$, the length of the lead has no influence upon the response time. This case corresponds to the "infinite line response", as the same result would be achieved if a step voltage supplied from an extremely long lead would be applied to the dividing system.

With no damping resistance, or $R_d < Z_L$, the response time taken from the actual beginning of the USR will always decrease proportionally with the lead length $l = \tau_L c_0$. This decrease of T is clearly produced by an overshoot of the USR (see Fig. 3.55).

As is seen from the computed USR, the determining factor is $R_d C_t$ providing a positive contribution to T.

For capacitor dividers, $R_t \to \infty$ and the same equation can be applied.

A second example (Fig. 3.56) simulates a pure resistor divider of low resistance value (2.32 kΩ), which was built from carbon composition resistors to achieve extremely low values of inductances. The stray inductances are therefore neglected in the equivalent circuit, but it comprises distributed stray capacitances to earth, which have been calculated from eqn. (3.34). The small input capacitance (5 pF) was estimated as only a very small top electrode was provided. The voltage divider was used for voltages up to 800 kV for steep front measurements. The lead length of 6 m was used for USR measurements only, and this example simulates this lead length. The computed USR shows again larger oscillations with no damping resistance in the lead. The shape of the oscillations deviate strongly from the USR of a pure resistor network (see Fig. 3.43), due to the efficiency of the stray capacitances. Only the infinite line response is smooth. For $R_d = 100\ \Omega$, also the input voltage of the divider is plotted to show the distortion introduced by the divider and to see the interactions between the divider and the lead. The small capacitive reflection is mostly suppressed by the divider. For this equivalent circuit, again the response time can be computed by eqn. (3.67). The result is

$$T = T^0 - \tau_L = \frac{1}{1 + (R_d/R_t)}$$
$$\times \left[\frac{R_t C_e}{6} + R_d \left(C_p + \frac{C_e}{2} \right) - \tau_L \left(1 - \frac{Z_L}{R_t} \right) \left(1 - \frac{R_d}{Z_L} \right) \right] \quad (3.93)$$

where $R_t C_e/6 = T_t$, the response time of the divider. Figure 3.57 shows oscillograms of the actually measured responses. The lead was placed parallel to the ground and the unit step voltage generator was mounted at the wall of the laboratory, which was shielded by a Faraday cage. There is a

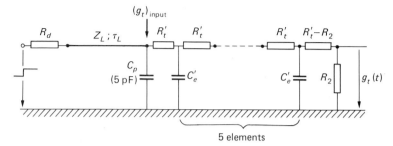

(a) $R_t' = 232\,\Omega;\ \ R_t = \Sigma R_t' = 2\cdot32\ \text{k}\Omega\ ;\ \ R_e \ll R_t';\ \ Z_L = 272\,\Omega$

          $C_e' = 5\ \text{pF};\ \ \ C_e = \Sigma C_e' = 25\ \text{pF};$ $\tau_L = 20\ \text{ns}$

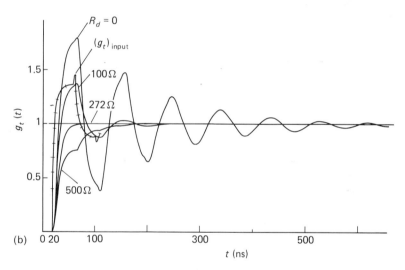

FIG. 3.56. Computed USR for low value resistor voltage divider. (a) Equivalent circuit. (b) Computed USR (for divider input).

very good agreement between the computed and measured values, the USR and the response time.

Finally, the third example (Fig. 3.58) explains the existence of a real time delay between the output and input voltage of a resistor voltage divider. This example is similar to the first one, but the resistors are distributed and comprise a small inductive time constant of $L_t/R_t = 5$ nsec. Stray capacitances in parallel to each section, however, are neglected. The USR of the output voltage starts now with a time delay of about 15–20 nsec related to

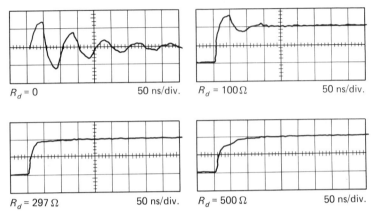

FIG. 3.57. Measured unit step response for the resistor voltage divider. $R = 2320\ \Omega$, with 6-m lead, according to Fig. 3.56.

the input voltage. This delay is caused by the travel time of the divider, $\tau_t = \sqrt{L_t C_e}$, which is about 22 nsec. A stray capacitance C_p' will only theoretically suppress this travel time, as was shown in reference 53. The very small C_e values assumed in this example should simulate a very good

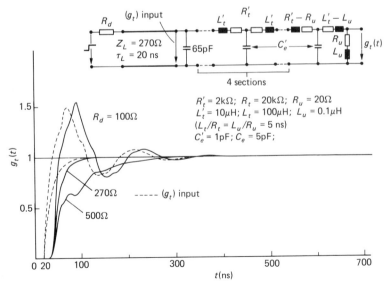

FIG. 3.58. Computed USR of resistor divider with inductance.

shielded divider. This rise time of the response is accordingly quite short. If the response time is calculated as before, an additional small negative term within the brackets [eqn. (3.93)] would appear, being $-R_d L_t/(R_t)^2$. Whereas this term is negligible, the additional time delay decreases the computed response time of the dividers, $R_t C_e/6$. This effect may thus be taken into account by a reduction of this value by a factor of 3/4, and for this the Standards[6] recommend a theoretical contribution of the response time for resistor dividers according to $R_t C_e/8$.

Though many carefully performed investigations[57] have confirmed the validity of such analytical treatment, a pure theoretical treatment of the transfer characteristics of voltage dividing systems will not satisfy the actual needs. In practice, an experimental unit step response has to prove the performance of the systems used, as inaccurate constructions may heavily disturb this response. There are still some unsolved problems inherent to response measurements, but they cannot be treated here in detail. The most difficult problem is related to the fact that the actual "input terminals" of our voltage measuring system (Fig. 3.35) are separated by a long distance due to the dimensions of the test object. A unit step voltage, however, cannot be generated with simple means between two terminals of large distance, though an attempt was made very recently by Schwab et al.[77] to reach this goal experimentally. The existence of a voltage defined by a potential difference between distant points is, of course, not justified in high-frequency alternating electromagnetic fields; but we still may assume that actual currents charging the test objects within a short but finite time will produce a quasistationary field and through it a potential difference for which the expression "voltage" is justified. For the measurement of a unit step response, which can be produced by small unit step voltage generators for some ten or hundred volts, the lead to the voltage divider must be lengthened to reach this generator, which in general will be placed at the ground return. Thus, the layout of the procedure for measuring the "experimental unit step response" is formed by a "square loop arrangement" as shown in Fig. 3.59 and recommended by the Standards.[6,60] The step generator a to c must have approximately zero impedance while generating the voltage step and during the subsequent response. Any fast switching device, c, which short-circuits a constant voltage, which was used to charge the measuring system as long as all transients disappeared, is applicable. Very suitable switches are mercury-wetted relays or a gap of about 1 mm spacing having a nearly uniform field which is caused to spark over. Larger gaps are not satisfactory as they do not have a sufficiently short

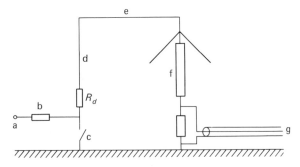

FIG. 3.59. The unit step method. (a) To d.c. supply or impulse generator. (b) Resistor. (c) Step
generator. (d) Added vertical lead, length h. (e) High-voltage lead, length l, height h, above
ground. (f) Voltage divider. (g) To oscilloscope.

time to break down nor provide sufficiently low impedances after sparkover. By this means the unit step voltage amplitude is always very low in
comparison with the rated voltage of the voltage dividing systems; the
linearity of the voltage output to voltage input must therefore be checked
by other means. The small voltage output of the voltage divider will
generally also be too low to be recorded with normal impulse oscilloscopes,
providing no internal amplitude amplifiers. Oscilloscopes having higher
sensitivity will have to be used, but they should have response characteristics similar to those which are replaced.

The added vertical lead d can be made from the same conductor
provided for the h.v. lead e,[6] though the surge impedances according to
eqns. (3.90) and (3.91) are then different. This difference is, however, not
large and may in general be neglected. For more accurate measurements the
adaption of the diameter for the vertical lead is possible to achieve either the
same mean value for the surge impedance [eqn. (3.91)] or to provide equal
and constant surge impedance per unit length by a conical-shaped lead.[78]
In any case, we can assume that the theory of the measuring system is
applicable, and thus the influence of this vertical lead may well be computed
from eqn. (3.67). The simplest way to account for this lead is to perform a
response measurement without any damping resistor, $Z_d(s) = R_d = 0$.
Equation (3.67) is thus reduced to

$$T^0 = T_t + \tau_L \frac{Z_L}{Z_t(0)}, \qquad (3.94)$$

where τ_L involves both leads, the horizontal as well as the vertical one, or
$\tau_L = \tau_h + \tau_v$. At the oscilloscope, the response will start at a zero point

which is delayed by τ_{de} as shown in Fig. 3.39. As this delay is approximately given by τ_L, we indicate the experimentally recorded response time by

$$T_n = T^0 - \tau_{de} = T_t + (\tau_h + \tau_v)\left(\frac{Z_L}{Z_t(0)} - 1\right).$$

The real response time in our measuring circuit with the horizontal lead only and without any damping resistor in the lead will also be controlled by eqn. (3.94). This actual response time T thus becomes with $\tau_{de} = \tau_h$

$$T = T_t + \tau_h\left(\frac{Z_L}{Z_t(0)} - 1\right).$$

The difference of both equations provides

$$T = T_n + \tau_v\left(1 - \frac{Z_L}{Z_t(0)}\right). \tag{3.95}$$

This simple relationship T is recommended by IEC or other Standards today. The disadvantage of this method is obvious, however, if the oscillations are taken into account, by which any response with undamped lead is disturbed. The procedure of the necessary integration to achieve the response time is troublesome and will often lead to inaccurate results.

To improve the method, the same test circuit (Fig. 3.59) may be used, but a few responses can be recorded with different types of R_d values. Small resistors of low inductance may be used, so that $Z_d(s) = R_d$. Then T_{kd}, eqn. (3.70), will be zero, and eqn. (3.67) can be rearranged to

$$T^0\left(1 + \frac{R_d}{Z_t(0)}\right) = T_t + \tau_L\frac{Z_L}{Z_t(0)}$$

$$+ R_d\left[\frac{\tau_L}{Z_L} + \frac{T_t}{Z_t(0)} + T_{kt}\left(\frac{1}{Z_L} + \frac{1}{Z_t(0)}\right)\right]. \tag{3.96}$$

If now T^0 or $T_n = T^0 - \tau_L$ is evaluated by the measurements, the left-hand side of this equation will increase proportionally to R_d, as all other terms are not influenced by the change of R_d. The recorded responses are no longer oscillatory, if R_d is not too small. The steepness of this line is also a measure for the sensitivity of the response time upon the magnitude of the damping resistor. The extrapolation for $R_d = 0$ is possible by a best fitting line. The same procedure as explained before may also be used to account for the additional vertical lead.

The main advantage of these methods is also the possibility to evaluate the response time T_t of the actual voltage divider. The influence of any lead can easily be eliminated by calculation only, as the remaining term $\tau_L Z_L/Z_t(0)$ (for $R_d = 0$) is known with adequate accuracy.

The uncertainties of the unit step method are related to the starting point, i.e. the value of τ_{de} in Fig. 3.39, of the response. This starting point on the "toe" region is influenced by electromagnetic waves radiated from the leads between step generator and the divider. These phenomena have been thoroughly investigated by an International Research group;[53] the methods for the computation of these phenomena are based upon Maxwell's equations, which can either be solved in the time domain[79] or in the frequency domain.[80] The solutions are very sophisticated and cannot be treated within this chapter, whose principal goal has been to introduce the problems only.

3.6.6 The L.V. Arm of the Measuring System

Besides the more general remarks made in section 3.6.1 concerning this matter, some additional problems are treated concerning adequate construction and layout of the l.v. arm of our measuring system. Many distortions in the response can be related to this part of the system.

For d.c. and a.c. voltage dividers, the design of the l.v. arm is not critical, if only steady-state voltages have to be recorded. However, if any fast transients have to be transmitted from the voltage divider to the recording instrument (see Fig. 3.35, items 5 to 7), the l.v. arm of the voltage divider itself may introduce large disturbances to the response. Let us first discuss the adequate impedance matching necessary to transmit impulse voltages from the divider to the recording instrument.

In Fig. 3.60 the somewhat simplified equivalent circuits for the matching procedures for the different types of dividers are sketched. The signal cable is mainly treated as lossless, so that the surge impedance $Z_k = \sqrt{L_k/C_k}$ becomes independent of frequency, and the travel time $\tau_k = \sqrt{L_k C_k}$ is a plain value. For resistor voltage dividers, Fig. 3.60(a), the cable matching is simply done by a pure ohmic resistance $R = Z_k$ at the end of the signal cable. The transmission line theory provides the well-known background for this procedure, the reflection coefficient becomes zero and any unit step voltage appearing across R_2 is undistorted transmitted by the cable. As the

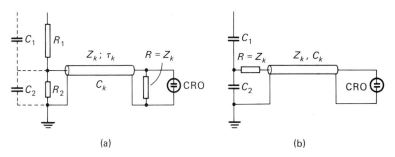

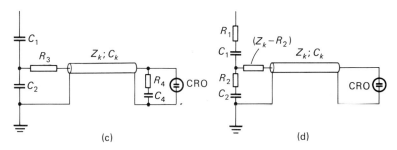

Fig. 3.60. Circuits for signal cable matching. (a) Resistor or parallel-mixed capacitor-dividers. (b) Capacitor dividers, simple matching. (c) Capacitor dividers, compensated matching. (d) Damped capacitor divider, simple matching.

input impedance of the signal cable is $R = Z_k$, this resistance is in parallel to R_2 and forms an integral part of the dividers l.v. arm. The low value of this resistance R, i.e. typically 50 to 75 Ω, should in fact suggest to consider a signal cable with losses. These losses are in reality dependent upon frequency due to the skin effect, and the response of such a cable becomes complex. Whereas the theory of this problem may be found elsewhere,[85,86] the result of this theory shows clearly that the best matching can be achieved with R equal to the surge impedance Z_k defined for high frequencies. For longer signal cables the d.c. resistance for the conductors (inner conductor and shield) will form a voltage dividing system between R_2 and R, which may decrease the voltage across R by an amount of 1% in order of magnitude. As this amount can easily be taken into account by d.c. resistance measurements only, this value should be checked. The unit step response from a lossy cable, characterized by a steep increase within a few nanoseconds to values of more than 90% of the final value and a slow trippling up to the final value, will introduce larger errors if the impulses to be transmitted are shorter than 0.5 to 1 μsec. At least an experimental test is recommended to check the signal cable with regard to this additional error.

For parallel-mixed resistor-voltage dividers the same procedure for cable matching, Fig. 3.60(a), can be used. A matching resistor R, coaxially designed to meet the high-frequency requirements, will not reflect energy. The input impedance of the recording instrument, however, should not comprise appreciable input capacitance, as otherwise too heavy reflections will appear. The l.v. arm for this type of divider reflects also heavily due to the parallel capacitance to R_2.

For capacitor voltage dividers, Fig. 3.60(b) or Fig. 3.60(c), the signal cable cannot be matched at its end. A low ohmic resistor in parallel to C_2 would load the l.v. arm of the divider too heavily and decrease the output voltage with time. To avoid travelling wave oscillations, the cable can be terminated at its input end. A voltage step of constant amplitude at C_2, i.e. $C_2 \to \infty$, will be halved by $R = Z_k$ at the cable input end, at R and Z_k forms a voltage divider. This halved voltage travels to the open end and is doubled by reflection. Thus the original amplitude of the voltage across C_2 appears at the input of the recording instrument. The reflected wave charges the cable to its final voltage amplitude, and is absorbed by R, as the capacitor C_2 forms a short-circuit.

In reality, C_2 is of finite value and is therefore discharged during these transient events. The computation shows that the discharge period is very close to twice the travel time. After this time, the cable capacitance is charged to the final voltage, and from this we obtain two ratios of the voltage divider, namely:

$$n_o = \frac{C_1 + C_2}{C_1} \qquad \text{for } t = 0;$$

$$n_e = \frac{C_1 + C_2 + C_k}{C_1} \qquad \text{for } t \gtrless 2\tau_k.$$

The signal cable, therefore, introduces an initial "overshoot" of the voltage of $\Delta V = (n_e/n_o) - 1 = C_k/(C_1 + C_2)$, which may well be neglected for short or medium cable length, and high values of C_2, i.e. high ratios of the voltage dividers. Capacitor dividers are often used for field testing of transient voltages, and longer cables thus are often necessary. The response can be improved by transferring part of the l.v. capacitor C_2 to the cable end and connecting it in series with a resistor, Fig. 3.60(c). This system, first treated by Burch,[81] offers some opportunities to decrease the overshoot effect. Burch proposed to make both matching resistances equal and $R_3 = R_4 = Z_k$. If then the condition $C_1 + C_2 = C_3 + C_k$ is satisfied, the initial and the infinite time values of the voltage become the same, and the original overshoot of about $C_k/(C_1 + C_2)$ is reduced to about 1/6. There are, however, further opportunities to improve the response as recently demonstrated by Zaengl.[82] For damped capacitor dividers, the resistors R_1 and R_2 necessary within the l.v. arm are for the reflected wave in series to the matching impedance at the l.v. arm, see Fig. 3.60(d). As R_2 is very small in comparison to R_1, the value of this matching resistor must only be reduced by the small value of R_2. The methods of Fig. 3.60(c) can also be applied.

Whereas matching resistors for coaxial cables, i.e. resistors between inner

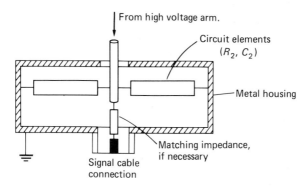

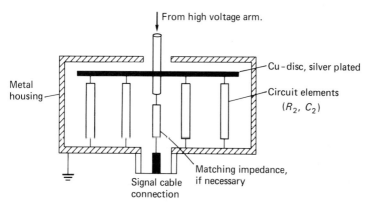

Fig. 3.61. Sketched cross-sections of possible layouts for the l.v. arm of voltage dividers.

and outer conductors, are commercially available, the series resistors for all capacitor dividers are an integral part of the divider's l.v. arm. It may well be recognized that the path to earth for the reflected wave should not be hindered by too high inductances. This condition dictates the need for every l.v. capacitor to have a very low inductance. The theoretical value of this inductance is given by the ratio of the divider, which divides also the overall inductance of the stacked capacitor column. The physical size of the capacitance C_2 values necessary to reduce the high voltage to a measurable quantity is, however, relatively large. The coaxial arrangement of any circuit elements used within the l.v. arm is a condition which should be strictly followed. In Fig. 3.61 simple cross-sections of possible layouts of the l.v. arm are sketched. Radially arranged elements tend to give even lower inductance values. The metal housing avoids the impact of electromagnetic fields. By the coaxial connection of the original cable, the input loop of this cable will not "see" any effective magnetic field, which contributes to reduced voltages by the transient currents. Therefore, the current paths must be evenly distributed within the coaxially arranged elements. A too low inductance may easily be increased by the addition of small wire loops in series with the elements. For more information reference should be made to the literature.[84,87]

REFERENCES

1. A. J. Schwab. *High Voltage Measurement Techniques.* MIT Press, Cambridge, Ma., 1972.
2. W. Betz, A. Schroke and K. Forger. *Elektrizitätszähler und Messwandler.* G. Graun, Karlsruhe, 1959.
3. W. Hermstein. Entwicklungstendenzen im Wandlerbau. *Elektrizitatswirtschaft* **68** (1969), pp. 246–257.
4. A. Draper. *Electrical Machines*, Longmans, London, 1976.
5. IEC Publication 52 (1960). Recommendations for Voltage Measurements by Means of Sphere-gaps (one sphere earthed).
6. IEEE Standard Techniques for High Voltage Testing. IEEE, 1978.
7. E. Kuffel and A. S. Husbands. *Proc. IEE* **108A** (1961), p. 302.
8. H. E. Feigel and W. A. Keen. *Trans. AIEE* **76,** 1 (1957), p. 307.
9. E. Kuffel. *Proc. IEE* **108A** (1961), p. 295.
10. W. G. Standring, D. H. Browning, R. C. Hughes and W. J. Roberts. *Proc. IEE* **110** (1963), pp. 1077–1081.
11. S. Guindehi. *Bull. SEV* **61** (1970), pp. 97–104.
12. T. E. Allibone and D. Dring. *Proc. IEE* Vol. 119, No. 9 (1972), pp. 1417–1422.
13. W. Link. PhD Thesis, TU Stuttgart, No. 203 (1975).
14. E. Peschke. PhD Thesis, TU Munich (1968).
15. E. Kuffel. *Proc. IEE* **106C** (1959), p. 133.

16. F. O. MacMillan and E. G. Starr. *Trans. AIEE* **49** (1930), p. 859.
17. P. L. Bellaschi and P. H. McAuley. *Electric Journal* **31** (1934), p. 228.
18. J. R. Meador. *Trans. AIEE* **53** (1934), p. 942.
19. W. Dattan. *Elektrotech. Z.* **57** (1936), p. 377.
20. R. Davis and G. W. Bowdler. *JIEE* **82** (1938), p. 645.
21. J. M. Meek. *JIEE* **93** (1946), p. 97.
22. A. J. Kachler. 2nd Int. Symp. on High Voltage Engg., Zurich, 1975, pp. 217–221.
23. W. Schultz. Erratic breakdown in air due to impurities in the presence of direct and alternating voltages. 3rd Int. Symp. on High Voltage Engg., Milan 1979, Report 52.05.
24. D. Peier and H. Groschopp. *PTB—Mitteilungen* **87** (1977), pp. 396–398.
25. W. O. Schumann. *Elektrische Durekbruchfeldstarke von Gasen.* Springer, Berlin, 1923.
26. E. Kuffel and M. Abdullah. *High-Voltage Engineering,* Pergamon Press, 1970.
27. G. A. Schroeder. *Zeitschr. f. Angew. Physik* **13** (1967), pp. 296–303.
28. H. A. Boyd, F. M. Bruce and D. J. Tedford. *Nature* **210** (1966), pp. 719–720.
29. P. Boening. *Das Messen, hoher elektrischer Spannungen.* Verlag G. Braun, Karlsruhe, 1953.
30. P. Paasche. *Hochspannungsmessungen,* VEB Verlag Technik, Berlin, 1957.
31. H. House, F. W. Waterton and J. Chew. 1000 kV standard voltmeter. 3rd Int. Symp. on High Voltage Engg., Milan, 1979, Report 43.05.
32. J. H. Park. *J. Res. Nat. Bur. Stand.* **66C,** 1 (1962), p. 19.
33. R. Davis. *J. Sci. Inst.* **5** (1928), pp. 305 and 354.
34. R. F. Goosens and P. G. Provoost. *Bull. SEV* **37** (1946), pp. 175–184.
35. D. Peier and V. Graetsch. 3rd Int. Symp. on High Voltage Engg., Milan, 1979, Report 43.08.
36. C. T. R. Wilson. *Phil. Trans.* **(A)221** (1920), p. 73.
37. H. Kleinwaechter. *Archiv. f. techn. Messen (ATM),* June 1970, R62-R64.
38. W. Clausnitzer. *Trans. IEEE* **IM 17** (1968), p. 252.
39. L. W. Chubb and C. Fortescue. *Trans. AIEE* **32** (1913), pp. 739–748.
40. W. Boeck. *ETZ-A* **84** (1963), pp. 883–885.
41. W. Zaengl. *Arch. Techn. Messen. ATM,* Blatt V 3383-6 and V 3383-7 (1961).
42. O. Voelcker and W. Zaengl. *Arch. Techn. Messen. ATM,* Blatt V 3383-5 (1961).
43. R. Peiser and W. Strauss. Impulse peak voltmeter with extended measuring possibilities. 3rd Int. Symp. on High Voltage Engg. (ISH), Milan, 1979, Report 72.07.
44. A. Bertschinger and M. Brandestini. Impulse peak-voltmeter with a novel memory-circuit. 2nd Int. Symp. on High Voltage Engg. (ISH), Zurich, 1975, pp. 194–198.
45. J. G. Graeme. *Designing with Operational Amplifiers.* McGraw-Hill, New York, 1977.
46. W. Schulz. High-voltage ac peak measurement with high accuracy. 3rd Int. Symp. on High Voltage Techn., Milan, 1979, Report 43.12.
47. W. Bucklen *et al.* Understanding the fundamentals eases signal-processing tasks. *EDN* **26,** March/April 1981, No. 6/7/8.
48. R. Malewski and A. Dechamplain. Digital impulse recorder for high-voltage laboratories. *Trans. IEEE* **PAS 99** (1980), pp. 636–649.
49. A. Keller. Symposium on Precision Electrical Measurements, NPL, London, 1955.
50. H. R. Lucas and D. D. McCarthy. *Trans. IEEE* **PAD 89** (1970), pp. 1513–1521.
51. U. Brand and M. Marckmann. Outdoor high-voltage compressed gas capacitors using SF$_6$. 2nd Int. Symp. on High Voltage Engg., Zurich, 1975.
52. D. L. Hillhouse and A. E. Peterson. *Trans. IEEE* **IM 22** (1973), No. 4.
53. IRR-IMS Group. Facing uhv measuring problems. *Electra* No. 35 (1974), pp. 157–254.
54. W. Zaengl. *Arch. Techn. Messen (ATM),* Blatt Z 130-3 (1969).
55. H. Luehrmann. *ETZ-A* **91** (1971), pp. 332–335.
56. F. Leclère. "Les oscillographes du laboratoires à très haute tension des renardieres", *EdF* Bull. de la Direction des Etudes et Recherches, Serie B, No. 1 (1971), pp. 71–88.

57. High voltage measurements, present state and future developments. *Rev. Gen. Electr*, Special Issue, June 1978.
58. A. Rodewald. Fast transient currents on the shields of auxiliary cables after switching operations in hv substations and hv laboratories, IEEE PES Winter Meeting, New York, 1979, Paper No. A79 086-0.
59. A. Rodewald. *Bull. SEV* **69** (1978), pp. 171–176.
60. IEC Publication 60-4 (1977). High-voltage test techniques, Part 4: Application Guide for Measuring Devices.
61. A. Asner. *Bull. SEV* **52** (1961), pp. 192–203.
62. F. Creed, R. Kawamura and G. Newi. *Trans. IEEE PAS* **86** (1967), pp. 1408–1420.
63. W. Zaengl. *Bull. SEV* **61** (1970), pp. 1003–1017.
64. W. Zaengl and K. Feser. *Bull. SEV* **55** (1964), pp. 1250–1256.
65. P. R. Howard. Errors in recording surge voltages. *Proc. IEE* **II/99** (1952), pp. 371–383.
66. A. F. Rohlfs, J. F. Kresge and F. A. Fisher. *Trans. AIEE* **76** (1957), Part I, pp. 634–646.
67. D. Pellinen and M. S. Di Capua. *Rev. Sci. Instr.* **51** (1980), pp. 70–73.
68. P. L. Bellaschi. *Trans. AIEE* **52** (1933), pp. 544–567.
69. T. Harada, T. Kawamura, Y. Akatsu, K. Kimura and T. Aizawa. *Trans. IEEE PAS* **90** (1971), pp. 2247–2250.
70. R. Krawczynski. Correction of the high voltage measuring system by means of l.v. transmission line. 2nd Int. Symp. on High Voltage Engg., Zurich, 1975, Report 3.1-07.
71. R. Elsner. *Arch. Elektrot.* **33** (1939), pp. 23–40.
72. T. Harada *et al. Trans. IEEE PAS* **95** (1976), pp. 595–602.
73. A. Schwab and J. Pagel. *Trans. IEEE PAS* **91** (1972), pp. 2376–2382.
74. W. Breilmann. Effects of the leads on the transient behavior of coaxial divider for the measurement of high ac and impulse voltage. 3rd Int. Symp. on High Voltage Engg., Milan, 1979, Report 42.12.
75. W. Zaengl. *Bull. SEV* **56** (1965), pp. 232–240.
76. H. Dommel. *Trans. IEEE PAS* **88** (1969), pp. 388–399.
77. A. Schwab, H. Bellm and D. Sautter. 3rd Int. Symp. on High Voltage Engg., Milan, 1979, Report 42.13.
78. H. Luehrmann. *Archiv. fur Elektrot.* **57** (1975), pp. 253–264.
79. N. Ari. Electromagnetic phenomena in impulse voltage measuring systems. *Trans. IEEE PAS* **96** (1977), pp. 1162–1172.
80. K. H. Gonschorek. 3rd Intern. Symp. on High Voltage Engg., Milan, 1979, Report 42.02.
81. F. G. Burch. On potential dividers for cathode-ray oscillographs. *Phil. Magazine*, Series 7, **13** (1932), pp. 760–774.
82. W. Zaengl. *ETZ-A* **98** (1977), pp. 792–795.
83. K. Feser. *Trans. IEEE PAS* **93** (1974), pp. 116–127.
84. R. Malewski and N. Hylten-Cavallius. *Trans. IEEE PAS* **93** (1974), pp. 1797–1804.
85. Ramo, Whinnery and van Duzer. *Fields and Waves in Communication Electronics*. J. Wiley, 1965.
86. H. G. Unger. *Theorie der Leitungen*. Vieweg, 1966.
87. T. Harada *et al.* Development of high-performance low voltage arms for capacitive voltage dividers. 3rd Int. Symp. on High Voltage Engg., Milan, 1979, Report 42.14.
88. G. W. Bowdler. *Measurements in High-voltage Test Circuits*. Pergamon Press, 1973.
89. E. Rinaldi, F. Poletti and A. Zingales. Constructive improvements in impulse peak voltmeters. 4th Int. Symp. on High Voltage Engg., Athens, 1983, Report 61.02.
90. Q.-C. Qi and W. Zaengl. Investigations of errors related to the measured virtual front time T_1 of lightning impulses. *Trans. IEEE PAS* **102** (1983), pp. 2379–2390.
91. N. Hylten-Cavallius *et al.* A new approach to minimize response errors in the measurement of high voltages. *Trans. IEEE PAS* **102** (1983), pp. 2077–2091.

Chapter 4

ELECTROSTATIC FIELDS
AND FIELD STRESS CONTROL

In response to an increasing demand for electrical energy, operating transmission level voltages have increased considerably over the last two decades. Designers are therefore forced to reduce the size and weight of electrical equipment in order to remain competitive. This, in turn, is possible only through a thorough understanding of the properties of insulating materials and knowledge of electric fields and methods of controlling electric stress.

This chapter is therefore devoted to a discussion of some of the problems encountered when analyzing even relatively simple but practical insulating systems. Teaching experience has shown that this is a necessary prerequisite in order to gain a clearer understanding of the behaviour of insulating materials. However, no attempt will be made here to introduce the basic field equations, or to treat systematically the numerous methods available for calculating electrostatic fields as this may be found in many books.[1-4]* Rather, this chapter is intended to provide some fundamental understanding of the importance of the interaction between fields and materials involved within an electrical insulation system by discussing some selected examples.

In h.v. engineering most of the problems concerned with the electrical insulation of high direct, alternating and impulse voltages are related to electrostatic and sometimes electrical conduction fields only. It should be emphasized, however, that the permissible field strengths in the materials are interlinked with the electrostatic field distributions and thus the problems may become extremely difficult to solve.

---

* Superscript numbers are to References at the end of the chapter.

4.1 ELECTRICAL FIELD DISTRIBUTION AND BREAKDOWN STRENGTH OF INSULATING MATERIALS

It is often assumed that a voltage V between two electrodes may be adequately insulated by placing a homogeneous insulating material of breakdown strength E_b, which is considered as a characteristic constant of the material, between these electrodes. The necessary separation d may then simply be calculated as $d = V/E_b$. Although the electrodes are usually well defined and are limited in size, the experienced designer will be able to take care of the entire field distribution between the electrodes and will realize that in many cases only a small portion of the material is stressed to a particular maximum value E_{max}. One may conclude that the condition $E_{max} = E_b$ would provide the optimal solution for the insulation problem, which thus could be solved by field analysis only. This is true only when E_b has a very specific value directly related to the field distribution and can be calculated for very well-known insulating materials, such as gases (see Chapter 5, section 5.8). However, for most solid and liquid dielectrics such values are only approximately known. Hence a special approach is necessary to solve the insulation problem with fair accuracy.

These statements will be elucidated and confirmed by considering the simple example of an insulation system shown in Fig. 4.1, which represents a rod-plane electrode configuration insulated by air at atmospheric pressure. Whereas the gap length and the air density are assumed to remain constant, the diameter D of the hemispherically shaped rod will change over a very wide range as indicated by the dashed lines. Two field quantities may be defined for rods of any diameter D. These are the maximum field strength E_{max} at the rod tip and the mean value of the field strength $E_{mean} = V/d$. With these two quantities a "field efficiency factor" η is defined as

$$\eta = \frac{E_{mean}}{E_{max}} = \frac{V}{dE_{max}} \tag{4.1}$$

originally proposed by Schwaiger.[6] This factor is clearly a pure quantity related to e.s. field analysis only. In a more complex electrode arrangement E_{max} may appear at any point on an electrode, not necessarily coinciding with the points providing the shortest gap distance, d. η equals unity or 100% for a uniform field, and it approaches zero for an electrode with an edge of zero radius.

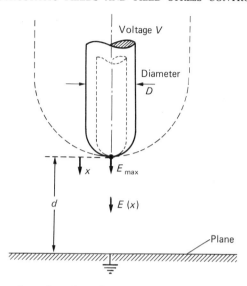

FIG. 4.1. Rod-to-plane electrode configuration [with different efficiency factor $\eta = V/(dE_{max})$].

If the breakdown of the gap is caused by E_{max} only, then the breakdown voltage V_b is obtained from eqn. (4.1) as

$$V_b = E_{max} d\eta$$
$$= E_b d\eta \quad \text{(with } E_{max} = E_b\text{).} \tag{4.2}$$

This equation illustrates the concept of the field efficiency factor. As $1 \geqslant \eta \geqslant 0$ for any field distribution, it is obvious that field non-uniformities reduce the breakdown voltage.

Let us now check the validity of eqn. (4.2) with experimental results. In Fig. 4.2 the d.c. breakdown voltage V_b is shown for the electrode arrangement of Fig. 4.1 for $d = 10$ cm as function of η. The dashed straight line corresponds to eqn. (4.2) with $E_b = 26.6$ kV/cm, a value which agrees well with measured breakdown field intensities in atmospheric air under normal conditions (temperature 20°C; pressure 101.3 kPa; humidity 11 g/m^3) for a *uniform* field $\eta = 1$. The highest breakdown voltage of the gap $V_b = 26.6 \times 10 = 266$ kV can also be found in Chapter 5, eqn. (5.103), or in the calibration tables for measuring sphere gaps discussed in Chapter 3, Table 3.3, for spheres of large diameters, i.e. $D \geqslant 100$ cm. With small gaps the field distribution is uniform in the highly stressed regions. The meas-

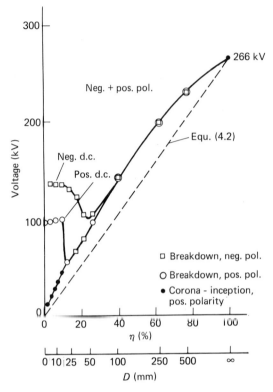

FIG. 4.2. Breakdown and corona inception voltage for the electrode arrangement Fig. 4.1 in atmospheric air (normal conditions) with $d = 10$ cm, for positive and negative d.c. voltage [η see eqn. (4.1)].

ured breakdown voltages, obtained with positive and negative d.c. voltages, are also shown over wide ranges of η or D, the correlation of which can be computed approximately using eqn. (4.20), or more accurately by a numerical computation for this special rod-plane system using the charge simulation method.[7] The differences are remarkable. The lowest measured V_b values are polarity dependent; the reason for the dependence of breakdown voltage upon polarities is explained in Chapter 5, section 5.12. Except when $\eta = 100\%$, the breakdown voltages are always higher than those predicted by eqn. (4.2). For $\eta > 0.3$ for negative and about 0.1 for positive polarity, the breakdown is not preceded by any noticeable predischarge (corona, partial discharge; see Chapter 5, section 5.11); thus it is obvious that E_b in eqn. (4.2) is *not* a constant value for a given gap length. A calculation of breakdown field strength in atmospheric air using the streamer breakdown criterion [see eqn. (5.90)] and the relevant field distribution within the gap would confirm the dependence of the breakdown strength E_b upon rod or sphere diameter D or—more accurately— upon the actual field distribution. In reality, the lowest breakdown voltage is not reached with the smallest values of η. Below the minimum breakdown voltages, the sparkover of the gap is influenced by predischarges, which, for lower voltages, partially bridge the gap and thus produce charged particles, completely altering the field distribution due to space charges. Computation of the breakdown voltages in this region based upon physical parameters only is inaccurate due to a lack of precise knowledge of the physical data and complications introduced due to the moving space charge.

This example, which is typical for most insulation media, demonstrates the complexity of the problems, i.e. the interaction between the static field distribution, field changes due to discharge development, and parameters related to the insulation materials. Further complications arise from differences in behaviour with direct, alternating and impulse voltages. For any other material, the results would be different, even for the same electrode configuration. The proper design of insulation systems is therefore very difficult. Nevertheless, the maximum field intensity E_{max} within any insulation system may be considered as a significant quantity, even though it only serves as a rough guide.

In practice, data on the dielectric stresses in the insulation materials used in h.v. equipment obtained by field analysis must be supplemented by extensive tests in which the breakdown stresses are experimentally determined for similar insulation arrangements. Computations of the stresses are most advanced in gaseous dielectrics. Tests necessary for most of the other materials need not, however, involve complete experimental models which precisely simulate the actual equipment. In general, breakdown stresses are dependent upon the field distribution within high field regions, as will be shown in Chapter 5 for gaseous dielectrics. Thus, models representing only those regions in which high stresses occur are, in general, sufficient; this offers definite advantages. Apart from saving time and costs by simplifying the experimental insulation assemblies, the required voltage levels may often also be reduced significantly, as the models can be reduced in size using electrode configurations in which the low field regions are absent.

4.2 FIELDS IN HOMOGENEOUS, ISOTROPIC MATERIALS

Many electrical insulation systems contain only one type of dielectric material. Most materials may be considered to be isotropic, i.e. the electric field vector $\mathbf{E}$ and the displacement $\mathbf{D}$ are parallel. At least on the macroscopic scale many materials at uniform temperature may also be assumed to be homogeneous. The homogeneity is well confirmed in insulating gases and purified liquids. Solid dielectrics are often composed of large molecular structures forming crystalline and amorphous regions so that the homogeneity of the electrical material properties may not be assured within microscopic structures. The materials will also be assumed to be constant; that means the electric susceptibility is not a function of electric field strength. On a macroscopic basis, the permittivity ε will then simply be a scalar quantity correlating $\mathbf{D}$ and $\mathbf{E}$, $\mathbf{D} = \varepsilon\mathbf{E}$.

At this stage it is assumed here that the influence of electrical conductivity σ on the field distribution may be ignored; this is justified for most insulating materials when they are stressed by alternating voltages at frequencies above 0.1 to 1 Hz. Thus, simple electrostatic field theory may be applied to most of the practical applications concerned with power frequency or impulse voltages. With direct or slowly alternating voltages the use of simple electrostatic field theory is greatly impeded by conduction phenomena. In the limiting case, the field is purely given by conduction and the correlation between field strength E and current density j is $\mathbf{j} = \sigma\mathbf{E}$, where σ may be highly dependent upon time due to relaxation phenomena, upon temperature and often also upon field intensity. This problem is only mentioned here to emphasize the difficulties encountered with d.c. voltage applications.

The following examples for electrostatic field distributions are typical for h.v. insulation systems:

The Uniform Field Electrode Arrangement

The realization of homogeneous fields within a finite volume of insulating material is very difficult. Using parallel metal plates of limited dimensions creates the problem of a proper stress control at the edges of the plates. The field problem becomes thus three-dimensional, though a rotational symmetry exists if the parallel plates are circular discs.

Depending upon the material to be tested, the breakdown strength may be very sensitive to local high fields within the whole electrode arrangement. Therefore, the highest stress should only be present in the homogeneous field region, where the plates are in parallel. A certain profile of electrodes is necessary outside the plane region to limit the dimensions, but the field strength at the curved edges should never exceed the value $E = V/d$, if V is the applied voltage and d the distance between the parallel plates. Rogowski[6] proposed electrodes for uniform fields for axially symmetrical systems whose profile follows the analytical function first introduced by Maxwell,

$$z = \frac{a}{\pi}(w + 1 + e^w) \tag{4.3}$$

where z and w represent the complex coordinates in the z- and w-planes. Substitution of the coordinates for the complex values $z = x + iy$ and $w = u + iv$ and separation of the real and imaginary parts gives

$$x = \frac{a}{\pi}(u + 1 + e^u \cos v);$$

$$y = \frac{a}{\pi}(v + e^u \sin v). \tag{4.4}$$

Assuming two infinite, parallel "plates" in the w-plane, the coordinates of which are given by $v = \pm\pi = \text{const}$, it can be recognized from eqn. (4.4) that these plates are transformed into the z-plane to the left half-plane only. All other lines $v = \text{const}$ with $-\pi < v < +\pi$ can be assumed to be other equipotential lines, and all lines $u = \text{const}$ with $-\infty \leqslant u \leqslant +\infty$ can be assumed to be field lines in the w-plane, representing a uniform field distribution. These lines appear in the z-plane as shown in Fig. 4.3, providing the electrical field distribution of parallel plates terminating at $x = 0$. The concentration of the equipotential lines, $v = \text{const}$, within the z plane may well be recognized at, or in the vicinity of, the edges of the plates.

The parallel plates, $v = \pm\pi$, are thus inadequate to fulfil the demand for field distribution whose intensity is limited to the field strength within the homogeneous part of the arrangement, i.e. for $u \lesssim -\pi$. It is obvious that the field strength along equipotential lines for which $-\pi < v < +\pi$ provide

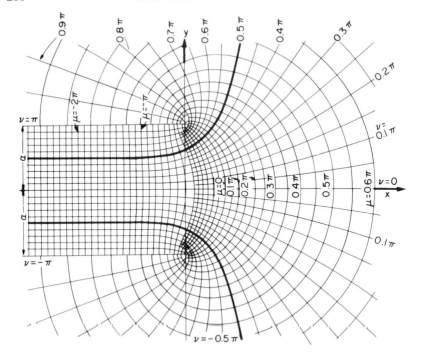

FIG. 4.3. Transformation of a square grid from a w-plane in the displayed z-plane by eqn. (4.3): Rogowski's profile ($v = \pm \pi/2$).

better conditions. For quantitative assessment the field strength within the z-plane may be computed in several ways, as shown:

From the conjugate complex field strength in the z-plane

$$E_z^* = E_x - iE_y = i\frac{dw}{dz} = i\frac{1}{\dfrac{dz}{dw}} \tag{4.5}$$

the absolute values could be computed by $|E_z^*| = \sqrt{E_x^2 + E_y^2}$.

A second possibility is given by

$$E_z = E_x + iE_y = -\operatorname{grad} v = -\left[\left(\frac{\partial v}{\partial x}\right) + i\left(\frac{\partial v}{\partial y}\right)\right] \tag{4.6}$$

which needs a partial differentiation only.

Finally, the absolute value of E_z may be computed by

$$|E_z| = \frac{1}{\sqrt{\left(\dfrac{\partial x}{\partial v}\right)^2 + \left(\dfrac{\partial y}{\partial v}\right)^2}}, \tag{4.7}$$

a method which is easiest to apply to our separated analytical function, eqn. (4.4). Combining eqns. (4.4) and (4.7), we easily may find the field strength as

$$|E_z| = \frac{\pi}{a\sqrt{1 + e^{2u} + 2e^u \cos v}} = f(u\,;v). \tag{4.8}$$

To quantify this expression with any applied voltage it is necessary to perform a calibration with the field intensity within the original w-plane. If the line $v = \pi$ is at potential $\phi = V$ and the line $v = -\pi$ at potential $\phi = -V$, the magnitude of the field strength in the w-plane is $|E_w| = 2V/2\pi = V/\pi$. Hence, the absolute magnitude in the z-plane becomes $|E_w|\,|E_z|$ or

$$|E_z| = \frac{V}{a\sqrt{1 + e^{2u} + 2\,e^u \cos v}}. \tag{4.9}$$

For $u \lesssim 3\text{--}5$, $|E_z|$ is practically constant and $= V/a$, but for $u = 0$ and $v = \pm\pi$, i.e. at the edges of the plates, $|E_z|$ increases to infinite values. There are, however, many equipotential lines in the z-plane for which $|E_z|$ is always limited to values $\lesssim V/a$. The general condition for this behaviour is given by $\cos v \gtrsim 0$ or v within $\pm(\pi/2)$. As the strongest curvature of an equipotential line will provide the smallest possible electrode arrangement, Rogowski has chosen the profile $\cos v = 0$ or $v = \pm\pi/2$, the so-called 90°-Rogowski profile, which is marked by a heavier solid line in Fig. 4.3. Along this line the field strength has its maximum values between the plates in the "homogeneous field region" $u \lesssim -(3\text{--}5)$ and decreases gradually within the curvature with increasing values u. As for all field lines starting at the curved part, the field strength decreases to a minimum value for $v = 0$, breakdown should not occur between the curved regions of the electrodes. The actual distance of two metal electrodes shaped in this way would be $d = a$, and eqns. (4.4) and (4.9) indicate the necessity of dimensioning the electrodes in accordance to the maximum gap length $d = a$, necessary for the breakdown tests. For smaller gap lengths and the same profile, the field strength at the curved profile will decrease relative to the homogeneous field region. Disc-shaped electrodes would have the rotational centre at a field line for $u \simeq -5$ or less providing any size or volume of a homogeneous field region desired. The rotation of the profile about the rotational centre converts the field to the third dimension. The additional increase of the field strength components in the x-direction by this additional curvature is, however, in general negligible. Machining of such profiles has to be carried out very carefully. An efficient test could be made to demonstrate the performance of the electrodes. Breakdown tests in pressurized sulphur hexafluoride (SF_6), a gas very sensitive to local field variations, must display all sparking events in the plane centre of the electrodes.

The decrease of field intensity at the outer curvature of the Rogowski profile could be prevented by a decrease of the radius of curvature, providing smaller dimensions or diameters of the disc electrodes. Profiles approaching constant field intensities at the electrode surface with magnitudes V/d also outside of the uniform field regions are, for instance, Bruce's profile[5] and Borda's profile.[6] Borda's profiles give a completely constant field intensity along the electrode surface, but they are also based on a two-dimensional calculation so that the uniformity will disappear if this profile is applied to an axisymmetric electrode. Improvements can be made by very accurate numerical, computer-aided calculations, taking the actual surroundings as additional boundary conditions into account. For Borda's profile, such optimization was recently performed by Okubo et al.[13]

Coaxial Cylindrical and Spherical Fields

Electrode configurations providing two-dimensional cylindrical or three-dimensional spherical fields are used in h.v. equipment, as well as in laboratories for fundamental research or field stress control. In a short treatment of the well-known coaxial arrangements, we shall demonstrate the fundamental differences only; some special cases give useful comparison.

Cross-sections of coaxial cylinders and concentric spheres are sketched in Figs. 4.4(a) and (b), and different notations are used to distinguish between the radii of cylinders (r_1, r_2) and spheres (R_1, R_2). The electrical field distribution is symmetrical with reference to the centre of the cylinder axis or the centre point of the sphere. In both cases the lines of force are radial and the field strength E is only a function of the distance x from the centres.

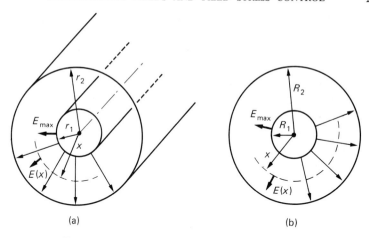

FIG. 4.4. Coaxial cylinders (a) and concentric spheres (b).

The cylinders are then uniformly charged over their surface with a charge per unit length Q/l, and the spheres with a charge Q, if a voltage V is applied to the two electrodes. Using Gauss's law, the field strength $E(x)$ at x is derived from the following:

Coaxial cylinder:
$$E(x) = \frac{Q/l}{2\pi\varepsilon}\frac{1}{x}$$

$$= \frac{V}{\ln(r_2/r_1)}\frac{1}{x}, \tag{4.10}$$

Coaxial spheres:
$$E(x) = \frac{Q}{4\pi\varepsilon}\frac{1}{x^2}$$

$$= \frac{V}{(R_2 - R_1)/R_1 R_2}\frac{1}{x^2}, \tag{4.11}$$

where the subscripts 1 and 2 refer to inner and outer radii respectively. The main difference between the two field distributions is the much faster decrease of the field strength with distance x in the three-dimensional case.

Therefore, for equal geometries ($r_1 = R_1$; $r_2 = R_2$) E_{max} will always be higher in the sphere configuration. As E_{max} is reached for $x = r_1$ or $x = R_1$ respectively, we obtain for:

Coaxial cylinders:
$$E_{max} = \frac{V}{r_1 \ln(r_2/r_1)}. \tag{4.12}$$

Coaxial spheres: $E_{\max} = \dfrac{V}{R_1(1 - R_1/R_2)}.$ (4.13)

Note that the denominator in eqn. (4.12) will always be larger than that in eqn. (4.13), confirming the statement made above.

Let us consider a few simple examples. Spheres or sphere-like electrodes are often used as terminating electrodes of h.v. equipment, placed at the top of a bushing or a voltage divider, etc. Neglecting the influence of the structure connected to the sphere, we may roughly estimate its necessary diameter $2R_1$ assuming the ground potential is far away, i.e. $R_2/R_1 \gg 1$ in eqn. (4.13). Therefore, $E_{\max} \simeq V/R_1$. Theoretically, atmospheric air insulation would provide a breakdown strength for large sphere diameter of about 25 kV/cm under normal conditions. Irregularities involved in the production of large electrodes and unavoidable dust particles in the air (see Chapter 3, section 3.1.1) will reduce the permissible breakdown field strength to about $E_b = 12$–15 kV/cm. Therefore, the diameters necessary to avoid discharge inception, or even breakdown will be

$$(2R_1) \simeq 2\hat{V}/E_b.$$ (4.14)

For an a.c. voltage of 1 MV (r.m.s. value) diameters of about 1.9 to 2.4 m are acceptable. In this case, the greatest uncertainty is related to the breakdown strength E_b at the electrode surface used, i.e. the surface irregularities of the electrodes.[15]

A cylindrical conductor used for partial discharge-free connections in h.v. test circuits in laboratories is always limited in length, and no discharges should occur at the end of the cylinder. Obviously, a sphere of larger diameter than that for the cylindrical conductor must be located at the end, as shown in Fig. 4.5a. The earthed walls of the laboratory will form the outer diameters of the sphere and the cylinder, and we may approximately assume that the field distributions at both electrodes are independent upon each other. Equal maximum values $E_{\max}$ are then achieved by setting eqns. (4.12) and (4.13) equal. Thus the condition

$$\frac{R_1}{r_1} = \frac{\ln(r_2/r_1)}{(1 - R_1/R_2)} \simeq \ln(r_2/r_1)$$ (4.15)

displays the necessary ratio of the diameters. As the "radius" r_2 or R_2 of the laboratory may well be assumed to be twenty times the radii of the electrodes, this ratio becomes at least 3. For small diameters, the breakdown field strength of gases are not equal for even the same radii, as

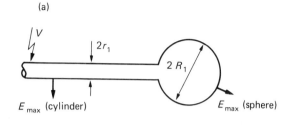

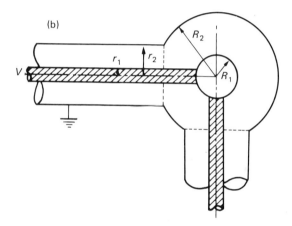

FIG. 4.5. Typical "coaxial" arrangements. (a) Cylinder ended by a sphere within a laboratory. (b) Busbar arrangement in GIS.

the increase of E_b is larger with decreasing radii for spherical fields. Exact values, therefore, can only be obtained by exact field computations and taking the properties of the insulation medium into account.

Busbars for SF_6-insulated, metal-enclosed equipment (GIS) are typical coaxial cylindrical arrangements. If the busbar must change the direction, a "knee" or elbow will be necessary, as shown in Fig. 4.5b. This problem may easily be solved by an interconnection of a coaxial sphere with coaxial cylinder configurations, if the edges at the earthed conductors arising at the intersections are adequately rounded. All dimensions are now interlinked, and as a starting point it will first be necessary to demonstrate optimum dimensioning. For every coaxial or concentric system there is an optimum ratio of the radii, as the field stresses E_{max} reach high values for a given voltage V for small ratios of the radii as well as with too small dimensions. For coaxial cylinders we may rewrite eqn. (4.12) as

$$V = E_{max} r_2 \left(\frac{r_1}{r_2}\right) \ln\left(\frac{r_2}{r_1}\right) \qquad (4.16)$$

and search for an optimum ratio (r_2/r_1), for which the highest voltage can be insulated with a given breakdown strength $E_b = E_{max}$ of the insulation material. For not too small diameters we may well neglect the fact that E_b depends upon r_1 for all gases or other insulation materials [see Chapter 5, section 5.9, eqn. (5.111)]. Thus, $E_{max} = E_b$ as well as r_2 can be treated to be constant and the differentiation of eqn. (4.16) with respect to r_1 gives the condition $dV/dr_1 = 0$ for

$$\ln(r_2/r_1) = 1; \quad (r_2/r_1)_{opt} = e \simeq 2.72$$
$$(V_b)_{opt} = E_b r_1. \qquad (4.17)$$

This ratio is obviously a very important one in dimensioning h.v. cables or coaxial conductors insulated by homogeneous materials of any permittivity. The field efficiency factor η defined by eqn. (4.1) in coaxial cylindrical system is, according to eqn. (4.12),

$$\eta_{cyl} = \frac{1}{\left(\dfrac{r_2}{r_1} - 1\right)} \ln\left(\frac{r_2}{r_1}\right). \qquad (4.18)$$

For $(r_2/r_1) = e$, this efficiency factor becomes 58% and is therefore quite high. Highest breakdown voltages can actually be reached with ratios of r_2/r_1 very close to the optimum value, which is demonstrated in Fig. 4.6 for SF_6-insulated cylindrical conductors within the most interesting range of r_1/r_2. For small ratios, i.e. for small diameters of the inner conductor, no direct breakdown will occur for $E_{max} = E_b$; similar to Fig. 4.2, the actual breakdown voltage is increased by corona discharges.

For the concentric sphere arrangement, the same statements will be applicable. The optimum values for breakdown can be derived from eqn. (4.13), resulting in:

$$(R_2/R_1)_{opt} = 2; \quad (V_b)_{opt} = E_b R_1/2. \qquad (4.19)$$

The field efficiency factor becomes in general terms

$$\eta_{sphere} = (R_1/R_2) \qquad (4.20)$$

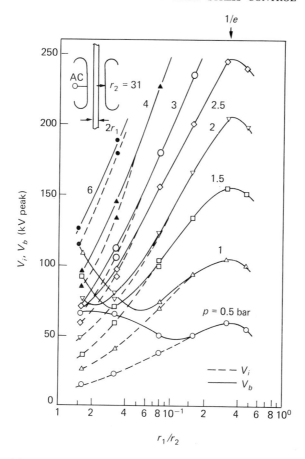

FIG. 4.6. Breakdown (V_b) and discharge inception (V_i) voltages in coaxial cylindrical system SF$_6$ insulation, in dependency of the ratio r_1/r_2. Parameter: gas pressure p. Temperature: 20°C (see reference 16).

and thus is only slightly smaller for $(R_2/R_1)_{opt}$ than that found for the coaxial cylinders with optimum conditions.

Now we may solve the example shown in Fig. 4.5b. If the busbar is optimally designed, i.e. $r_2 = er_1$, and r_1 was calculated by eqn. (4.12) for given values of breakdown voltage $V = V_b$ and breakdown field strength $E_{max} = E_b$, one may apply equal breakdown conditions for the concentric sphere arrangement. Equating the values V_b/E_b for the two systems, we obtain

$$R_1(1 - R_1/R_2) = r_1 \ln(r_2/r_1) = r_1,$$

a condition which obviously has many solutions depending upon the magnitude of R_2. We may, however, select the optimum ratio R_2/R_1 for spheres, and thus we obtain the conditions

$$R_1 = 2r_1, \quad R_2 = \frac{4}{e}r_2,$$

and accordingly the different gap distances related to r_1:

$$R_2 - R_1 = \left(\frac{4}{e}\frac{r_2}{r_1} - 2\right)r_1 = 2r_1,$$

$$r_2 - r_1 = \left(\frac{r_2}{r_1} - 1\right)r_1 \simeq 1.72r_1.$$

These conditions are quite favourable in practice, as the outer sphere diameter is not much bigger than that of the cylindrical system. The gap distance $(R_2 - R_1)$, however, is larger than $(r_2 - r_1)$, which could be expected by the more inhomogeneous field distribution within the three-dimensional field of the sphere arrangement.

Sphere-to-sphere or Sphere-to-plane

In practice, the sphere-to-sphere arrangement is used for measuring high voltages with sphere gaps (Chapter 3, section 3.1.1); sphere-to-plane gaps are widely used for fundamental breakdown studies. The field distribution can be computed analytically if the spheres are assumed to become charged to their potential without any connecting leads. The influence of connecting leads upon the field distribution was recently investigated with a charge simulation program by Steinbigler.[7] The analytical results are presented here, based upon the method of image charges.[1] Another possible solution based upon bipolar coordinates can be found in the literature.[17]

In Fig. 4.7 two spheres of equal diameter $2R$ separated by distance b between centres are assumed to have the potential $+V$ and $-V$ respectively. Then—and only then—the field distribution is completely symmetrical with reference to an imaginary plane P placed between the two

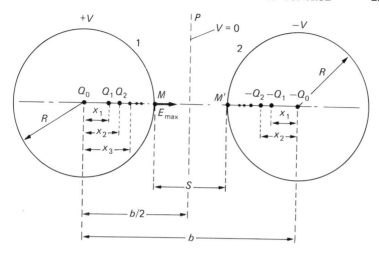

FIG. 4.7. Sphere-to-sphere or sphere-to-plane arrangement.

spheres, if the plane has zero potential. Zero potential also exists at distances far away from the spheres. With a point charge $Q_0 = 4\pi\varepsilon_0 RV$ at the centre of the left sphere (1) the surface of this sphere would exactly represent an equipotential surface and could be replaced by a metal conductor, if the right sphere (2) and the plane would not be present. A charge $-Q_0$ placed at the centre of sphere (2) will produce a symmetrical field distribution with reference to the plane P, but this charge makes the potentials at the surface of the imaginary spheres nonequipotential. An improvement of these potentials is possible by placing additional image charges $+Q_1$ and $-Q_1$ in both spheres at a certain distance from their centres. This statement is confirmed by a well-known solution of the electrostatic field problem concerning a point charge in the vicinity of a conducting sphere by the image charge technique. A point charge Q of zero potential and a smaller point charge Q' distant from Q and opposite in polarity are producing a field distribution, for which the zero equipotential surface is formed by a sphere. This sphere does include Q', but not at its centre. The amount of the charge Q' with reference to Q and the distance from the centre of the imaginary sphere may easily be computed by consideration of boundary conditions. Applying this principle to our problem, one may treat the disturbing charge $-Q_0$ of sphere (2) such as the above-mentioned point charge outside of the system (1) and find the necessary image charge $+Q_1$ within this sphere by

$$|Q_1| = Q_0 \frac{R}{b} = 4\pi\varepsilon_0 RV \frac{R}{b}$$

placed at a distance

$$x_1 = \frac{R^2}{b}$$

from the centre. The charges $+Q_0$ and $+Q_1$ inside of sphere (1) and the charge $-Q_0$ outside would make the surface of sphere (1) precisely equipotential to $+V$; but there is also a charge $-Q_1$ within sphere (2) necessary to gain symmetry with reference to P, and this charge again disturbs the equipotential character of both sphere surfaces. To compensate for these charges, further image charges $+Q_2$ inside sphere (1) and $-Q_2$ inside sphere (2) with magnitudes

$$|Q_2| = Q_1 \frac{R}{(b-x_1)} = 4\pi\varepsilon_0 RV \frac{R}{(b-x_1)} \cdot \frac{R}{b}$$

at distances $x_2 = R^2/(b-x_1)$ from their centres must be added, and this process must be continued indefinitely to reach precisely equipotential sphere surfaces. The potentials or field intensities between the two spheres could now be computed with the knowledge of the charge intensities and their position with reference to the sphere centres. The most interesting quantity is the field strength along a field line of highest field intensity, which is obviously within the shortest distance M–M' of both spheres. As the potentials ϕ at any distance r from a point charge are proportional to $1/r$ and the field strength $E(r) = -\text{grad } \phi$ thus proportional to $1/r^2$, the total field intensity is equal to the sum of the single intensities of all image point charges inside of both spheres. The maximum field strength at the points M and M' is, therefore, given by

$$E(R) = E_{\max} = \frac{1}{4\pi\varepsilon_0} \left\{ \sum_{n=0}^{\infty} \frac{Q_n}{(R-x_n)^2} + \sum_{n=0}^{\infty} \frac{Q_n}{(b-R-x_n)^2} \right\}$$

$$= RV \sum_{n=0}^{\infty} \left\{ \prod_{k=1}^{n} \left(\frac{R}{b-x_{k-1}} \right) \right\} \left\{ \frac{1}{(R-x_n)^2} + \frac{1}{(b-R-x_n)^2} \right\}, \quad (4.21)$$

where

$$Q_n = Q_{n-1} \frac{R}{(b-x_{n-1})} = 4\pi\varepsilon_0 RV \prod_{k=1}^{n} \left(\frac{R}{b-x_{k-1}}\right);$$

$$x_n = \frac{R^2}{(b-x_{n-1})}; \quad \text{with } n = 1, 2, 3 \ldots$$

$$x_0 = 0.$$

The same expression can be used to compute the field intensity at any point on the line M–M', if the R values in the expressions $(R-x_n)^2$ and $(b-R-x_n)^2$ are replaced by a distance x measured from the centre of the sphere (1) and the point considered between M and the plane P, i.e. $R \leqslant x \leqslant b/2$.

The capacitance between the two spheres can be calculated according to Gauss's Law, as the real total charge on metal spheres replacing the imaginary spheres is equal to the sum of all charges Q_n:

$$C = \sum_{n=0}^{\infty} \frac{Q_n}{2V} = 2\pi\varepsilon_0 R \sum_{n=0}^{\infty} \left\{ \prod_{k=1}^{n} \left(\frac{R}{b-x_{k-1}}\right) \right\},$$

where again $x_0 = 0$.

Numerical evaluation of eqn. (4.21) for different (b/R) ratios displays the following approximation for the maximum field strength E_{max}, if $S > R$:

$$E_{max} \simeq 0.9 \frac{V}{S/2} \frac{R+S/2}{R} \tag{4.22}$$

where $S = b - 2R$ is equal to the distance M–M', and V equals to the potentials as defined in Fig. 4.4, i.e. half the voltage across the two spheres.

For a sphere-to-plane arrangement, the same equation can be used, if $S/2$ is then equal to the gap distance and V identical to the voltage applied.

As mentioned before, eqn. (4.21) may be applied to compute the field intensities between oppositely charged metal spheres along a field line of highest field strength, i.e. between the shortest distance M–M'. Numerical examples for the evaluation of this equation are shown in Fig. 4.8 for different values of S/R to demonstrate the increasing nonuniformity of the electrostatic field with increasing S/R ratios. The field strength values are normalized with reference to the mean values E_{mean} according to eqn. (4.1); by this the field efficiency factor η may directly be computed from the maximum values of the field intensity. This "isolated" sphere-to-sphere

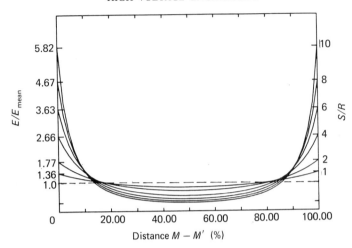

FIG. 4.8. Electric stress distribution along the axis M–M' of the sphere-to-sphere arrangement (Fig. 4.7) for various S/R ratios.

arrangement is only an approximation of actual electrode arrangements, i.e. sphere gaps for the measurement of the peak values of high voltages (see Chapter 3, section 3.1.1).

Two Cylindrical Conductors in Parallel

We choose this electrode configuration for comparison with the field distribution between two oppositely charged spheres as treated above. If two or more cylindrical conductors would be at the same potential with reference to predominantly earth potential far away from the parallel conductors, the configuration of so-called "bundle conductors" is formed, a system extensively applied in h.v. transmission lines. Due to the interaction of the single conductors the maximum field intensity at the conductors is reduced in comparison to a single cylindrical conductor, so that the corona inception voltage can significantly be increased. Solutions of the field distributions for such bundle conductors are possible by the complex variable technique, i.e. conformal mapping.[6]

For our comparison, we have to charge the two cylindrical conductors with opposite polarity to each other. Thus the field distribution can be calculated by assuming only two line charges $\pm Q/l = \pm \rho_l$ running in parallel and eccentrically placed within the conductors. This statement is

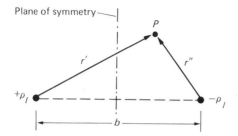

FIG. 4.9. Two line charges $\pm\rho_l$ in parallel.

confirmed by a short calculation based upon Fig. 4.9, in which the two line charges $\pm\rho_l$ are spaced by a distance b. At any point P within the plane the potential ϕ_p may be found by the principle of superposition. As the field intensity of an individual line charge is $E(r) = \rho/(2\pi\varepsilon r)$, with r being the distance from the charge, the potentials may be found by integration. Superposition leads to

$$\phi_p = \frac{\rho_l}{2\pi\varepsilon}\ln\frac{r''}{r'} + K \qquad (4.23)$$

when r' and r'' are defined in Fig. 4.9 and K is a constant found from boundary conditions. For equal line charges of opposite polarity and the potential zero at infinite distances, there is also zero potential, i.e. $\phi_p = 0$ at the plane of symmetry, $r' = r''$. Thus $K = 0$ for this special case of equal charges.

For all other ratios $r''/r' =$ const, also ϕ_p is constant and may lead to any positive or negative potentials. However, all constant ratios of r''/r' generate cylindrical surfaces. These surfaces T may be assumed to be cylindrical conductors of different diameters.

Interested in two conductors of equal diameters, the two line charges will be eccentrically but symmetrically placed within these two conductors as shown in Fig. 4.10. The eccentric position, indicated by the distance c between the line charges and the centres M of the conductors, can easily be found for constant ratios r_1''/r_1' and r_2''/r_2' for the points P_1 or P_2 positioned at A,B or C,D. Omitting this simple calculation, we find for equal radii $r_1 = r_2 = r$

$$c = \sqrt{\left(\frac{b}{2}\right)^2 + r^2} - \frac{b}{2} = \frac{a}{2} - \sqrt{\left(\frac{a}{2}\right)^2 - r^2} \; ;$$

$$a = \sqrt{b^2 + (2r)^2}. \qquad (4.24)$$

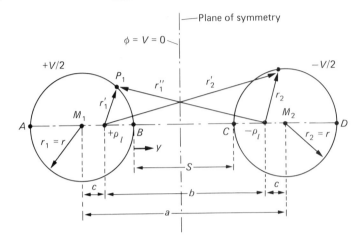

Fig. 4.10. Two equal cylindrical conductors in parallel, symmetrically charged, Fig. 4.7, and the parallel cylindrical conductors, Fig. 4.10, for equal voltages applied.

The distance $c = (a-b)/2$ becomes for $r \ll (a/2)$ very small which demonstrates that for larger gaps the fields in the vicinity of the conductor surface will not be much disturbed in comparison to single conductors. For thinner conductors, we may calculate the field distribution along the flux line for the highest density, i.e. between B and C, where the field strength is highest. The potential $\phi(y)$ along this line starting at $B(y = 0)$ is provided by eqn. (4.23), as

$$\phi(y) = A \ln\left(\frac{r''}{r'}\right) = A \ln\left[\frac{\left(\dfrac{b+S}{2}\right)-y}{\left(\dfrac{b-S}{2}\right)+y}\right]$$

where A is a constant given by boundary conditions and S is the gap distance. Assuming a total potential difference or voltage of V between the two conductors, A is given by $\phi(y) = +V/2$ for $y = 0$ and thus

$$A = \frac{V/2}{\ln\left(\dfrac{b+S}{b-S}\right)}.$$

The field strength $E(y)$ becomes therefore

$$
\begin{aligned}
E(y) &= -\frac{d\phi(y)}{dy} = A\left[\frac{1}{\left(\dfrac{b+S}{2}\right)-y} + \frac{1}{\left(\dfrac{b-S}{2}\right)+y}\right] \\
&= \frac{V}{2}\frac{b}{\left[\left(\dfrac{b}{2}\right)^2-\left(y-\dfrac{S}{2}\right)^2\right]\ln\left(\dfrac{b+S}{b-S}\right)}.
\end{aligned}
\tag{4.25}
$$

The field distribution is symmetrical to $y = S/2$. For convenience, the distance $b = f(a, r)$ might be expressed by the gap distance also. Then

$$
E(y) = \frac{V}{S}\frac{\sqrt{\left(\dfrac{S}{2r}\right)^2+\left(\dfrac{S}{r}\right)}}{\left[1+\dfrac{y}{r}-\dfrac{y^2}{rS}\right]\ln\left(1+\dfrac{S}{2r}+\sqrt{\left(\dfrac{S}{2r}\right)^2+\dfrac{S}{r}}\right)}.
\tag{4.26}
$$

The field distribution between two conductors can easiest be discussed by relating eqn. (4.26) with the maximum field intensity $E_{\max}$ for $y = 0$. This ratio becomes

$$
\frac{E(y)}{E_{\max}} = \frac{1}{1+\dfrac{y}{r}-\dfrac{y^2}{rS}} = \frac{r}{r+y\left(1-\dfrac{y}{S}\right)}.
$$

In comparison to a single charged cylindrical conductor, for which this field strength ratio would be given by $r/(r+y)$ only—see eqn. (4.10)—it is obvious that for all values $y/S \ll 1$ the parallel conductor is of diminishing influence. As the minimum value of E is reached for $y = S/2$, the ratio $E_{\min}/E_{\max}$ becomes

$$
\frac{E_{\min}}{E_{\max}} = \frac{1}{1+(S/4r)}.
$$

A comparison of the field distributions between the sphere-to-sphere gap and the parallel cylindrical conductors is plotted in Fig. 4.11. Again we can recognize that the cylindrical fields are more uniform for the same ratios of gap distance and radii.

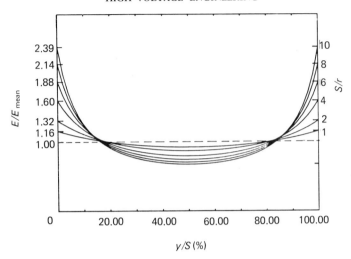

FIG. 4.11. Field strength distribution between two cylindrical conductors of equal radii r, for different ratios S/r, with S = gap distance (see Fig. 4.10). (Compare with Fig. 4.8.)

Field Distortions by Conducting Particles

Up to now we have treated "macroscopic" fields acting between conducting electrodes with dimensions suitable to insulate high voltages by controlling the maximum electrical field strength by large curvatures of the electrodes. In actual insulation systems the real surface of any conductor may not be really plane or shaped as assumed by macroscopic dimensions, or the real homogeneous insulation material may be contaminated by particles of more or less conducting nature. Though a real surface roughness of an electrode, or the real shape of particles within the insulating material may be very complex, the local distortion of the electrical field which can be assumed to be "microscopic" in dimensions can easily lead to partial discharges or even to a breakdown of the whole insulation system.

To account for such phenomena two results of field distributions produced by spheroidal conducting particles are shown. The results are based upon one of the most powerful methods for solving Laplace's equation, the method of separation of variables, extensively treated in the book of Moon and Spencer.[3]

The first example is related to prolate spheroids formed within a prolate

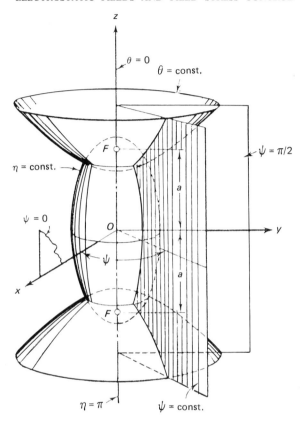

FIG. 4.12. Prolate spheroidal coordinates. The coordinate surfaces are prolate spheroids, η = const, hyperboloids, θ = const, and meridian planes, ψ = const (see reference 3, p. 237).

spheroidal coordinate system (η, Θ, ψ) shown in Fig. 4.12, which is related to rectangular coordinates by the equations

$$x = a \sinh \eta \sin \Theta \cos \psi;$$

$$y = a \sinh \eta \sin \Theta \sin \psi;$$

$$z = a \cosh \eta \cos \Theta. \tag{4.27}$$

The prolate spheroids are surfaces of constant η values, for which

$$\left(\frac{x}{b}\right)^2 + \left(\frac{y}{b}\right)^2 + \left(\frac{z}{c}\right)^2 = 1, \tag{4.28}$$

where $b = a \sinh \eta$; $c = a \cosh \eta$. The variable η may be changed from 0 to $+\infty$. For $\eta \to \infty$, $\sinh \eta \simeq \cosh \eta$, and thus $b \simeq c$, i.e. the spheroid becomes a sphere. For $\eta \to 0$, the spheroid approaches a straight line segment of length $2a$ on the z-axis, as $z = a$ for $\Theta = 0$. Due to the rotational symmetry with reference to the z-axis, the cross-sections of the spheroid for constant z-value planes are circles. The surfaces of constant Θ values are hyperboloids, and for the special case of $\Theta = \pi/2$ the hyperboloid becomes the xy-plane. Ψ is the angle measured about the z-axis, and the range of Ψ is taken as $0 \leqslant \Psi \leqslant 2\pi$. Surfaces of constant Ψ are half-planes containing the z-axis.

The solution of Laplace's equation for this coordinate system is treated in reference 3. The results depend upon the boundary conditions, i.e. assuming scalar potentials for constant values $\eta = \eta_0$, as well as for distances far away of the centre, $\eta \to \infty$, i.e. for a sphere of infinite large diameter. The lengthy calculations are not shown here, but it may well be recognized that two

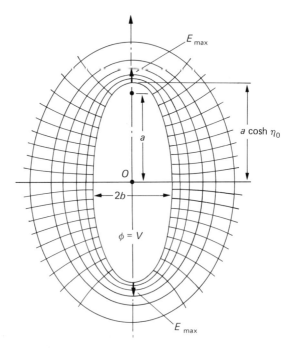

FIG. 4.13. Electrostatic field about the spheroid of Fig. 4.12 with $\eta = \eta_0$, $\phi = V$ (see reference 3, p. 245).

special cases are of interest. A charged spheroid of potential $\phi = V$ for $\eta = \eta_0$ with a reference potential $\phi = 0$ far away from the spheroid, and a spheroid within an otherwise uniform field $E = E_0 = $ constant. In both cases the field strength $E(z)$ along a flux line in the z-direction ($x = y = 0$) is of main interest; no simple analytical expressions, however, can be achieved as Legendre functions are involved in the solutions. Therefore, only some field distributions and maximum potential gradients are reproduced from computations.[3]'

In Fig. 4.13 the electrostatic field about a charged spheroid with potential $\phi = V$ within free space ($\phi = 0$ for $\eta \to \infty$) displays the field enhancement along the z-axis for a ratio of $b/a \simeq 0.436$. The maximum field strength E_{max} will heavily increase with decreasing ratios b/a, as the curvature at this point increases. The numerical evaluation of E_{max} is shown in Fig. 4.14. Slim

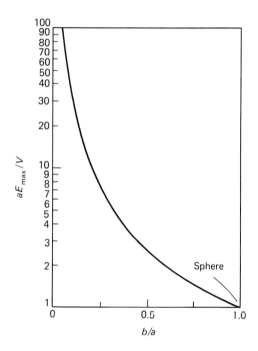

FIG. 4.14. Maximum potential gradient near a charged metal spheroid as affected by the shape of the spheroid. Major semi-axes a, minor semi-axes b, potential of spheroid V. The ordinate (aE_{max}/V) approaches infinity as $b/a \to 0$ and falls to a value of unity for a sphere (see reference 3, p. 246).

spheroids may be assumed to simulate capped wires whose length is large in comparison to its diameter.

Of more importance is the second case, for which a spheroid of either high permittivity equivalent to a conducting spheroid or a real metal particle placed within a dielectric material in which an originally constant uniform field E_0 was present. A field map is shown in Fig. 4.15. The potential $\phi = 0$ being present not only at the surface of the spheroid, but also for all values $z = 0$, i.e. a plane in the xy-direction, simulates also a macroscopic plate-to-plate electrode arrangement, which would produce a uniform field; if a protrusion is present at the plates whose shape is identical with half of the spheroid, the field is distorted heavily in the vicinity of this

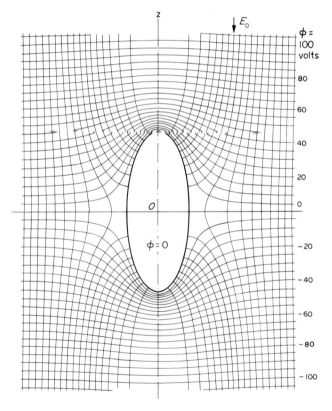

FIG. 4.15. Field distribution produced by a spheroid of high permittivity ($\varepsilon_2/\varepsilon_1 \rightarrow \infty$) within a uniform electrostatic field, E_0 (see reference 3, p. 257).

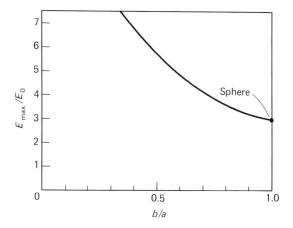

FIG. 4.16. Maximum potential gradient at a metal spheroid introduced into a uniform electric field. Here a and b are semi-axes of the ellipse, Fig. 4.13 (see reference 3, p. 258).

protrusion only. The map indicates that the large distortion is limited to dimensions about equivalent to the dimensions of the protrusion only, a region of the field which can be named "microscopic". Again, for different shapes of the spheroid the maximum values E_{max} can be calculated with reference to the uniform field strength E_0, the result of which is shown in Fig. 4.16. For $b = a$, i.e. a sphere, E_{max}/E_0 equals to 3, the well-known field enhancement factor for a half-sphere placed upon a plate electrode within a parallel plane-to-plane arrangement. Again, for slender spheroids the E_{max} values will increase to very high values, independently of the absolute size of the spheroids. Such high E_{max} values are responsible for electron emission at metal surfaces. Critical electron avalanches in gases, however, are produced not only by this high value, but also from the field distribution in the vicinity of E_{max}, so that the absolute values of the dimensions a and b become significant also.

4.3 FIELDS IN MULTIDIELECTRIC, ISOTROPIC MATERIALS

Many actual h.v. insulation systems, e.g. a transformer insulation, are composed of various insulation materials, whose permittivities are different from each other. The main reasons for the application of such multidielec-

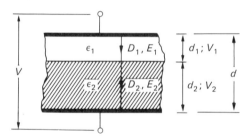

FIG. 4.17. Different dielectrics within a uniform field region.

tric systems are often mechanical ones, as gaseous or fluid materials are not able to support or separate the conductors. Layer arrangements may also be applied to control electrical stresses. The aim of the section is, therefore, to treat some fundamental phenomena for such systems.

Only few examples have been chosen to demonstrate principally the dangerous effects. Analytical methods for field computations in multidielectric systems containing predetermined shapes of the electrodes as well as the interfaces of the dielectrics are severely restricted. Adequate solutions are in general only possible by numerical computations or experimental field plotting techniques.

4.3.1 Simple Configurations

Due to the effect of reduced electrical breakdown strength at the interface of two different insulation materials, the interfaces in highly stressed field regions should be arranged normal to the field lines. The "parallel-plate capacitor" containing two layers of different materials represented by their permittivities ε_1 and ε_2 is therefore typical for many applications. Figure 4.17 shows the arrangement and the dimensions assumed. For real dielectric materials and a.c. voltages, the conductivity of the materials can be neglected and hence no free charges are built up at the interface between the two layers. The displacement vectors $\mathbf{D}_1$ and $\mathbf{D}_2$ are then equal, starting from and ending at the equal free charges on the plates only. As $D = \varepsilon E$, the ratio of the field strength becomes

$$\frac{E_1}{E_2} = \frac{\varepsilon_2}{\varepsilon_1} \qquad (4.29)$$

and as the field remains uniform in each layer, the voltage V or potential difference between the two plates is

$$V = E_1 d_1 + E_2 d_2$$

where d_1, d_2 are the individual thicknesses of the two dielectrics. Introducing eqn. (4.29) into this equation, we obtain the following absolute values of E_1 and E_2 with reference to the voltage applied.

$$E_1 = \frac{V}{\varepsilon_1 \left(\dfrac{d_1}{\varepsilon_1} + \dfrac{d_2}{\varepsilon_2} \right)} = \frac{V}{d} \frac{\varepsilon_2/\varepsilon_1}{\dfrac{d_1}{d}\left(\dfrac{\varepsilon_2}{\varepsilon_1} - 1\right) + 1} = \frac{V}{d_1 + d_2 \left(\dfrac{\varepsilon_1}{\varepsilon_2}\right)}. \qquad (4.30)$$

$$E_2 = \frac{V}{\varepsilon_2 \left(\dfrac{d_1}{\varepsilon_1} + \dfrac{d_2}{\varepsilon_2} \right)} = \frac{V}{d} \frac{1}{\dfrac{d_1}{d}\left(\dfrac{\varepsilon_2}{\varepsilon_1} - 1\right) + 1}. \qquad (4.31)$$

This relationship demonstrates some essential effects.

(a) The partial replacement of a given dielectric material of ε_1, for instance a gas within a gap of uniform field, by a material of higher permittivity ε_2 decreases according to eqn. (4.30) the "effective gap distance" $d' = d_1 + d_2(\varepsilon_1/\varepsilon_2)$ defined by the unaltered field strength E_1 in the original gap, as the *equivalent thickness* of the layer "2" becomes $d_2(\varepsilon_1/\varepsilon_2)$ only. Alternatively, for V_1, d and $(\varepsilon_1/\varepsilon_2)$ remaining constant, the field stress E_1 will always *increase* if the thickness of the layer "2" with higher permittivity is increased.

Though no distinct relationships exist between the permittivity of an insulation material and its permissible breakdown field strength, gases with the lowest values of ε close to ε_0, the permittivity of the free space, are in general most sensitive to high field stresses, primarily if the gas pressure is only equal to atmospheric pressure or lower. Partially replacing of the gas with solid materials thus does *not* improve the dielectric strength of an air- or gas-insulated system, as the gas will now be even more stressed than in the original system.

(b) The continuous increase of both field intensities E_1 and E_2 in the parallel plate system with increasing thickness d_2 for $\varepsilon_1 < \varepsilon_2$, given by eqns. (4.30) and (4.31) can numerically be demonstrated in Fig. 4.18. The worst case is displayed for conditions when $d_1 \to 0$, i.e. very thin layers of the low permittivity material, as the field strength increases to a value $(\varepsilon_2/\varepsilon_1)$ times the field in a system filled with one type material of any permittivity.

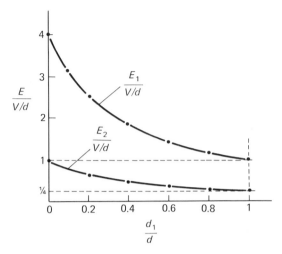

FIG. 4.18. Relative values of field strength E_1 and E_2 in the system of Fig. 4.17 for constant voltage V and gap distance d by varying d_1 and $d_2 = d - d_1$ for $\varepsilon_2/\varepsilon_1 = 4$.

"Sandwiched" or multidielectric insulation systems can therefore be dangerous if the layers are of very different permittivities. However, it is also very difficult in h.v. insulation technology to avoid such or similar arrangements due to production problems. Examples are the continuous tight contact between metal electrodes and solid insulation materials, or between insulation material interfaces. The remaining voids may then become filled with gases, the breakdown strength of which may be calculated by applying Paschen's Law treated in Chapter 5, if the dimensions and discharge parameters of the gases are known. Only for very thin gaseous layers may the breakdown strength of the gas be high enough to fulfil the requirements.

Thus it is essential to avoid any voids or bubbles within a solid or fluid insulation system, though this was demonstrated by a uniform field configuration only. Actual voids can be more complex in shape, and then the field strength will be more or less reduced (see section 4.3.2).

(c) Either eqn. (4.30) or (4.31) may be used to calculate the resultant or effective mean value of the permittivity of any homogeneous mixture of dielectric materials, such as in the case of resin- or oil-impregnated kraft papers which are extensively used in h.v. apparatus. The two-dielectric system can be subdivided into an infinite number of layers with materials designated by their intrinsic properties ε_1 and ε_2 and the resultant permittivity ε_{res} can be defined as

$$D = \varepsilon_{res}E \tag{4.32}$$

where D and E are macroscopic mean values. As the microscopic values E_1 or E_2 will remain unchanged by multiple layers, we can write

$$D = \varepsilon_{res}E = \varepsilon_1 E_1 = \varepsilon_2 E_2$$

or after replacement of E_1 or E_2 from eqn. (4.30) or (4.31) and rearranging the numbers

$$\varepsilon_{res}E = \frac{1}{\dfrac{(d_1/d)}{\varepsilon_1} + \dfrac{(d_2/d)}{\varepsilon_2}}\left(\frac{V}{d}\right).$$

As before, V/d represents the mean value of the field strength within the mixture, and the distances can be replaced by relative volumes v_1 and v_2 as the relationships d_1/d and d_2/d represent also the volumes of the two materials. Therefore

$$\varepsilon_{res} = \frac{1}{(v_1/\varepsilon_1) + (v_2/\varepsilon_2)} \tag{4.33}$$

or for a mixture of n materials

$$\varepsilon_{res} = \frac{1}{(v_1/\varepsilon_1) + (v_2/\varepsilon_2) + \ldots + (v_n/\varepsilon_n)} \tag{4.34}$$

with

$$\sum_{i=1}^{n} v_i = 1$$

or 100%.

A kraft paper in which 75% of the volume is filled with cellulose ($\varepsilon_2 \simeq 6\varepsilon_0$) should be impregnated with mineral oil ($\varepsilon_1 \simeq 2.2\varepsilon_0$). Then $v_1 = 25\%$ and $\varepsilon_{res} \simeq 4.19\varepsilon_0$, which is less than one could expect by a merely linear interpolation.

(d) Multidielectric insulation systems provide distinct advantages if made of thin layers making up flexible slabs and which are well impregnated by fluids or even gases of high breakdown strength such as SF_6. Single layers may have weak points of low breakdown strength; overlapping of many layers will provide a statistical distribution of the weak points not spread throughout the insulation. Oil-impregnated h.v. power cables are typical multilayer insulation systems.

(e) The consistency of the electric flux density at interfaces without free charges can in *nonuniform* electrode arrangements be used to make the field stress more uniform. A typical example is the coaxial cable or coaxial capacitor with sandwiched dielectric materials sketched in Fig. 4.19a. Applying Gauss's Law to each of the individual interfaces forming

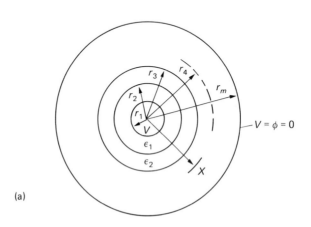

(a)

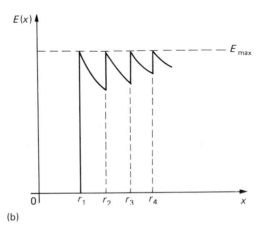

(b)

Fig. 4.19. Coaxial cable with layers of different permittivity. (a) Geometry. (b) Field distribution for $\varepsilon_1 r_1 = \varepsilon_2 r_2 = \dots \varepsilon_n r_n = $ const.

equipotential areas within the field being symmetrical with reference to the centre of the cylinder axis, one may easily derive the field strength $E(x)$ as

$$E(x) = \frac{V}{\varepsilon_x x \sum\limits_{n=1}^{m} \frac{1}{\varepsilon_n} \ln\left(\frac{r_n+1}{r_n}\right)} \quad (4.35)$$

with V the voltage applied across all of the m layers, and ε_x the inherent value of permittivity within the layer of distance x from the centre.

For cylindrical conductors within each layer, $E(x)$ is proportional to $1/x$, as this is the case for cylindrical conductors; the discontinuities within the field distributions caused by the interfaces are recognized in eqn. (4.35) as for $x \leqslant r_n$ and $x \geqslant r_n$ two different values of $E(x)$ will appear in the equation. As the maximum values of $E(x)$ are always at the locations $x \geqslant r_n$, it is possible to maintain the same values $E_{\max}$ within every layer of the dielectric, if $\varepsilon_x r_n$ remains constant. With $\varepsilon_x = \varepsilon_1, \varepsilon_2, \ldots, \varepsilon_n$ for the individual layers the conditions can be written as

$$\varepsilon_1 r_1 = \varepsilon_2 r_2 = \ldots = \varepsilon_n r_n = \text{constant.}$$

The field distribution for this condition is sketched in Fig. 4.19b. The actual applicability is, however, restricted by the limited availability of dielectric materials capable of taking full advantage of this effect. However, in h.v. oil-filled power cables high-density cellulose papers may be used for the layers close to the inner conductors, whose resultant permittivity $\varepsilon_{\mathrm{res}}$ is somewhat higher after impregnation than that for a lower density paper used for larger diameters.

4.3.2 Dielectric Refraction

In the case when the electrical displacement vector $\mathbf{D}$ meets the interface between two media of different permittivities at an angle other than 90°, the direction of this vector will change in the second dielectric. In general, it can be assumed that no free charges are present at the interface and only polarization charges define the boundary conditions. Then the angles of incidence and refraction are related as follows:

$$\frac{\tan \alpha_1}{\tan \alpha_2} = \frac{E_{t1}/E_{n1}}{E_{t2}/E_{n2}} = \frac{E_{n2}}{E_{n1}} = \frac{D_{n2}/\varepsilon_2}{D_{n1}/\varepsilon_1} = \frac{\varepsilon_1}{\varepsilon_2}. \quad (4.36)$$

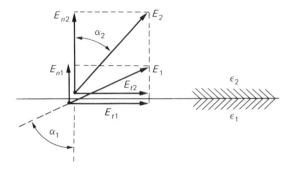

FIG. 4.20. The law of refraction applied to field intensities E for $\varepsilon_1 > \varepsilon_2$.

These quantities are illustrated in Fig. 4.20 for the conditions $\varepsilon_1 > \varepsilon_2$. In practical systems stressed with d.c. voltages the accumulation of free charges at the interface will take place, caused by the differing conductivities of the materials (interfacial polarisation). For a.c. voltage applications eqn. (4.36) may be applied.

Figure 4.21 shows the case when two different dielectrics are placed between parallel plane electrodes, the interface of which is not perpendicular to the electrode surface. We observe a compression of equipotential lines at the corner P increasing the field strength at that point.

If the angle between interface and electrode in this corner is $<90°$, the field intensity at point P becomes theoretically infinite.[8,9] This may

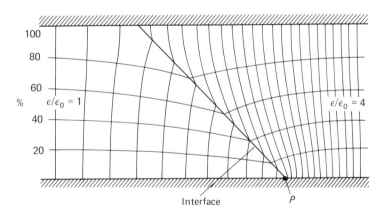

FIG. 4.21. Two different dielectric materials between plane electrodes.

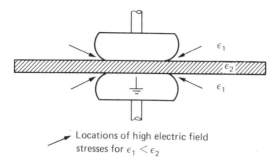

Locations of high electric field stresses for $\epsilon_1 < \epsilon_2$

FIG. 4.22. Breakdown tests on solid dielectric plate materials (ε_2). ↗: locations of high electrical field stresses for $\varepsilon_1 < \varepsilon_2$.

correspond to the case when a solid dielectric is only partly attached to the electrode, leaving a void filled with dielectric materials of inadequate breakdown strength. A typical example occurs during testing of breakdown strength of solid dielectrics in the form of plates only shown in Fig. 4.22. The metal disc electrodes may be of Rogowski's profile, for which the breakdown could always be achieved within the uniform field region if only one insulation material is present. If plates of solid material with permittivity ε_2 are tested in atmospheric air only, for which the breakdown strength as well as the permittivity $\varepsilon_1 \simeq \varepsilon_0$ is much lower than the corresponding values for the solid material, even for voltages much lower than the breakdown voltage, many partial discharges will appear starting from the edges as indicated in the figure. These discharges will spread over the surface of the solid dielectric and will cause breakdown outside the uniform field region. To avoid this phenomenon, either compressed gases of very high dielectric strength must be used or insulation fluids, whose permittivity ε_1 should be higher than ε_2 to avoid field enhancement, if the breakdown strength of the fluid is not as high as that of the solid dielectric. Therefore, the testing of the insulation strength of solid materials in which no electrodes can be embedded becomes a troublesome and difficult task.

However, the law of refraction given by eqn. (4.36) can be used to control the electric field, i.e. to improve the dielectric strength of an insulation system. Typical examples include spacers of solid materials used in metal-enclosed gas insulated substations discussed briefly in section 4.2. The coaxial cylindrical conductors are not only insulated by compressed sulphur hexafluoride (SF$_6$) but also partly by spacers necessary for

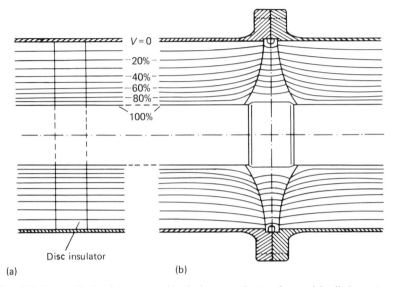

(a)   (b)

FIG. 4.23. Epoxy disc insulator supporting the inner conductor of a coaxial cylinder system.
(a) Simple disc spacer: No refraction of equipotential lines. (b) shaped spacer for approximate
constant tangential field stress at the interface gas insulator.

mechanical support of the inner conductor. If only a disc of solid material
would be used as shown in Fig. 4.23a, the flux lines would not be refracted
or distorted and the field strength $E(x)$ along the interface between gas and
solid material would follow eqn. (4.10). This means that only tangential
components of the electric field, E_t, are stressing the interface and E_t is not
constant along the surface. As the permissible E_t values at boundaries are
always lower than field magnitudes within the adjacent materials, the
spacers can be formed in such a way, that all E_t components along the
interface remain nearly constant. One possible solution is shown in
Fig. 4.23b, and the same equipotential lines as in Fig. 4.23a are used
to demonstrate the change of the field distribution. The field map for this
example was computed by numerical methods (see section 4.5).

4.3.3 Stress Control by Floating Screens

The necessity for applying electrostatic stress control in h.v. apparatus
was demonstrated up to now for fields in homogeneous materials as well as

for multidielectric insulation systems. But in all examples only two metal electrodes have been used whose potential was fixed by the applied voltage. For homogeneous or single dielectric materials the field stress control was thus only possible by providing an adequate shape or contour for these electrodes, and Rogowski's profile (Fig. 4.3) may be considered an example. The insertion of multidielectric systems between the main electrodes provided also means for stress control, as shown for the case of coaxial cables and its two-dimensional field configuration (Fig. 4.19). For this special case, the interface between layers of differing permittivity was equipotential. Dielectric interfaces for general three-dimensional insulation systems, however, are often difficult to shape such as to provide equipotential surfaces, which would avoid any tangential field intensities with its limited breakdown strength.

Equation (4.36) indicates that flux lines penetrating from a dielectric of high permittivity into one of much lower permittivity are forced to leave the material nearly perpendicular to its surface. This means that the equipotential lines or surfaces in the dielectric of smaller permittivity are forced to be nearly parallel to the interface as is found for metal electrodes. A dielectric of very high ε_r values thus behaves similarly to an electrically conducting material, and for $\varepsilon \rightarrow \infty$ the boundary conditions for metal surfaces are reached. For this reason insulation systems, including floating screens, whose potential is solely controlled by the field distribution of the dielectric materials attached to the screens, can be treated as a multidielectric system.

Field stresses are controlled by means of such screens in many h.v. apparatus such as capacitor-type cable terminations,[14] bushings, potential transformers, etc. The "capacitor bushing" or "field stress controlled bushing" will be treated as a typical example and will demonstrate the complexity of the problems involved. Bushings are used to run a high-potential cylindrical conductor H through a grounded wall or barrier W (see Fig. 4.24). The wall may consist of a partially conducting concrete or brick, a grounded metal tank of a transformer or any other metal-enclosed h.v. apparatus. The insulation materials used on both sides of the wall can, therefore, be different. For transformers mineral oil insulation inside the tank is typical and atmospheric air is commonly used outside. For this case, the bushing also provides sealing. The main task, however, is provided by the electrical insulation of the conductor H from the wall and its mechanical support by an insulation system, which is as compact as possible.

To demonstrate the actual complex problems involved in the design of field stress controlled bushings, reference is first made to Fig. 4.24a. The

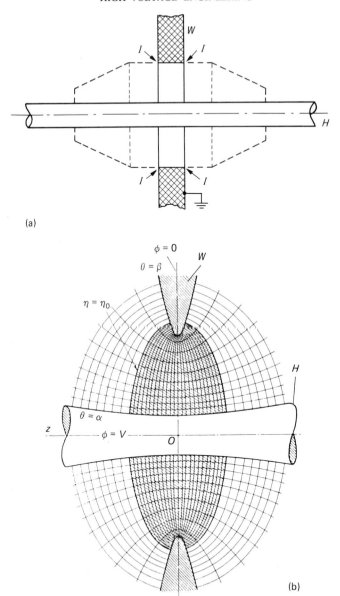

Fig. 4.24. Simple bushing arrangements for introduction into the problems solved by capacitor bushings, Fig. 4.25. (a) The problem. (b) A theoretical solution.[3]

barrier W perpendicular to the plane of drawing contains a circular opening in which the cylindrical conductor H is centred. Even without taking into account the mechanical support and assuming a homogeneity of the insulation material used, the numerical calculation or graphical field mapping would show that the high field intensity regions are at the conductor surface within the plane of the wall and at the edged contours I of the wall opening. To support the cylindrical conductor and to avoid a breakdown between the wall and the conductor caused by the high field regions, we may add a solid insulation material as shown by dashed lines. The solid dielectric would withstand the high field stresses in the vicinity of the cylindrical conductor; at I at the wall opening; however, the high tangential components of the field intensities at the interface between solid and gaseous (or liquid) dielectrics used on both sides of the wall would cause surface discharges and lead to relatively low flashover voltages.

One solution to the problem is to use special contours conducting electrodes and the solid-type insulator supporting the h.v. conductor. An adequate solution proposed by Moon and Spencer[3] is shown in Fig. 4.24b, displaying a field map for a three-dimensional arrangement computed with an oblate spheroidal coordinate system. The electrodes W and H are shaped to give equipotential lines. The solid dielectric is shaped such that it prevents refraction of flux lines; the equipotential lines, calculated analytically, remain unchanged. Though the field intensities are still highest at the shaped conductors, the improvement of field distribution in comparison to the simple configurations of Fig. 4.24a is clear. As far as we know, bushings of this type have never been used, though they could be manufactured nowadays using epoxy resins as the insulation material.

In practice, the solution is in the introduction of floating electrodes, as will be shortly demonstrated. Let the cylindrical h.v. conductor H be surrounded by many layers of thin dielectric sheets of permittivity ε where ε is considerably higher than ε_0, the permittivity of vacuum or air used for the "external" insulation of the bushing. Figure 4.25a shows a simplified cross-sectional view of such an arrangement, in which the dielectric sheets of different lengths are interleaved with thin conducting foils providing the floating electrodes; these are shown by the thicker lines. Neglecting now the influence of the dielectric conductivity, i.e. the permittivity ε_0, of the external insulation, which is acceptable for a large number of conducting foils, we may treat this system as an arrangement of coaxial cylindrical capacitor units which are series connected. Thus a "capacitor bushing" is formed. As indicated, the length $l_0, l_1, \ldots, l_n$ of the sheets is increasing from

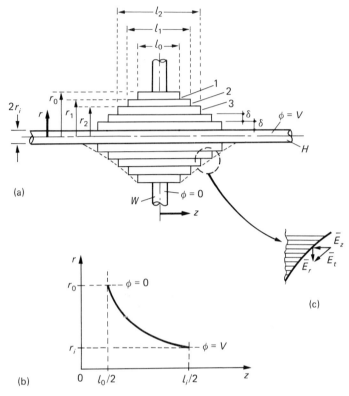

FIG. 4.25. Capacitor bushing. (a) Coaxial capacitor arrangement. (b) Profile of conductory foils for constant radial field intensity $\bar{E}_r$ (mean value). (c) Definition of field intensity components.

the wall W to the centre conductor H, and the conditions for the different lengths can be provided by boundary conditions.

Let us assume the simplest boundary condition, for which the *mean* value of the field intensity $\bar{E}_r$ acting within the sheets remains constant. If every sheet is of equal thickness δ, each of the coaxial capacitor units is stressed by equal voltages $\Delta V = \bar{E}_r\delta$, if all capacitances are equal. Then $C_1 = C_2 = \ldots = C_n$ with

$$C_1 = \frac{2\pi\varepsilon l_0}{\ln\left(r_0/r_1\right)},$$

$$C_2 = \frac{2\pi\varepsilon l_1}{\ln\left(r_1/r_2\right)},$$

or

$$\frac{l_0}{\ln(r_0/r_1)} = \frac{l_1}{\ln(r_1/r_2)} = \ldots = \frac{l_n}{\ln(r_n/r_{n+1})}. \qquad (4.37)$$

Apart from this exact solution, an approximation is possible for thin sheets. Then $r_{n+1} = r_n - \delta$ and $(\delta/r_n) \ll 1$ even for the smallest radius r_i of the inner conductor, yielding

$$\ln(r_n/r_{n+1}) = \ln\left[\frac{1}{1-(\delta/r_n)}\right] \simeq \delta/r_n.$$

With this approximation, eqn. (4.37) becomes

$$l_0 r_0 \simeq l_1 r_1 \simeq \ldots \simeq l_n r_n, \qquad (4.38)$$

where $0 \leqslant n \leqslant N$, with N equal to the total number of sheets. As N is quite high, we may replace the discrete numbers l_n and r_n by the variables $z = l/2$ (Fig. 4.25a) and r. Equation (4.38) then defines a two-dimensional profile or contour of the conducting foil edges as sketched in Fig. 4.25b. The given boundary condition provides a hyperbolic profile, along which the potential ϕ increases steadily between r_0 and r_i. Neglecting the actual discontinuities of the field intensities produced by the conducting foils, we can now recognize the constant value of the mean radial field strength $\bar{E}_r$ as indicated in the figure. Whereas $\bar{E}_r$ stresses the insulation material of the sheets only, an even more significant component of a field intensity is introduced by the conducting foil edges, as sketched in Fig. 4.25c. The solid material from the active part of the capacitor bushing also shares a boundary with the surrounding dielectric material, in general atmospheric air, or mineral oil.

This interface is also heavily stressed by a tangential field intensity E_t, which has the components of $\bar{E}_r$ and $\bar{E}_z$, the latter defined as a mean value of the potential difference $\Delta\phi$ between each adjacent foil and the increase $\Delta l = 2\Delta z$ in sheet length, i.e. $\bar{E}_z = \Delta\phi/\Delta l$. For the small values of $\Delta\phi$, Δl and Δr provided by the large amount of sections we may write in differential terms

$$d\phi = -\bar{E}_r dr = 2E_z dz$$

$$\bar{E}_z = -(1/2)\bar{E}_r \frac{dr}{dz} \qquad (4.39)$$

with the boundary conditions shown in Fig. 4.25b or eqn. (4.38) $\bar{E}_r = V/(r_0 - r_i)$ and $dr/dz = -(2/l_0r_0)r^2$, and thus

$$\bar{E}_z = \frac{V}{(V_0 - V_i)l_0r_0}\,r^2 = \frac{V}{(r_0 - r_1)l_0r_0}\,r^2. \tag{4.40}$$

This dependency shows the strong increase of the axial field strength with increasing diameter of the dielectric sheets. It contributes to a non-homogeneous potential distribution at the surface of the laminated unit, as the mean value of the tangential field intensity according to Fig. 4.25c is

$$\bar{E}_t = \sqrt{(\bar{E}_r)^2 + (\bar{E}_z)^2}, \tag{4.41}$$

if the surface is very close to the foil edges. $\bar{E}_t$ is therefore, still highest in the vicinity of the grounded wall, and the optimum value of the flashover voltage will not be reached.

In practice, such a dimensioning of a capacitor bushing due to constant mean values of the radial field intensity is not adequate and the calculations performed only indicate the problems. One could readily see, however, that the conducting foils can be used to control the internal fields E_r as well as the field strength distribution along the boundaries E_t, and that it will not be possible to keep both these values constant. The dimensioning of bushings thus becomes a very difficult task, if also other important factors are taken into account. First, the surrounding insulation materials cannot be neglected. Secondly, h.v. bushings, in general, are not made from a single dielectric material, which is often provided by oil- or resin-impregnated kraft paper. Protection of the active part is provided by porcelain or other solid insulation material housings, having different permittivities and introducing additional field refraction at the interfaces of the differing materials. Due to the heat generated within the h.v. conductor H the permissible radial field intensity may be lower than within the outer regions. Finally, careful attention must be paid to the edges of the conducting foils which form regions of locally high fields, as the equipotential lines will not necessarily leave the foils at the edges, but in its vicinity only. Therefore, foils made from semiconducting materials of still adequate conductivity are sometimes used to adapt the potentials at the foil edges to the field distribution forced by the dielectric materials outside the field-controlled regions. Analytical computations of bushing designs are, therefore, supplemented by numerical computations, which take into account the very different boundary conditions.[18,19]

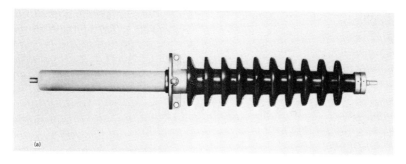

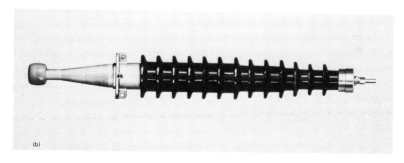

FIG. 4.26. Photographs of bushing (courtesy Micafil/Switzerland). (a) Wall bushing outdoor-indoor rated 123 kV/1250 A. (b) Transformer bushing with "dry" insulation, rated 170 kV a.c./630 A, BIL 750 kV.

Figure 4.26 shows two typical types of bushings, a transformer bushing with its asymmetry due to different external insulation, and a common wall bushing for air-to-air insulation, but one side indoor, the other side (porcelain) outdoor.

4.4 EXPERIMENTAL FIELD ANALYSIS TECHNIQUES

The rapid development of digital computers as a tool to solve the basic electrostatic field equations numerically may support the opinion that any treatment of experimental field analysis techniques, which have been developed during the early decades of this century, is obsolete. The development of very efficient computer programs for solving even three-dimensional fields including multidielectric materials has indeed reached a state today which may completely replace experimental techniques in the near future. Nevertheless, some reference will be made to those proven methods which are believed to be still useful not only for didactic reasons, but also during the early steps of h.v. apparatus development, for which the high costs of sophisticated numerical calculations are not justified. Further on the discussion of experimental techniques will help to appreciate the problems of electrostatic field distributions in the same way as the analytical methods do.

We define experimental field analysis techniques as methods in which the real physical system is replaced by any analogue system, and the quantities are much easier to measure. The direct measurement of field characteristics in real physical systems is often combined with experimental difficulties, especially if field quantities within solid dielectrics or within inconveniently small systems of interest are determined. The following experimental techniques have been extensively used in the past:

graphical field plotting,
electroconduction analogues,
resistor or impedance networks.

All these methods are extensively treated in reference 2, in which also the relevant publications dealing with their development are summarized. This section deals with analogue methods and discusses their limitation. Graphical field plotting methods were extensively used prior to the advent of computers, but today are rarely used and will not be discussed here.

4.4.1 Electroconductive Analogues

The analogy of Laplacian electrostatic and electric conduction fields, i.e. the replacement of any homogeneous, isotropic and linear dielectric material by a conductive material with the same fundamental structural properties, offers the opportunity to measure the potential distribution within the conducting material without major difficulties. Conduction fields generated by adequate current densities will continuously transport energy, whereas in an electrostatic field the energy is only stored. Therefore, the potential measurement can be made by voltage measurements which still may consume or dissipate energy. The ratio of consumed to transported energy, however, can be kept very small. Also integrated quantities, i.e. the current densities or currents, are very easy to measure.

The *electrolytic tank* has been widely used in the past for studying two-dimensional engineering field problems. In a simple form it consists of a *flat* tank constructed from insulating material, filled with an adequately conducting fluid of uniform height. The electrodes for which the potential distribution has to be determined are immersed in the liquid. The tank walls of insulating materials are areas in parallel to the current and therefore also field intensity vectors. The electric potentials are detected with fine wire probes immersed in the fluid and connected to a detector, which is either a voltmeter with very high input impedance or a null-indicator used in conjunction with a calibrated potentiometer.

For three-dimensional fields with axial symmetry, for instance the field distribution within a coaxial cable, a tank with sloping bottom can be used. For asymmetrical fields in homogeneous dielectrics the tank must be deep so that the three-dimensional scale model of the electrode system can be completely immersed. The tank walls in this case are often metal, whose potential serves as reference potential. Since the walls are equipotential surfaces, the field intensity vector is perpendicular to the surface and therefore often used to approximate equipotential lines at long distance from most interesting field regions. The electric potentials are detected in any selected planes by thin wire probes, which are insulated except the tips which provide a local contact with the fluid.

Though the electrolytic tank technique is basically very simple, some fundamental errors can be made. The main requirements include the use of adequate conducting liquids, of electrodes and probes, which are electrically and chemically compatible (effects of oxidation, corrosion, solubility, polarization, etc.). A simulation of multidielectric systems is also possible.

Electrolytic tanks are still used today. For efficient applications, the tanks are, in general, equipped with servo-operated probes and plotting tables, an example of which is shown in Fig. 4.27. The *conductive-sheet analogues* are, in principle, identical to electrolytic tank technique, if flat tanks with constant electrolyte depth are used. Very little additional equipment is necessary and, therefore, the method is appropriate for the primary design of equipment. In general, graphitized papers (Teledeltos paper), as applied for facsimile telegraphing purposes and for recording instruments, offer acceptable resistivity of several thousands ohms per square; the papers are in general quite uniformly conductive, though sometimes slightly anisotropic due to the manufacturing process. This anisotropy, however, is in the order of 1 to 2% only.

The conductive sheets are placed on suitable insulating materials such as

FIG. 4.27. Electrolytic tank, with servo-operated probe and plotting table (courtesy H. Weidmann AG, Rapperswil/Switzerland).

wood or soft plastic material, and the electrode configuration or other equipotential boundaries are produced by painting on the paper with a paint containing an adequately high percentage of silver. Non-conducting boundaries, i.e. those corresponding to flux lines, can simply be represented by cutting the paper to the shape of the boundary required.

After applying a.c. or d.c. voltages to the electrodes—the graphitized paper and silver painted electrode boundaries show no polarization effects—a simple metal or graphite pencil can be used as a probe to establish any equipotential lines. The voltages necessary are low ($\leqslant 50$ V) and the probe is connected to a balance detector as for electrolytic tanks. Once the equipotential lines are plotted, the orthogonal flow lines may be drawn. These could also be found by plotting the inverse potential distribution, i.e. by interchanging the conducting and non-conducting boundaries.

Multidielectric systems can partly be simulated by representing the higher permittivity regions with paper sheets in parallel. As only a mechanical pressure applied will not be sufficient to reach homogeneous conductivity within the stacked papers, the boundaries have to be fixed by equidistant metal needles or small nails. Three-dimensional problems are, however, difficult to simulate.[2]

The accuracy is somewhat lower than that reached with an electrolytic tank, due to the anisotropy of the paper.

4.4.2 Impedance Networks

The homogeneity of a resistive fluid material within the electrolytic tank provides a perfect analogue for the solution of Laplace's equation. Apart from some errors arising in practical applications, no inherent errors are theoretically introduced in this method. Subdividing the continuous resistive medium by small blocks and replacing these blocks by lumped resistances of adequate magnitude provides yet another analogue system, which is, however, discrete by nature and may not be as perfect as the electrolytic tank is. This new structure leads to a finite difference approximation to the differential operators, and inherent errors due to the imperfections of all finite difference methods must necessarily appear.

To demonstrate the principle only, let us imagine a flat electrolytic tank, i.e. a plate of resistive material with homogeneous resistivity and equal thickness, in which a two-dimensional current flow exists. If we subdivide this material into equal blocks as shown in Fig. 4.28a, each block can be represented by equal resistances. If the blocks are squares, the resistance of the block $ABCD$ with respect to its faces AB and CD will be R, and thus the points P_0 and P_1 could be connected by a lumped resistor of equal value. The same resistance can be regarded as due to the block $EFGH$ with its faces EF and GH, and therefore the point P_0 could be connected to P_2 by the same resistance. Equal procedures have to be carried out for resistances R between P_0–P_3 and P_0–P_4, and thus a network of identical resistors R as shown in Fig. 4.28b will represent the homogeneous material by a finite difference network.

Let us assume that the network is large and that the outside branches are connected to any voltages acting as boundary conditions. It is then possible to extract a current I_0 from the point P_0. By Kirchhoff's Law the sum of all currents flowing into P_0 must be zero; if the voltages at the five points P_0 to

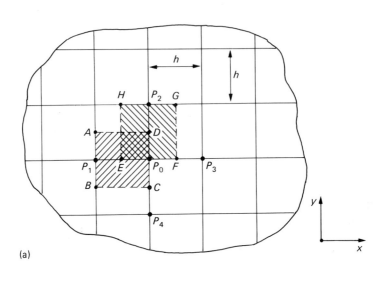

(a)

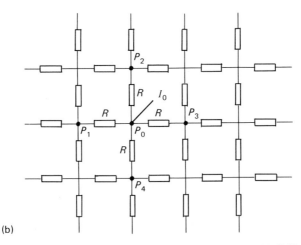

(b)

FIG. 4.28. Principle of impedance networks (two-dimensional). (a) Grid superimposed on resistive plate. (b) Equivalent resistance network.

P_4 are denoted by V_0 to V_4, it thus follows that

$$\frac{V_1 - V_0}{R} + \frac{V_2 - V_0}{R} + \frac{V_3 - V_0}{R} + \frac{V_4 - V_0}{R} = I_0$$

or

$$\sum_{i=1}^{4} V_i - 4V_0 = I_0 R. \tag{4.42}$$

For the homogeneous isotropic and linear medium of Fig. 4.28a the exact solution for the same problem is given by the two-dimensional Poisson's equation

$$\nabla^2 \phi = \frac{\partial^2 \phi}{\partial x^2} + \frac{\partial^2 \phi}{\partial y^2} = f(x, y) \tag{4.43}$$

where ϕ are the potentials at any point.

By expressing the potentials ϕ_1 to ϕ_4 at the points P_1 to P_4 and its derivatives at P_0 in terms of ϕ using Taylor's series, the finite difference form of the Laplace operator $\nabla^2 \phi$ is obtained at point P_0 by

$$(\nabla^2 \phi)_0 = \frac{1}{h^2} \left(\sum_{i=1}^{4} \phi_i - 4\phi_0 \right) - \varepsilon_0 \tag{4.44}$$

where h are the equal distances from the points P_1 to P_4 from P_0, and ε_0 is the truncation error term given by

$$\varepsilon_0 = \frac{2h^2}{4!} \left(\frac{\partial^4 \phi}{\partial x^4} + \frac{\partial^4 \phi}{\partial y^4} \right)_0 + \frac{2h^4}{6!} \left(\frac{\partial^6 \phi}{\partial x^6} + \frac{\partial^6 \phi}{\partial y^6} \right)_0 + \dots \tag{4.45}$$

The exact solutions of eqns. (4.44) and (4.45) contain obviously the approximation of our equivalent resistance network, as the error ε_0 becomes smaller with decreasing values of h. This fundamental error term, however, will never disappear, as it is impossible to increase the number of elements in Fig. 4.28b, unlimited for economic reasons. The voltages V in the equivalent network can be related to the potentials ϕ by a proportionality constant b as

$$V = b\phi. \tag{4.46}$$

Neglecting the truncation error ε_0 and equating the Laplace operator in eqn. (4.44) to a function f_0 to account for the Poisson's form, eqn. (4.43), we may rewrite eqn. (4.42) with eqn. (4.46) as

$$\frac{1}{h^2}\left(\sum_{i=1}^{4} \phi_i - 4\phi_0\right) = \frac{I_0 R}{bh^2} = f_0(x, y). \qquad (4.47)$$

Poisson's equation is thus solved by the resistive network if the current extracted from P_0 is equal to

$$I_0 = \frac{bh^2 f_0(x, y)}{R}.$$

Thus, the resistance network analogue can approximate the Laplace equation $(I_0 = 0)$ as well as Poissonian fields. Apart from truncation errors, additional errors are introduced by the boundary conditions, if the boundaries are continuous ones within the x-y plane, which is the general case. Within the mesh grid, however, the boundary conditions are always discrete points only. In addition, real boundaries will not in general intersect the mesh grid at provided mesh points; then irregular networks have to be made to account for the boundary conditions.

For simulation of electrostatic fields in h.v. technology, the application of this method is often not very useful. The most interesting and most effective regions of the fields are close to the shaped surfaces of the electrodes; these regions, however, are suffering from the discretization even more than areas far from the boundaries. Nevertheless, this method was widely used in different disciplines since the three-dimensional problems of Laplace- or Poisson-type can be tackled by an extension of the mesh grids to three-dimensional resistor networks; many partial differential equations may also be dependent upon time (diffusion, heat flow, wave equation, etc.) and they can still be solved by *impedance* networks also containing capacitances and inductances. There is no doubt, however, that all of the analogies will be replaced to a large extent by the numerical methods applying digital computers of high efficiency.

4.5 NUMERICAL METHODS

In recent years several numerical methods for solving partial differential equations and thus also Laplace's and Poisson's equations have become available. There are inherent difficulties in solving partial differential equations and thus in Laplace's or Poisson's equations for general two- or three-dimensional fields with sophisticated boundary conditions, or for insulating materials with different permittivities and/or conductivities. Each of the different numerical methods, however, has inherent advantages or disadvantages, depending upon the actual problem to be solved, and thus the methods are to some extent complementary.[20]

The aim of this chapter is to introduce the most widely used methods in such a way that a fundamental knowledge is provided and to give the user of a computer program an understanding of the limitations of the results and his computations.

4.5.1 Finite Difference Method (FDM)

Apart from other numerical methods for solving partial differential equations, the finite difference method (FDM) is quite universally applicable to linear and even nonlinear problems. Though this method can be traced back to C.F. Gauss (1777–1855), and Boltzmann has already demonstrated in 1892 in his lectures in Munich the applicability of difference equations to solve Laplace's equation, it was not until the 1940s that FDMs have been used widely.

The applicability of FDMs to solutions of general partial differential equations is well documented in specialized books.[21,22] More specific references concerning the treatment of electric and magnetic field problems with the FDM can be found in reference 23. The inherent relationship of the FDM to the impedance network method described earlier in this chapter and the advantage of setting up relatively simple computer programs gives didactic reasons for a short introduction to this numerical method.

This introduction is illustrated by two-dimensional problems for which Laplace's equation, or Poisson's equation, eqn. (4.43), applies. The field problem is then given within an x-y-plane, the area of which has to be limited by given boundary conditions, i.e. by contours on which some field quantities are known. It is also known that every potential ϕ and its distribution within the area under consideration will be continuous in nature. Therefore, an unlimited number of $\phi(x,y)$ values would be necessary to ascribe the potential distribution. As every numerical computation can provide a limited amount of information, only a discretization of the area will be necessary to exhibit nodes for which the solution may be found. Such nodes are produced by any net or grid laid down upon the area.

As any irregular net, however, would lead to inadequate difference equations replacing the original partial differential equation, and would thus be prohibitive for numerical computations, the FDM is in general applied to regular nets or polygons only. These restrictions will be understood clearer by the derivation of the differential equations. Regular polygons which can fill a plane are squares, triangles or hexagons, but squares or equilateral triangles are the only regular nets in common use. As also such square or triangular nets will in general not fit into the boundaries, we will derive the difference equations for rectangles, which can at least at given boundaries be formed in such a way that nodes can also be laid down upon the boundary. As squares are a particular case of rectangles, the result applies also for squares, and the inherent difficulties in using irregular nets are better understood.

In Fig. 4.29 such an irregular net of rectangles is sketched within the x-y-plane, with the sides of all rectangles parallel to the x- or y-axis. All points of intersection between the vertical and horizontal lines create nodes, but only five nodes will be of immediate special interest. These are the four neighbouring nodes, N, W, S, and E around a point P, which are given compass notations (N = north, etc.). Let us assume now that the potentials at these nodes, i.e. $\phi(S)$, $\phi(E)$, $\phi(N)$ and $\phi(W)$ are known either from given boundary conditions or other computational results. As the potential

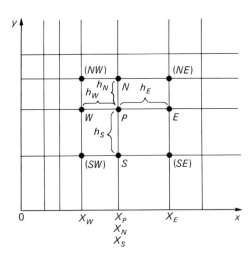

Fig. 4.29. Irregular rectangular net composed of horizontal and vertical lines, with node abbreviations.

within the field region is continuous, it is obviously possible to expand the potential at any point (x, y) by the use of Taylor's series. If this point is identical with node P, the series for the two variables x and y is given by

$$\phi(x, y) = \phi(P) + \frac{1}{1!}[(x - x_P)\phi_x(P) + (y - y_P)\phi_y(P)]$$

$$+ \frac{1}{2!}[(x - x_P)^2\phi_{xx}(P) + 2(x - x_P)(y - y_P)\phi_{xy}(P) + (y - y_P)^2\phi_{yy}(P)]$$

$$+ \frac{1}{3!}[(x - x_P)^3\phi_{xxx}(P) + 3(x - x_P)^2(y - y_P)\phi_{xxy}(P)$$

$$+ 3(x - x_P)(y - y_P)^2\phi_{xyy}(P) + (y - y_P)^3\phi_{yyy}(P)] + R'_{xy}(P) \qquad (4.48)$$

where the rest of the series $R'_{xy}(P)$ is of still higher order. In eqn. (4.48) the derivatives

$$\phi_x(P) = \left[\frac{\partial\phi(x, y)}{\partial x}\right]_P, \quad \phi_y(P) = \left[\frac{\partial\phi(x, y)}{\partial y}\right]_P, \quad \phi_{xy}(P) = \left[\frac{\partial\phi(x, y)}{\partial x\,\partial y}\right]_P, \quad \text{etc.}$$

are used for abbreviation.

Every potential $\phi(x, y)$ in the close vicinity of node P may be expressed by eqn. (4.48) with adequate accuracy, if the Taylor's series is interrupted by ignoring terms containing third derivatives of the potential, as they will be multiplied by small distances h to the power of 3 or more. Thus, the potentials of the nodes E, N, W and S can be expressed by the following equations, in which the small distances $(x - x_P)$ and $(y - y_P)$ are substituted by the proper values h_E, h_N, h_W and h_S:

$$\phi(E) = \phi(P) + h_E\phi_x(P) + \tfrac{1}{2}h_E^2\phi_{xx}(P) \qquad (4.49a)$$

$$\phi(N) = \phi(P) + h_N\phi_y(P) + \tfrac{1}{2}h_N^2\phi_{yy}(P) \qquad (4.49b)$$

$$\phi(W) = \phi(P) - h_W\phi_x(P) + \tfrac{1}{2}h_W^2\phi_{xx}(P) \qquad (4.49c)$$

$$\phi(S) = \phi(P) - h_S\phi_y(P) + \tfrac{1}{2}h_S^2\phi_{yy}(P). \qquad (4.49d)$$

The sums of eqns. (4.49a) and (4.49c), and eqns. (4.49b) and (4.49d) respectively yield to the following two equations:

$$\phi(E) + \phi(W) - 2\phi(P) = (h_E - h_W)\phi_x(P) + \tfrac{1}{2}(h_E^2 + h_W^2)\phi_{xx}(P), \qquad (4.50a)$$

$$\phi(N) + \phi(S) - 2\phi(P) = (h_N - h_S)\phi_y(P) + \tfrac{1}{2}(h_N^2 + h_S^2)\phi_{yy}(P). \qquad (4.50b)$$

The derivatives $\phi_x(P)$ and $\phi_y(P)$ may be expressed by the well-known first order approximations

$$\phi_x(P) \simeq \frac{\dfrac{h_W}{h_E}[\phi(E)-\phi(P)]+\dfrac{h_E}{h_W}[\phi(P)-\phi(W)]}{(h_E+h_W)}$$

$$= \frac{h_W}{h_E(h_E+h_W)}\phi(E)+\frac{(h_E-h_W)}{h_E h_W}\phi(P)-\frac{h_E}{h_W(h_E+h_W)}\phi(W) \quad (4.51a)$$

$$\phi_y(P) \simeq \frac{h_S}{h_N(h_N+h_S)}\phi(N)+\frac{(h_N-h_S)}{h_N h_S}\phi(P)-\frac{h_N}{h_S(h_N+h_S)}\phi(S). \quad (4.51b)$$

Introducing eqn. (4.51a) into (4.50a) and eqn. (4.51b) into (4.50b) will result in

$$\phi_{xx}(P) = \frac{2\phi(E)}{h_E(h_E+h_W)}+\frac{2\phi(W)}{h_W(h_E+h_W)}-\frac{2\phi(P)}{h_E h_W}, \quad (4.52a)$$

$$\phi_{yy}(P) = \frac{2\phi(N)}{h_N(h_N+h_S)}+\frac{2\phi(S)}{h_S(h_N+h_S)}-\frac{2\phi(P)}{h_N h_S}. \quad (4.52b)$$

With these approximations for the second derivatives of the potential functions in the x- and y-direction at node P it is now possible to solve Laplace's or Poisson's equation, which are recalled from eqn. (4.43):

$$\nabla^2\phi = \phi_{xx}+\phi_{yy} = \begin{cases} 0 & \text{(Laplacian region)} \\ -F(x,y) & \text{(Poissonian region)} \end{cases} \quad (4.53)$$

where $F(x,y) = \rho/\varepsilon$ for electrostatic fields within a medium of permittivity ε and containing distributed charges of density $\rho(x,y)$. The solution may then be written as

$$D_{EP}\phi(E)+D_{NP}\phi(N)+D_{WP}\phi(W)+D_{SP}\phi(S)+D_{PP}\phi(P)+\tfrac{1}{2}F(P) = 0 \quad (4.54)$$

with

$$D_{EP} = \frac{1}{h_E(h_E+h_W)}, \qquad D_{NP} = \frac{1}{h_N(h_N+h_S)},$$

$$D_{WP} = \frac{1}{h_W(h_E+h_W)}, \qquad D_{SP} = \frac{1}{h_S(h_N+h_S)},$$

$$D_{PP} = -\left(\frac{1}{h_E h_W}+\frac{1}{h_N h_S}\right).$$

This difference equation is a valid approximation of the original differential equation (4.53), but it should be recalled, that the validity is restricted to the individual point P under consideration. The same form is, however, valid for every node within a net.

Before further considerations we shall discuss briefly the common simplifications. For every two-dimensional problem most of the field regions can be subdivided by a regular square net as shown in Fig. 4.28a. Then $h_E = h_N = h_W = h_S = h$, and eqn. (4.54) is reduced to

$$\phi(E) + \phi(N) + \phi(W) + \phi(S) - 4\phi(P) + h^2 F(P) = 0. \qquad (4.55)$$

This equation is identical with eqn. (4.47) derived for impedance networks by much simpler considerations, for which the mathematical tools have thus been demonstrated. It may well be understood now that difference equations similar to eqn. (4.54) can be derived for other nets or other neighbouring nodes to P within our rectangular net shown in Fig. 4.29 if the proper derivations are performed. In this figure, for instance, one could involve the nodes NE, NW, SW and SE either neglecting the nodes N, W, S and E or including the nodes. In all cases, the unknown potential $\phi(P)$ can be expressed by the surrounding potentials which are assumed to be known for the single difference equation.

All difference equations, however, are approximations to the field equation due to the omission of higher order terms in eqns. (4.48) and (4.51). The error due to these approximations is known as truncation error, and it is important to investigate this error carefully if the values h are not chosen properly. The treatment of the truncation error is beyond the scope of this chapter and may be found elsewhere.[21,23]

The numerical evaluation of the difference equation (4.55) is obviously simple, but time-consuming. Considering any field problem to be treated will result in a subdivision of the finite plane by a predominantly regular net (of squares for the special case under consideration) which is supplemented by irregular elements at the boundaries, i.e. electrodes of known potentials. The whole net will then contain n nodes, for which the potential $\phi(P)$ is *not* known. It is obvious that we will obtain a system of n simultaneous equations according to eqn. (4.54), for which most of the D values are equal, due to the predominant square net. This equation may be written in matrix form as

$$[D]\{\phi\} = \{d\} \qquad (4.56)$$

where $[D]$ is the $n.n$ matrix of the coefficients D, $\{\phi\}$ is the column matrix of potentials, and $\{d\}$ is the column matrix of the sum of known potentials and terms $F(P)/2$ (if present for Poissonian field regions). There is clearly a small number of terms only in each row of $[D]$, and one can readily confirm that this matrix is essentially purely diagonal and symmetrical about the main diagonal. As the number of unknowns, however, is in general very large, the solution of eqn. (4.56) may be difficult even for machine computation. It is again beyond the scope of this book to treat the methods for solving this problem, as they are well documented in the literature.[23] It will only be mentioned that simpler problems, i.e. problems with a relatively small number of n, may readily be treated by hand computation using the concept of residuals and point relaxation. The simple procedures involved with these techniques have been the origin of the application of FDM before electronic computers became available. For bigger problems, machine computation is necessary, and iterative schemes are most efficient in combination with successive over-relaxation methods. The direct solution of eqn. (4.56) may, however, be restricted in application due to the high CPU storage necessary for the computer.

A final remark relates to the treatment of electrical fields within regions composed by different values of permittivity ε. There is no fundamental difficulty to take isotropic materials into account, for which the permittivities are not oriented. This is easily demonstrated by eqn. (4.55) applied to Laplacian fields ($F = 0$), if this equation is first multiplied by ε. Let us assume that the nodes E, P and W are at the interface between two materials ε_1 and ε_2, and node N belongs to the region with ε_1, node S to the region with ε_2. As the potential at the interface will still be continuous and only the normal component of the displacement vector is influenced [see eqn. (4.29)], the resultant field may also be composed by a superposition of two Laplacian fields. By this, eqn. (4.55) can be applied as

$$\phi(P) = \frac{1}{4}\left[\phi(E) + \phi(W) + \frac{2\varepsilon_1}{(\varepsilon_1 + \varepsilon_2)}\,\phi(N) + \frac{2\varepsilon_2}{(\varepsilon_1 + \varepsilon_2)}\,\phi(S) \right]. \quad (4.57)$$

It should be mentioned, however, that interfaces between the different ε regions are new boundaries and that again irregular rectangles have to be introduced in the vicinity of the interface, if the interface does not coincide with the points of a square net.

4.5.2 Finite Element Method (FEM)

By reviewing the theory of the FDM it was readily demonstrated that the partial derivatives of the basic field equations (4.53) have been replaced by their algebraic difference form, eqns. (4.52a, b), resulting in a system of algebraic equations (4.56) which have to be solved. Due to the approximations made during this derivation the algorithm was linear of the first order ("first order FDM algorithm").

Though there are different approaches to arrive mathematically at finite element approximations[24] and the most general approach is traced back to the variational problem of extremization of a specific functional, the most common basis is related to a very well-known physical property of fields. The FEM concerns itself with minimizing the energy in the whole field region of interest, when the field may be electric or magnetic, of Laplacian or Poissonian type.

In this section a specific rather than general treatment of the method will be presented. To reduce the size of equations, we will restrict ourselves to two-dimensional electric fields of Laplacian type. Convenient applications even for complicated Poissonian electric fields as, for instance, present around coronating h.v. lines are documented in references 28 and 29, as well as the practical application to magnetic fields.[25–27]

Let us consider a steady-state electrostatic field within a dielectric material whose conductivity may be neglected and whose permittivity may be dependent upon the direction of the field strength $\mathbf{E}$ (anisotropic material) or not (isotropic dielectric). Then as no space charge should be present or accumulated, the potentials would be excited from boundaries (metal electrodes) between which the dielectric material is placed. Assuming a cartesian coordinate system, for such a Laplacian field, the electrical energy W stored within the whole volume R of the region under consideration is

$$W = \iiint_V \left[\frac{1}{2} \left\{ \varepsilon_x \left(\frac{\partial \phi}{\partial x} \right)^2 + \varepsilon_y \left(\frac{\partial \phi}{\partial y} \right)^2 + \varepsilon_z \left(\frac{\partial \phi}{\partial z} \right)^2 \right\} \right] dx \, dy \, dz. \quad (4.58)$$

ε_x, ε_y and ε_z would be anisotropic permittivity coefficients, and it should be noted that even in an isotropic material with $\varepsilon_x = \varepsilon_y = \varepsilon_z = \varepsilon$ the absolute values of ε may change at boundaries between different dielectric materials. The reader may easily verify from any small volume element $dV = (dx \, dy \, dz)$ that the expressions $(\varepsilon \nabla^2 \phi / 2)$ within eqn. (4.58) are energy densities per unit volumes dV.

Furthermore, it is assumed that the potential distribution does not change in the z-direction, i.e. a two-dimensional case. Figure 4.30 displays the situation for which the field space is reduced from the volume R to the area A limited by boundaries with given potentials ϕ_a and ϕ_b (Dirichlet

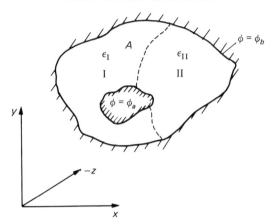

Fɪɢ. 4.30. Limited field area A within x–y-plane representing a two-dimensional field within space $(x, y, z$-coordinates). Dielectric material subdivided by dashed line into regions I and II.

boundaries). The dielectric may be subdivided into two parts, I and II, indicated by the dashed interface, for which the boundary condition is well known (see section 4.3), if no free changes are built up at the interface. The total stored energy within this area-limited system is now given according to eqn. (4.58) by

$$W = z \int\!\!\int_A \left[\frac{1}{2} \left\{ \varepsilon_x \left(\frac{\partial \phi}{\partial x} \right)^2 + \varepsilon_y \left(\frac{\partial \phi}{\partial y} \right)^2 \right\} \right] dx\, dy \qquad (4.59)$$

when z is a constant. W/z is thus an energy density per elementary area dA.

Before any minimization criteria based upon eqn. (4.59) can be applied, appropriate assumptions about the potential distribution $\phi(x, y)$ must be made. It should be emphasized that this function is continuous and a finite number of derivatives may exist. As it will be impossible to find a continuous function for the whole area A, an adequate discretization must be made.

For our two-dimensional problem it is possible to use rectangular or square elements, as was done for the FDM (see Fig. 4.29), or multiple node composite elements for three-dimensional regions. There are, however, definite advantages in using simple, irregularly distributed elements with an arbitrary *triangular* shape (or tetrahedrons for three-dimensional problems). Such triangles can easily be fitted to coincide with boundary shapes, i.e. the nodes of a triangular element system can be placed upon curved boundaries, a situation often met in h.v. insulation systems.

Figure 4.31 shows such a subdivision of a part of a two-dimensional region A (in Fig. 4.30) into triangular elements. Let us consider one of these elements (indicated by e) and the nodes i, j, and m, and formulate basic functions for the potential distributions $\phi(x, y)$ within this element. In the development of the FEM no *a priori* restrictions are placed on this basic function. However, for triangular elements, or a "triangular element family",[29] polynomials can be of higher order, such as

$$\phi(x, y) = \alpha_1 + \alpha_2 x + \alpha_3 y + \alpha_4 x^2 + \alpha_5 xy + \alpha_6 y^2 + \ldots, \qquad (4.60)$$

for which the inter-element compatibility can be improved. The increase in accuracy by applying higher order functions is compensated, however, by an increase in computation time and computation complexity, and thus most of the algorithms used are based upon a *first-order* approximation, i.e. a linear dependency of ϕ on x and y in eqn. (4.60). Following this simple basic function, this equation is reduced to

$$\phi(x, y) = \phi = \alpha_1 + \alpha_2 x + \alpha_3 y. \qquad (4.61)$$

This means that the potentials within each element are linearly distributed and the field intensity, whose components in the x- and y-directions can be computed for eqn. (4.61) by simple derivation, is constant. In this respect, the FEM and the FDM coincide.

For such a first-order approximation, the three coefficients α_1, α_2 and α_3

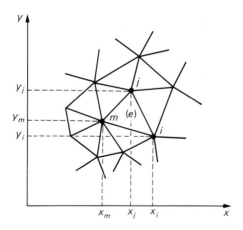

FIG. 4.31. A section of area A (Fig. 4.30) subdivided into irregular triangular elements. Notation of nodes i, j, m for element e.

for element e are easily computed by means of the three *a priori* unknown potentials at the respective nodes i, j and m, given by the equations

$$
\left.
\begin{aligned}
\phi_i &= \alpha_1 + \alpha_2 x_i + \alpha_3 y_i \\
\phi_j &= \alpha_1 + \alpha_2 x_j + \alpha_3 y_j \\
\phi_m &= \alpha_1 + \alpha_2 x_m + \alpha_3 y_m
\end{aligned}
\right\}
\tag{4.62}
$$

The coefficients may be computed applying Cramer's rule, the result being

$$
\alpha_1 = \frac{1}{2\Delta_e}(a_i \phi_i + a_j \phi_j + a_m \phi_m);
\tag{4.63a}
$$

$$
\alpha_2 = \frac{1}{2\Delta_e}(b_i \phi_i + b_j \phi_j + b_m \phi_m);
\tag{4.63b}
$$

$$
\alpha_3 = \frac{1}{2\Delta_e}(c_i \phi_i + c_j \phi_j + c_m \phi_m);
\tag{4.63c}
$$

where

$$
\left.
\begin{aligned}
a_i &= x_j y_m - x_m y_j \\
a_j &= x_m y_i - x_i y_m \\
a_m &= x_i y_j - x_j y_i
\end{aligned}
\right\}
\tag{4.63d}
$$

$$
\left.
\begin{aligned}
b_i &= y_j - y_m \\
b_j &= y_m - y_i \\
b_m &= y_i - y_j
\end{aligned}
\right\}
\tag{4.63e}
$$

$$
\left.
\begin{aligned}
c_i &= x_m - x_j \\
c_j &= x_i - x_m \\
c_m &= x_j - x_i
\end{aligned}
\right\}
\tag{4.63f}
$$

and

$$
\left.
\begin{aligned}
2\Delta_e &= a_i + a_j + a_m \\
&= b_i c_j - b_j c_i
\end{aligned}
\right\}
\tag{4.64}
$$

From eqn. (4.64) and Fig. 4.31, one may easily see that the symbol Δ_e is used to describe the area of the triangular element i, j, m.

With eqns. (4.61), (4.62) and (4.63), the potential distribution of the element can thus be related to the potentials of the adjoining nodes and simple numbers a_i, b_i, etc., for each element can be computed once division of the two-dimensional region into triangular elements has been performed. Introducing these values into eqn. (4.61) the result is (index e used for "element"):

$$\phi_e(x, y) = \frac{1}{2\Delta_e} [(a_i + b_i + c_i)\phi_i + \ldots$$

$$\ldots + (a_j + b_j + c_j)\phi_j + (a_m + b_m + c_m)\phi_m]. \quad (4.65)$$

This equation may also be written as

$$\phi_e = [N_i, N_j, N_m] \begin{Bmatrix} \phi_i \\ \phi_j \\ \phi_m \end{Bmatrix} \quad (4.66)$$

in which the functions N are the "shape functions", as they will depend upon the shape of the finite elements used. Such shape functions can be derived for many kinds and shapes of elements including the rectangles used for the FDM.[24]

With eqn. (4.65) or eqn. (4.61), the energy noted within the element is easily computed. According to eqn. (4.59), the partial derivatives for each element are:

$$\frac{\partial \phi}{\partial x} = \alpha_2 = f(\phi_i, \phi_j, \phi_m)$$

$$\frac{\partial \phi}{\partial y} = \alpha_3 = f(\phi_i, \phi_j, \phi_m) \quad (4.67)$$

However, as we are not interested in the absolute values of these energies, the components of the electric field intensities should not be introduced into eqn. (4.59) at this stage. The FEM is based upon the minimization of the energy within the whole system, and thus only derivatives of the energies with respect to the potential distribution are of interest. According to eqn. (4.59), the energy functional, i.e. the energy per unit length in the z-direction for our specific case, is for the element under consideration.

$$\chi^e = \frac{W_e}{z} = \frac{1}{2} \Delta_e \left\{ \varepsilon_x \left(\frac{\partial \phi}{\partial x} \right)^2 + \varepsilon_y \left(\frac{\partial \phi}{\partial y} \right)^2 \right\}_e \quad (4.68)$$

as $\iint dx\, dy$ provides the area of the element, Δ_e. For further consideration only, isotropic dielectric material is assumed within each individual element, i.e. $\varepsilon_x = \varepsilon_y = \varepsilon_e$.

Whereas the functional χ^e in eqn. (4.68) is only dependent upon the node potentials of the individual element [eqn. (4.67)], an equivalent functional χ for the whole system (area A, Fig. 4.30) will exist. The formulation regarding the minimization of the energy within the complete system may thus be written as

$$\frac{\partial \chi}{\partial \{\phi\}} = 0 \qquad (4.69)$$

where $\{\phi\}$ is the potential vector for all nodes within this system. For our specific element, the minimizing equations can easily be derived by differentiating eqn. (4.68) partially with respect to ϕ_i, ϕ_j and ϕ_m. Taking also eqns. (4.63) and (4.67) into account, the differentiation with respect to ϕ_i yields

$$\frac{\partial \chi^e}{\partial \phi_i} = \frac{1}{2}\varepsilon_e \Delta_e \left(2\alpha_2 \frac{\partial \alpha_2}{\partial \phi_i} + 2\alpha_3 \frac{\partial \alpha_3}{\partial \phi_i} \right)$$

$$= \tfrac{1}{2}\varepsilon_e(\alpha_2 b_i + \alpha_3 c_i)$$

$$= \frac{\varepsilon_e}{4\Delta_e}\left[(b_i^2 + c_i^2)\phi_i + (b_i b_j + c_i c_j)\phi_j + (b_i b_m + c_i c_m)\phi_m \right]. \qquad (4.70)$$

The set of all three equations may best be expressed in matrix form as

$$\frac{\partial \chi^e}{\partial \{\phi\}^e} = \frac{\varepsilon_e}{4\Delta_e}\begin{bmatrix} (b_i^2 + c_i^2) & (b_i b_j + c_i c_j) & (b_i b_m + c_i c_m) \\ & (b_j^2 + c_j^2) & (b_j b_m + c_j c_m) \\ \text{sym} & & (b_m^2 + c_m^2) \end{bmatrix} \begin{Bmatrix} \phi_i \\ \phi_j \\ \phi_m \end{Bmatrix}$$

$$= [h]^e \{\phi\}^e. \qquad (4.71)$$

The matrix $[h]^e$ is well known as the "stiffness matrix" for the individual element, as it contains the sensitivity of the functional with respect to the potentials. (Within a mechanical, elastic system, this matrix relates mechanical nodal forces to displacements.) It contains well-known geometric quantities [eqns. (4.63), (4.64)] and the material's permittivity ε_e.

It is now possible to establish a set of algebraic equations with which the still unknown potentials can be computed. No assumptions have been made so far concerning the *a priori* known potentials at the boundaries, and Fig. 4.30 displayed only the finite field regions with a Dirichlet boundary.

The triangular element (e) within Fig. 4.31 is surrounded by other triangular elements and it is seen that any node potential within such a system will depend upon the potentials of the surrounding nodes. The number of these nodes is dependent upon the triangular network, but that number is always small. Thus it is sufficient to demonstrate the last step with a set of only four triangular elements as shown in Fig. 4.32. The elements are numbered from 1 to 4, and the nodes by 1 to 5.

Application of eqn. (4.69) to this set of elements yields

$$\frac{\partial \chi}{\partial \phi_5} = 0, \tag{4.72}$$

where χ is the energy functional of the system with the four elements. Before this equation is evaluated, it is convenient to write the stiffness matrix, eqn. (4.71), as

$$[h]^e = \begin{bmatrix} (h_{ii})_e & (h_{ij})_e & (h_{im})_e \\ & (h_{jj})_e & (h_{jm})_e \\ \text{sym} & & (h_{mm})_e \end{bmatrix} \tag{4.73}$$

when

$$(h_{ii})_e = \frac{\varepsilon_e}{4\Delta_e}(b_i^2 + c_i^2);$$

$$(h_{ij})_e = \frac{\varepsilon_e}{4\Delta_e}(b_i b_j + c_i c_j);$$

$$\vdots$$

etc.

Replacing the index e by the individual numbers of the elements of Fig. 4.32, eqn. (4.72) results in

$$\frac{\partial \chi}{\partial \phi_5} = 0 = \tag{4.74}$$

(from element 1) $= [(h_{im})_1 \phi_2 + (h_{jm})_1 \phi_1 + (h_{mm})_1 \phi_5 + \dots$

(from element 2) $+ (h_{im})_2 \phi_3 + (h_{jm})_2 \phi_2 + (h_{mm})_2 \phi_5 + \dots$

(from element 3) $+ (h_{im})_3 \phi_4 + (h_{jm})_3 \phi_3 + (h_{mm})_3 \phi_5 + \dots$

(from element 4) $+ (h_{im})_4 \phi_1 + (h_{jm})_4 \phi_4 + (h_{mm})_4 \phi_5].$

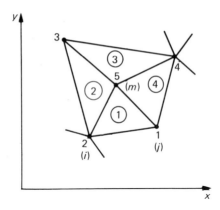

FIG. 4.32. Node 5 connected to four triangular elements (i, j, m identify element l).

This equation may be written as

$$H_{15}\phi_1 + H_{25}\phi_2 + H_{35}\phi_3 + H_{45}\phi_4 + H_{55}\phi_5 = 0 \qquad (4.75)$$

where

$$H_{15} = [(h_{im})_4 + (h_{jm})_1]$$
$$H_{25} = [(h_{im})_1 + (h_{jm})_2]$$
$$\vdots$$

$$H_{55} = \left[(h_{mm})_1 + (h_{mm})_2 + (h_{mm})_3 + (h_{mm})_4 \right] = \sum_{r=1}^{4} (h_{mm})_r.$$

If the potentials ϕ_1 to ϕ_4 were known, ϕ_5 could immediately be calculated from this equation. As, however, the potentials of the nodes 1 to 4 might still be embedded in a larger triangular network, for every unknown potential a corresponding equation has to be set up. For our system with Laplace conditions the FEM solution may thus be written as

$$\frac{\partial \chi}{\partial \{\phi\}} = 0 = [H]\{\phi\} \qquad (4.76)$$

indicating the assembly of the whole set of minimizing equations, which can be solved following the usual rules (see section 4.5.1).

This short detailed introduction of the FEM cannot demonstrate all the advantages and disadvantages of the method. In the application to electric field problems within insulation systems, the advantages may be summarized as follows:

(a) It is readily applicable to non-homogeneous systems (i.e. with materials of different permittivities) as well as to anisotropic systems [refer to eqn. (4.59)].

(b) The shapes and sizes of the elements may be chosen to fit arbitrary boundaries and the grid size may easily be adapted to the gradient of the potentials, i.e. small elements can be placed into regions with high gradients and vice versa.

(c) Accuracy may also be improved using higher order elements [compare with eqn. (4.60)], without complicating boundary conditions.

(d) Dielectric materials may also be treated as the case where conduction currents contribute to the potential distribution. This can be done by assuming complex permittivity with real and imaginary parts (i.e. $\varepsilon = \varepsilon' - j\varepsilon''$ where $\tan \delta = \varepsilon''/\varepsilon'$).[30]

For the calculation of electric field intensities within electric insulation systems, the only disadvantage of the FEM is still related to the limited and *a priori* unknown accuracy which can be achieved. Even for two-dimensional problems and highly divergent fields, a very large number of triangular elements or nodes would be necessary to obtain an adequate accuracy within the highly divergent field regions, which are responsible for the breakdown of the whole system. It should be remembered that the often used first-order algorithm [see eqn. (4.61)] does result in a *constant* field strength within each element [see eqn. (4.67)], which is only approximately correct for the case of continuous field distribution within homogeneous materials. Though the size of the elements can well be adapted to the divergence of the field distribution, too large a number of elements or nodes would be required for high accuracy. Efficient computation algorithms are necessary to solve eqn. (4.76), as the stiffness matrix $[H]$, though highly sparse and symmetric, will become very large.

Finally, Fig. 4.33 shows an example of a field computation using the FEM ("Unifield" program No. 4, Brown Boveri Co., Baden, Switzerland). Figure 4.33a displays the original triangular grid used for computation of a coaxial section of a GIS comprising a conical space r ($\varepsilon_r = 6.5$) within the gaseous insulation system ($\varepsilon_r \approx 1$). The result of this grid displayed by 5% equipotential lines (Fig. 4.33b) still shows some discontinuities, though much smaller triangular elements have been used in regions with high field

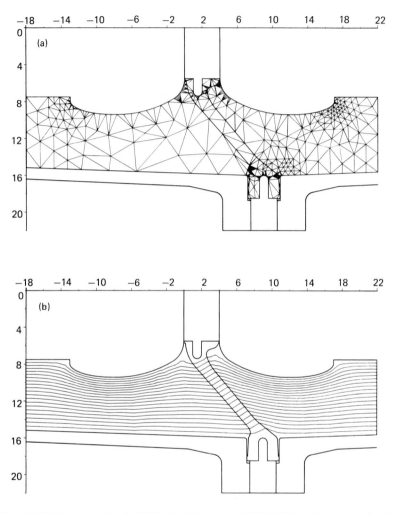

FIG. 4.33. Field computation by FEM. Coaxial section of GIS. (a) Triangular elements for the computation of a limited axial section comprising the spacer. (b) Result of the computation (5%-equipotential lines) based upon the grid displayed in (a). (c), (d) A section of (a) and (b) enlarged. Same axial and radial notations. (e) A section of the improved grid with a much higher number of elements in comparison to (a) or (c) respectively. (f) Equipotential lines due to (e) (courtesy of BBC, Baden, Switzerland).

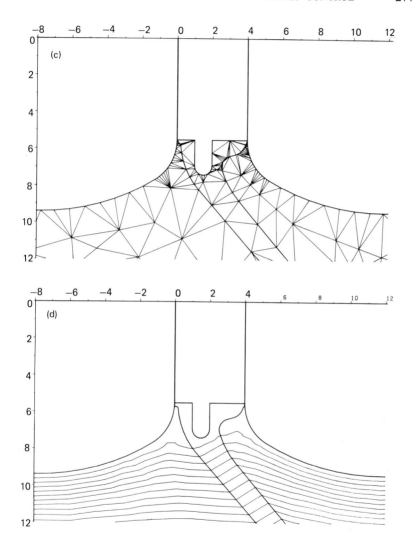

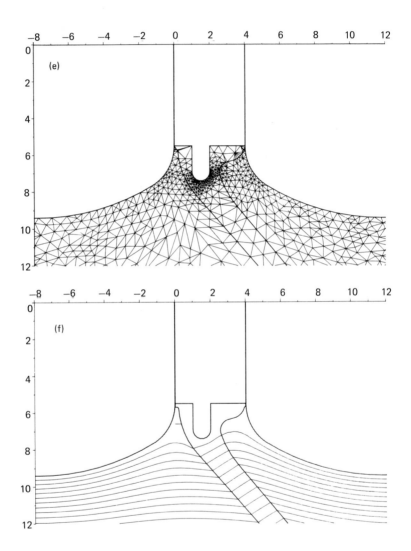

non-uniformity. Figures 4.33c and d are sections of the figures shown before. The same sections computed by a much higher grid density (see Figs. 4.33e, f) confirm the large improvement displayed by the new equipotential lines, the discontinuity of which disappeared.

4.5.3 Charge Simulation Method (CSM)

A third numerical method widely and successfully used today to calculate electric fields is known as the charge simulation method (CSM). Though the fundamentals of this method may be familiar to most electrical engineers, as it is based upon frequently used analytical field computation methods, it may be useful to review some fundamentals of Maxwell's equations.

The Poisson's equation may be written as

$$\text{div}\,(-\varepsilon\ \text{grad}\ \phi) = \text{div}\ \mathbf{D} = \rho \qquad (4.77)$$

(which is a differential form of Maxwell's equation) where $\mathbf{D}$ is the electric flux density and ρ is the volume charge density. In contrast to eqn. (4.43), in which the cartesian form of Poisson's equation was used, eqn. (4.77) is independent of any particular coordinate system. This equation may also be integrated by means of a volume integral, resulting in

$$\int_V \text{div}\ \mathbf{D}\ dV = \oint_A \mathbf{D}\ d\mathbf{A} = \int_V \rho\ dV. \qquad (4.78)$$

Here the volume integral of divergence is transferred to a surface integral with the closed surface A, and the volume integral applied to the charge density can easily be identified with the total charge enclosed by the surface A. Equation (4.78) represents the well-known Gauss's Law.

Gauss's Law gives an exact solution of Poisson's equation, and many direct methods for field computations are based upon this law.

We have seen that both the FDM (section 4.5.1) and the FEM (section 4.5.2) are directly based upon the *differential* form of a Maxwell equation [see eqn. (4.77)]. We noted also, in previous sections, that solving the differential equations, either analytically or numerically, involves difficulties inherent in the formulation of boundary conditions as well as due to inaccuracies arising within numerical procedures. On the other hand, Gauss's Law is much easier to apply, at least for the cases where some symmetry boundary conditions are apparent. This advantage was used by applying eqn. (4.78) to calculate analytically some simple field configurations, e.g. coaxial cylindrical or spherical fields (see section 4.2, p. 224), for which the integrals of the left-hand side of eqn. (4.78) could easily be solved due to symmetry conditions, arising from a concentration of the charge distribution (right-hand side of this equation) within line or point charges respectively.

Directly related to the application of Gauss's Law is the *method of images* (or image charges), which could be used to compute analytically some important problems by means of ready-made solutions, thus eliminating the need for formal solutions of Laplace's or Poisson's equations in differential form. This method, which can be traced to Lord Kelvin[31] and Maxwell,[32] was also used for field computation of a sphere-to-sphere arrangement.

More recently, Steinbigler[33] introduced this technique as an efficient method for digital computation of electric fields. Since its publication in English[34] this method (CSM) has been recognized to be very competitive and often superior to FEM or FDM, at least for treating two- or three-dimensional fields within h.v. insulation systems, particularly where high accuracies within highly divergent field areas are demanded. Though the efficiency and applicability of the CSM may not have been fully developed up to now, many recent publications have shown interest in this technique.[20,35–42]

The basic principle of CSM is very easy to formulate. Using the superposition principle, the potential functions of the fields of individual charges of any type (point, line or ring charges, for instance) can be found by a summation of the potentials (scalars) resulting from the individual charges. Let Q_j be a number n of individual charges, and ϕ_i be the potential at any point within the space (independent of the coordinate system used). The superposition principle results in

$$\phi_i = \sum_{j=1}^{n} p_{ij} Q_j \tag{4.79}$$

where p_{ij} are the *potential coefficients*, which are known for many types of individual charges by particular solutions of Laplace's or Poisson's equations mentioned earlier. Figure 4.34 displays a point charge Q_p and a line charge Q_l placed at the x- and y-axis respectively and an arbitrary point P_i at which the potential ϕ_i would apply.

Whereas the potential coefficients, $p_{ij}, \ldots$ are known, only additional boundary conditions enable us to relate ϕ_i with Q_j quantitatively. If the individual charges are placed *outside* the space in which the field is to be

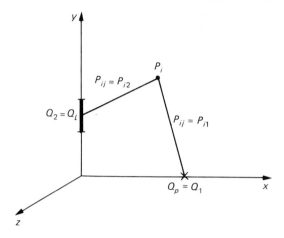

FIG. 4.34. A finite line charge Q_l and a point charge Q_p related to a field point P_i.

computed (or inside of a closed metal electrode, whose surface is an equipotential area), the magnitudes of these charges are related to the distributed surface charges which are physically bonded by the electric flux leaving or entering the surface of any electrode or conductor surrounding these charges. If n charges Q_j are assumed, we require also at least n known potentials to solve eqn. (4.79) for the *a priori* unknown charge magnitudes. This can easily be done by identifying the potentials ϕ_i with n potentials on the surface of the conductors ("contour points"), which are adequately placed at a given electrode configuration. If this potential is $\phi_i = \phi_c$, we may rewrite eqn. (4.79) as

$$\sum_{j=1}^{n} p_{ij} Q_j = \phi_c. \qquad (4.80)$$

This equation leads to a system of n linear equations for the n unknown charges

$$\begin{bmatrix} p_{11} & p_{12} & \cdots & p_{1n} \\ p_{21} & p_{22} & \cdots & p_{2n} \\ \vdots & & & \vdots \\ p_{n1} & p_{n2} & \cdots & p_{nn} \end{bmatrix} \begin{Bmatrix} Q_1 \\ Q_2 \\ \vdots \\ Q_n \end{Bmatrix} = \begin{Bmatrix} \phi_1 \\ \phi_2 \\ \vdots \\ \phi_n \end{Bmatrix} \qquad (4.80a)$$

or

$$[p]\{Q\} = \{\phi\}.$$

After this system has been solved, it is necessary to check whether the set of calculated charges fits the actual boundary conditions. It must be emphasized that only n discrete contour points of the real electrode system have been used to solve eqn. (4.80), and thus the potentials at any other contour points considered in this calculation might still be different from ϕ_c. Therefore, eqn. (4.79) must be additionally used to compute the potentials at a number of "check points" located on the electrode boundary (with known potential). The difference between these potentials and the given boundary potential is then a measure of the accuracy and applicability of the simulation. The development and introduction of special objective functions is thus an important procedure within the optimization of the CSM.[34–36]

As soon as an adequate charge system has been adopted, the potentials and the field strength within the space can be computed. Whereas the potentials are found by superposition, i.e. by eqn. (4.79) or the corresponding set of linear equations [compare with eqn. (4.80)], the field stresses are calculated by superposition of magnitudes and directional components. For a cartesian coordinate system for resistance, the x-coordinate $\mathbf{E}_x$ would then be for a number of n charges.

$$\mathbf{E}_x = \sum_{j=1}^{n} \frac{\partial p_{ij}}{\partial x} Q_j = \sum_{j=1}^{n} (f_{ij})_x Q_j \qquad (4.81)$$

where f_{ij} are "field intensity coefficients" in the x-direction. Before further considerations, the computation algorithm may be applied to a simple example. In Fig. 4.35a a symmetrical sphere-to-sphere electrode system is sketched symmetrically charged to $\pm V$. This condition implies zero-potential for the plane $z = 0$ as well as for the dielectric space at a distance from the spheres (unlimited dielectric space). Thus the field configuration is axisymmetric with the rotation centre being the z-axis. This simple example would be difficult to compute by FDM or FEM, as the space is unlimited.

Let us consider the case of two point charges $\pm Q_1$ and $\pm Q_2$ symmetrically placed along the axis at $r = 0$; $z = \pm 0.75/1.25D$ and only two contour points P_1, P_2 at $r = 0$ as shown in Fig. 4.35a. The symmetric arrangement of the charges (imaging) gives $V = 0$ at $z = 0$. Thus also a sphere-to-plane geometry is computed.

To solve eqn. (4.80), the potential coefficients for a point charge are necessary. The potential related to a point charge Q distant d is given by:

$$\phi = \frac{Q}{4\pi\varepsilon} \frac{1}{d} = pQ \qquad (4.82)$$

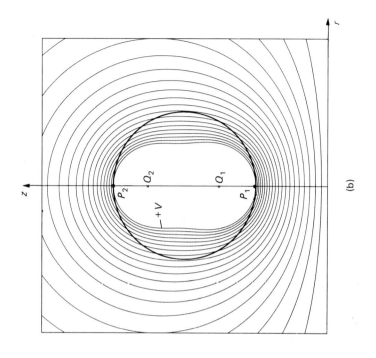

(b)

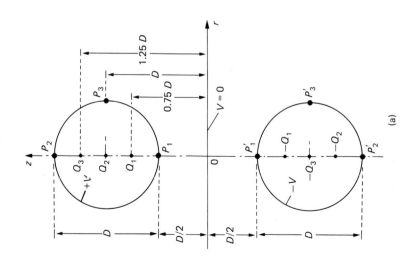

(a)

284

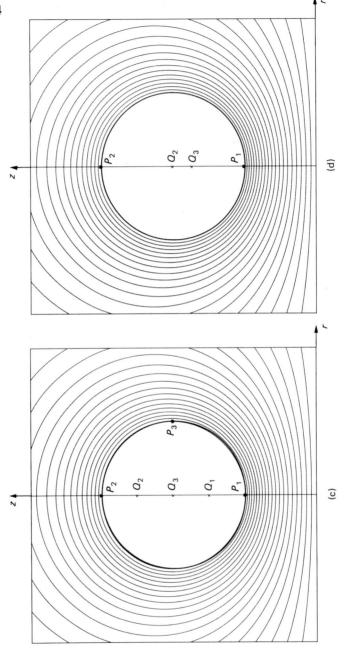

Fig. 4.35. Example for CSM. (a) Sphere-to-sphere electrode arrangement. (b) to (d) Computed results. (For more information see text.)

or

$$p = \frac{1}{4\pi\varepsilon d}.$$

Thus the potential coefficients p_{ij} are dependent upon the distance d between the charges Q_j and the contour P_i. For our r-z-coordinate system, the coefficients may be expressed by

$$p_{ij} = \frac{1}{4\pi\varepsilon\sqrt{r_i^2 + (z_i - z_j)^2}} \tag{4.82a}$$

from simple geometric considerations. Let the computer now solve the four simple equations using eqn. (4.80), in order to obtain the magnitudes of Q_1 and Q_2, and to compute a sufficient set of other potentials within the r-z-coordinate system. These potentials can be used to draw equipotential lines; such lines are shown in Fig. 4.35b for part of the positive z-axis. The result may appear disappointing, since the equipotential line $+V$ deviates grossly from the circle, representing the cross-section of the sphere. An agreement of the computed and given potential is only found for the contour points P_1, P_2, but for other contour points a disagreement extending up to about 39% can be observed. This suggests a very poor simulation and bad assumption of point charges. Therefore, we may add a third point charge Q_3 and contour point P_3, as also indicated in Fig. 4.35a, and repeat the calculations. The result is now shown in Fig. 4.35c. The disagreement between the real contour of the electrode and the computed equipotential line $\phi = +V$ is now very small, not exceeding 1.98%, an error difficult to see within the figure. This means that the simulation was greatly improved and it is easy to see that more charges improve the computation. We can, however, also find excellent solutions using only two simulation charges placed at proper positions. This was done in Fig. 4.35d, where again only two charges and two contour points were used to solve the problem. The largest deviation for the computed potential $\phi = V$ from the sphere is now less than 0.2%.

This simple example demonstrates two essential features concerning an effective application of the CSM. The first relates to the proper selection of the *types* of simulation charges, and the second to a suitable *arrangement* of the charges and contour points.

Various other charge types are available for which the potential coefficients are known from analytical solutions. For our example, the

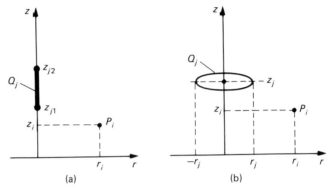

FIG. 4.36. Finite straight line charges (a) and toroidal line (ring) charges (b), with constant charge densities. Total charge: Q_j.

application of toroidal line charges (ring charges) of constant charge density and centred on the axis of symmetry would have been an effective method of discretization. One could also use infinite or finite line charges, or even plane or curved surface charges. The complexity of computation, however, in general increases with the complexity of the simulation charges used, as the potential coefficients become more difficult to compute numerically. As an exercise, only the coefficients for finite line charges and toroidal line charges are reproduced here. With the notations of Fig. 4.36, the potential coefficients are for:

Finite straight line charges (Fig. 4.36a)

$$p_{ij} = \frac{1}{4\pi\varepsilon(z_{j2}-z_{j1})} \ln \frac{(z_{j2}-z_i+\gamma_1)(z_{j1}+z_i+\gamma_2)}{(z_{j1}-z_i+\delta_1)(z_{j2}+z_i+\delta_2)}, \qquad (4.83)$$

where

$$\gamma_1 = \sqrt{r_i^2+(z_{j2}-z_i)^2}; \quad \gamma_2 = \sqrt{r_i^2+(z_{j1}+z_i)^2},$$

$$\delta_1 = \sqrt{r_i^2+(z_{j1}-z_i)^2}; \quad \delta_2 = \sqrt{r_i^2+(z_{j2}+z_i)^2}.$$

A suitable application of eqn. (4.81) leads also to analytical expression for the field strength components in the r- and z-directions (Q_j individual line charges):

$$E_r = \sum_{j=1}^{n} \frac{Q_j}{4\pi\varepsilon(z_{j2}-z_{j1})} \left[\frac{z_{j2}-z_i}{r_i\gamma_1} - \frac{z_{j1}-z_i}{r_i\delta_1} + \frac{z_{j1}+z_i}{r_i\gamma_2} - \frac{z_{j2}+z_i}{r_i\delta_2} \right], \qquad (4.84a)$$

$$E_z = \sum_{j=1}^{n} \frac{Q_j}{4\pi\varepsilon(z_{j2}-z_{j1})} \left[\frac{1}{\gamma_1} - \frac{1}{\delta_1} - \frac{1}{\gamma_2} + \frac{1}{\delta_2} \right]. \qquad (4.84b)$$

Ring charges (Fig. 4.36b)

$$p_{ij} = \frac{1}{4\pi\varepsilon} \frac{2}{\pi} \left[\frac{K(k_1)}{\alpha_1} - \frac{K(k_2)}{\alpha_2} \right], \tag{4.85}$$

where

$$\alpha_1 = \sqrt{(r_i+r_j)^2 + (z_i-z_j)^2}, \quad \alpha_2 = \sqrt{(r_i+r_j)^2 + (z_i+z_j)^2},$$

$$\beta_1 = \sqrt{(r_i-r_j)^2 + (z_i-z_j)^2}, \quad \beta_2 = \sqrt{(r_i-r_j)^2 + (z_i+z_j)^2},$$

and

$$k_1 = \frac{2\sqrt{r_j r_i}}{\alpha_1}, \quad k_2 = \frac{2\sqrt{r_j r_i}}{\alpha_2}$$

with the complete elliptic integrals of the first kind $K(k)$ and the second kind $E(k)$.

The field stress components become

$$E_r = \sum_{j=1}^{n} \frac{-Q_j}{4\pi\varepsilon} \frac{1}{\pi r_i} \left\{ \frac{[r_j^2 - r_i^2 + (z_i-z_j)^2] E(k_1) - \beta_1^2 K(k_1)}{\alpha_1 \beta_1^2} \right.$$

$$\left. - \frac{[r_j^2 - r_i^2 + (z_i+z_j)^2] E(k_2) - \beta_2^2 K(k_2)}{\alpha_2 \beta_2^2} \right\} \tag{4.86a}$$

$$E_z = \sum_{j=1}^{n} \frac{-Q_j}{4\pi\varepsilon} \frac{2}{\pi} \left\{ \frac{(z_i-z_j) E(k_1)}{\alpha_1 \beta_1^2} + \frac{(z_i+z_j) E(k_2)}{\alpha_2 \beta_2^2} \right\}. \tag{4.86b}$$

As far as the most suitable arrangement of discrete charges within an electrode is concerned, these may either be found by optimization techniques based upon objective functions[35] or a more practical approach is by the definition of and assignment factor,[34] which relates the successive distances of the contour points with the distances between a contour point and the adjoining corresponding charge. Details of this method may be found in the literature.

For a field space containing only one type of dielectric material ($\varepsilon = $ constant), the application of the CSM to real three-dimensional problems does not present fundamental difficulties. Even sophisticated electrode configurations can be treated by means of discrete charges and images, at least if types of charges with variable charge densities are used (ring charges with periodically variable charge distribution,[34] multipoles,[39] elliptic cylinder charges,[37] axispheroidal charges.[38] Even electric fields with even moving space charges can be treated.[34]

In contrast to the simple solutions within the FDM or FEM for treating multidielectric materials, the CSM when used for field calculations in systems composed of two or more materials increases the cost. This may be understood by considering the fundamental mathematical solutions and the physical mechanisms involved. The CSM is directly based upon physical charges and in every dielectric *material* polarization processes take place. Whereas in a homogeneous material placed between electrodes the *absolute* value of its permittivity does not contribute to the field strength (or potentials), but only the flux density D, the field distribution at the boundaries of different materials is heavily distorted due to the dipole charges at the boundaries which do not have counterparts at the adjacent medium. The law of dielectric refraction [section 4.3.2, eqn. (4.36)], results from this physical effect and is associated with an infinitely thin layer of bonded charges located in the two media. The free surface charges physically present due to electrical conduction of the interface surface also contribute to field distortions,[40] but the common dielectric refraction is not related to such additional charges.

This realignment of dipoles within different dielectric materials must thus be considered within the CSM. An exact solution with CSM must be based upon the physical dipole surface charge density as has been shown recently.[47] But continuous surface charges can also be simulated by discrete charges by replacing the surface charge density at metal electrodes, whose potential is a fixed value, by discrete charges within this electrode. This method, originally presented by P. Weiss,[34] will be presented briefly through a simple example.

Figure 4.37 displays a cross-section of a part of an insulation system, in which a metal electrode with fixed potential, $\phi = \phi_c$, meets two adjoining dielectric materials I and II. The actual shapes of the two-dimensional surfaces of the three different boundaries (electrode-dielectric I, electrode-dielectric II, dielectric I-dielectric II) determine the optimal types of discrete charges simulating the problem. Thus, the localized charges 1–7 will represent point charges as well as intersections with line or ring charges. From earlier considerations it is obvious that a part of the charges (nos. 1–3, denoted as n_E) have been placed inside the electrode, i.e. *behind* the metal surface. However, the same is correct for the charges placed on both sides of the dielectric interface (nos. 4–7), as the influence of the dipolar charges within dielectric I upon the field in dielectric II can be simulated by the discrete charges nos. 4 and 5 within dielectric I and vice versa. It was also shown earlier that a limited number of contour points placed at a

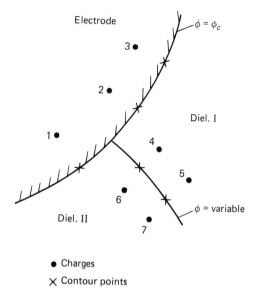

FIG. 4.37. Simulation of a dielectric boundary by discrete charges.

ϕ = constant boundary is necessary, which is equal to the number of simulated charges within an electrode, and thus a number of $n_E = 3$ contour points (nos. 1–3) is adequate. For the dielectric interface, however, it will be sufficient for our example to place only two contour points corresponding to the two pairs of simulation charges (nos. 4 and 6, nos. 5 and 7), as each contour point belongs to dielectric I as well as to dielectric II. Equal numbers of charges, designated by n_B, on both sides of the dielectric interface are thus convenient and they should be placed at positions equally distributed between the mutual contour points and adjacent charges respectively. For our example, n_B is 2 only.

Now it is possible to set up a system of equations for our unknown charges based upon well-known boundary conditions. These boundary conditions can be subdivided into three parts.

(1) The electrode-dielectric interface is a boundary with known potential, $\phi = \phi_c$. The absolute magnitude of the surface charge density at this electrode is, due to the polarization mechanisms in both dielectric materials, dependent upon the relative permittivity ε_r of the dielectric materials, as $D = \varepsilon E = \varepsilon_r \varepsilon_0 E$, where ε_0 is the permittivity of vacuum. Also

the absolute magnitudes of our simulation charges would depend upon these materials' constants. However, it is not necessary to take these physical effects into account, which are indeed included within our potential coefficients [see eqns. (4.82), (4.82a) etc.]. For any homogeneous dielectric material, the electric field may be computed independent of any relative permittivity ε_r, and the potential coefficients, for which eqn. (4.82) is one example only, are in general always computed by assuming $\varepsilon = \varepsilon_0$, or any other number as long as the simulated charges are not used to derive capacitance values from the results, which is also possible. It is easy to understand, however, that the absolute magnitudes of the discrete charges used within our system are based upon a superposition of potentials. And thus we can use the known potential at the electrode interface to derive *two* sets of equations due to the two dielectrics used. The first set of three equations based upon the three or n_E contour points takes only dielectric I into account, for which the charges within dielectric II can be neglected:

$$\sum_{j=1}^{n_E} Q_j p_{ij} + \sum_{j=n_E+1}^{n_E+n_B} Q_j p_{ij} = \phi_c. \qquad (4.87a)$$

$$\underset{(1-3)}{} \qquad \underset{(4-5)}{}$$

Using eqns. (4.88) and (4.89) subject to two new boundary conditions, the electric field within dielectric II could be computed, as all Q_j charges within eqn. (4.87a) which are not yet known, define the potentials within this material.

For the computation of the field distribution within dielectric I, the same considerations apply. But now we neglect the charges within dielectric I, which results in an equal set of three or n_E equations, as

$$\sum_{j=1}^{n_E} Q_j p_{ij} + \sum_{j=n_E+n_B+1}^{n_E+2n_B} Q_j p_{ij} = \phi_c. \qquad (4.87b)$$

$$\underset{(1-3)}{} \qquad \underset{(6-7)}{}$$

(2) The potential at the dielectric interface is unknown. We know, however, that due to the continuity of the potential at either side of the interface, the potentials must be *equal* at each contour point. As the charges within the electrode (nos. 1–3) will not disturb the continuity condition, the potentials due to the charges within the dielectric materials must satisfy the

condition

$$\sum_{j=n_E+1}^{n_E+n_B} Q_j p_{ij} = \sum_{j=n_E+n_B+1}^{n_E+2n_B} Q_j p_{ij}. \qquad (4.88)$$

$$(4\text{--}5) \qquad\qquad (6\text{--}7)$$

This equation refers to a number of n_B ($=2$) contour points, giving an equal number of new equations, in which those charges Q_j are involved, which have not yet been used within eqn. (4.87a) or eqn. (4.87b) respectively. It should be noticed that this potential continuity condition implies that the field stress components tangential to the interface are equal.

(3) Finally, the third boundary condition refers to the continuity of the normal component of the electric flux density crossing the dielectric interface, or the discontinuity of the normal components of the field intensity [see eqn. (4.29)]. To include this condition, the "field intensity coefficient" f_{ij} must be considered [see eqn. (4.81)], being the contribution of the charge j to that component of the field vector, which is normal to the dielectric boundary at a contour point i. These factors are in general also known from analytical computations, as this applies to the potential coefficients p_{ij}, and specific f_{ij} values can be taken directly from the earlier equations [(4.84) or (4.86)] for line or ring charges. Then for any normal component $(E_n)_i = Q_j f_{ij}$, this condition may be written as

$$\varepsilon_I \left[\sum_{j=1}^{n_E} Q_j f_{ij} + \sum_{j=n_E+n_B+1}^{n_E+2n_B} Q_j f_{ij} \right] = \varepsilon_{II} \left[\sum_{j=1}^{n_E} Q_j f_{ij} + \sum_{j=n_E+1}^{n_E+n_B} Q_j f_{ij} \right] \qquad (4.89)$$

$$(1\text{--}3) \qquad (6\text{--}7) \qquad\qquad\qquad (1\text{--}3) \qquad (4\text{--}5)$$

where ε_I, ε_{II} are the permittivities of the two dielectrics. This equation refers again to a number of n_B contour points, and thus a total number of $(n_E + 2n_B)$ linear equations are given for the calculations of the same number of unknown charges. This procedure demonstrates the difficulties involved with the implementation of dielectric boundaries, as a significant number of additional charges increases the computational efforts.

The recent development referring to CSM are two-fold

(a) In practice, the adequate shaping of electrode configurations within insulation systems is an essential task, as field stresses may well be reduced and kept low by this method. Such electrode optimization techniques are either based upon an interactive process in which the contour points are shifted after each computation of the field stresses[41] or are based upon a superposition of fixed simulation charges representing the original insulation system and additional "optimization" charges by which the field distribution will be changed due to a given objective function.[36,42]

(b) The application of discrete simulation charges used in the charge simulation technique provides at least a very reliable and efficient method to solve many two- and three-dimensional problems. However, it should be recognized that the option of surface charges at electrode or dielectric boundaries, i.e. distributed layers of charge sources in free space, offers definite advantages, as by such a simulation the role of physical charges which are the origin of electric flux densities is taken directly into account. A full treatment of this extended CSM is beyond the scope of this chapter, and only a few comments regarding the procedure, which is fundamentally similar to the CSM, will be made. While in the discrete CSM the individual charges Q_j may be found from known potentials, ϕ_c, at boundaries and individual potential coefficients, p_{ij} [see eqn. (4.80)], the relation between potential boundaries and charge densities is expressed by integral equations in which the "potential coefficients", which are metric coefficients, are much more difficult to compute. In general, Fredholm's integral equations have to be solved. This method and procedure is still in the developing stage and the reader is referred to the literature for further consideration.[43–45]

In summarizing the features of the CSM with reference to the FDM, the following statements can be made.

For the specific tasks of field calculations within h.v. insulation systems, in which in general Dirichlet boundary conditions are given, all types of interfaces are predominantly curved and field distributions are of utmost interest in highly stressed areas, the inherent feature of CSM to simulate curved interfaces by relatively simple means is a big advantage.

Field regions must not be limited by a closed boundary, as the solution is not based upon a computation of potentials within a given field space. Nevertheless, potentials and even field stresses can be computed based upon analytical (i.e. exact) solutions within any point of the field region as soon as a proper charge distribution [see eqn. (4.80)] is found.

Proper charge distributions and thus field simulations need in general less computation times for digital computers, as fewer linear equations are involved and thus the potential coefficient matrix $[p]$, eqn. (4.80a), is similar, though densely occupied, in comparison with adequate matrix equations within the FDM or FEM.

The accuracy of this method may be controlled more strictly at least qualitatively, as indicated in Fig. 4.35.

With a reasonable amount of computation three-dimensional fields without any symmetry can be handled.

Adequate application of the CSM needs more fundamental knowledge in field computation, as the proper choice of adequate simulation charges is of great importance.

The greatest disadvantages of the CSM is related to multidielectric problems, though the current developments based upon surface changes may greatly improve the method.

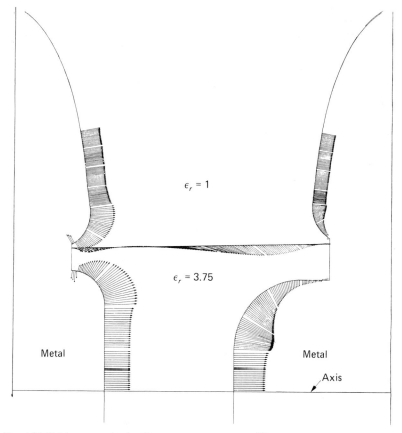

FIG. 4.38. Field computation by CSM with surface charges.[45] Epoxy spacer between parallel plate electrodes.

This section will be concluded with an example of a numerical field computation based upon the CSM with surface simulation charges.[45] Figure 4.38 shows the computed arrangement as well as the essential sections of the fields computed. A cylindrical epoxy spacer ($\varepsilon_r = 3.75$) with recessments is placed between parallel electrodes shaped at the outer parts similar to Bruce's profile, but also recessed to reduce the field intensity at the triple point (gas-solid-electrode interface). Outside the spacer, gas insulation ($\varepsilon_r = 1$) is provided, and the whole system is placed within a cylindrical metal pressure vessel with zero potential, the vessel not being shown. As the diameter of the vessel is large compared with the diameter of the electrode system, for the field calculation zero potential is assumed also in infinite space.

The result of the computation is displayed by a number of field stress arrows starting at the points at which the field intensity is computed. These sites are located at the electrode contours as well as at the interface between gas and dielectric, for which the normal and tangential components of the field intensities are of utmost interest. As the length of each arrow is proportional to the absolute value of the field strength, and the direction of an arrow displays the field direction at each site, these components are directly detectable. No tangential components act at the electrode-dielectric interfaces, and normal components can barely be noted in the upper part of the spacer. This example is taken from an investigation concerning surface charge accumulation at the gas-dielectric interface under a d.c. voltage application. The experimental investigations showed a high accumulation of positive or negative surface charges after applying high d.c. voltages to the electrode for a long time, i.e. up to hours, but the polarity and magnitude of these charges are directly related to this original electrostatic field, i.e. the field before charge is deposited and fixed to the interface.

REFERENCES

1. B. D. Popovic. *Introductory Engineering Electromagnetics*. Addison-Wesley, 1971.
2. D. Vitkovitch. *Field Analysis: Experimental and Computational Methods*. D. Van Nostrand, 1966.
3. P. Moon and D. E. Spencer. *Field Theory for Engineers*. D. Van Nostrand, 1961; *Field Theory Handbook*. Springer, 1961.
4. J. D. Kraus and K. R. Carver. *Electromagnetics* 2nd ed. McGraw-Hill, New York, 1973.
5. F. M. Bruce. Calibration of uniform field spark gaps for high voltage measurements at power frequencies. *Proc. IEE* **94**, Part II (1947), p. 138.

6. H. Prinz. *Hochspannungsfelder*. Oldenbourg, Munich, 1969.
7. H. Steinbigler. Anfangsfeldstaerken und Ausnutzungsfaktoren rotations-symmetrischer Elektrodenanordnungen in Luft. Dr.-Thesis, TH Munich, 1969.
8. T. Takuma, T. Kouno and H. Matsuba. Field behaviour near singular points in composite dielectric arrangements. *Trans. IEEE EI 13* (1978), pp. 426–435.
9. P. Weiss. Fictious peaks and edges in electric fields. *3rd Int. Symp. on High Voltage Engg.*, Milan, 1979, Report 11.21.
10. K. Wechsler and M. Riccitiello. Electric breakdown of a parallel solid and liquid dielectric system. *Trans. AIEE* **80**, Part III (1961), pp. 365–369.
11. E. A. Cherney. High voltage flashover along a solid-liquid interface. Conf. on El. Ins. and Diel. Phenomena, Annual Report 1970, pp. 187–190.
12. H. Kärner and H.-J. Voss. The particle influenced breakdown of insulating surfaces in SF_6 under oscillating switching impulse voltage. 3rd Int. Symp. on High Voltage Engg., Milan, 1979, Report 32.04.
13. H. Okubo, T. Amemiya and M. Honda. Borda's profile and electrical field optimization by using charge simulation method. 3rd Int. Symp. on High Voltage Engg., Milan, 1979, Report 11.16.
14. B. M. Weedy. *Underground Transmission of Electric Power*. J. Wiley, 1980.
15. K. Feser. Bemessung von Elektroden im UHV-Bereich am Beispiel von Toroidelektroden für Spannungsteiler. *ETZ-A* **96** (1975), pp. 207–210.
16. S. Sangkasaad. Dielectric strength of compressed SF_6 in nonuniform fields. Dr.-Thesis, ETH Zurich, No. 5738 (1976).
17. G. W. Carter and S. C. Loh. The calculation of the electric field in a sphere-gap by means of bipolar coordinates. *Proc. IEE* **106C** (1959), pp. 108–111.
18. A. Roth. *Hochspannungstechnik*. 5th ed., Springer-Verlag, Vienna/New York, 1965.
19. H. Singer. Ein Rechenverfahren von Steuerbelaegen in Durchfuehrungen und Kabelendverschluessen. 2nd Int. Symp. on High Voltage Engg., Zurich, 1975, Report 1.1-12.
20. M. D. R. Beasley *et al.* Comparative study of three methods for computing electric fields. *Proc. IEE* **126** (1979), pp. 126–134.
21. G. E. Forsythe and W. R. Wasow. *Finite-Difference Methods for Partial Differential Equations*. John Wiley, 1960.
22. H. Rutishauser. *Vorlesungen über numerische Mathematik. Bd. 2: Differentialgleichungen und Eigenwertprobleme*. Birkhaüser-Verlag, 1976.
23. K. J. Binns and P. J. Lawrenson. *Analysis and Computation of Electric and Magnetic field Problems*, 2nd ed. Pergamon Press, 1973.
24. O. C. Zienkiewicz. *The Finite Element Method in Engineering Science*. McGraw-Hill, London, 1971 (3rd ed. 1977) (in German: *Methode der finiten Elemente*, Carl Hanser, 1975).
25. N. A. Demerdash and T. W. Nehl. An evaluation of the methods of finite elements and finite differences in the solution of nonlinear electromagnetic fields in electrical machines. *Trans. IEEE* **PAS 98** (1979), pp. 74–87.
26. P. Unterweger. Computation of magnetic fields in electrical apparatus. *Trans. IEEE* **PAS 93** (1974), pp. 991–1002.
27. E. F. Fuchs and G. A. McNaughton. Comparison of first-order finite difference and finite element algorithms for the analysis of magnetic fields. Part I: Theoretical analysis, Part II: Numerical results. *Trans. IEEE* **PAS 101** (1982), pp. 1170–1201.
28. W. Janischewskyj and G. Gela. Finite element solution for electric fields of coronating dc transmission lines. *Trans. IEEE* **PAS 98** (1979), pp. 1000–1012.
29. W. Janischewskyj, P. Sarma Maruvada and G. Gela. Corona losses and ionized fields of HVDC transmission lines. CIGRE-Session 1982, Report 36-09.
30. O. W. Andersen. Finite element solution of complex potential electric fields. *Trans. IEEE* **PAS 96** (1977), pp. 1156–1160.

31. W. Thomson (Lord Kelvin). Reprint of *Papers on Electrostatics and Magnetism.* Macmillan, London, 1872.
32. J. C. Maxwell. *A Treatise on Electricity and Magnetism.* 3rd ed. Clarendon Press, Oxford, 1891.
33. H. Steinbigler. Anfangsfeldstaerken und Ausnutzungsfaktoren rotationssymmetrischer Elektrodenanordnungen in Luft. Dr.-Thesis, Techn. Univ. Munich, 1969.
34. H. Singer, H. Steinbigler and P. Weiss. A charge simulation method for the calculation of high voltage fields. *Trans. IEEE* **PAS 93** (1974), pp. 1660–1668.
35. A. Yializis, E. Kuffel and P. H. Alexander. An optimized charge simulation method for the calculation of high voltage fields. *Trans. IEEE* **PAS 97** (1978), pp. 2434–2440.
36. F. Yousef. Ein Verfahren zur genauen Nachbildung und Feldoptimierung von Elektrodensystemen auf der Basis von Ersatzladungen. Dr.-Thesis, Techn. Univ., Aachen, 1982.
37. S. Sato *et al.* Electric field calculation in two-dimensional multiple dielectric by the use of elliptic cylinder charge. 3rd Int. Symp. on High Voltage Engg., Milan, 1979, Report 11.03.
38. S. Sato *et al.* Electric field calculation by charge simulation method using axi-spheroidal charge. 3rd Int. Symp. on High Voltage Engg., Milan, 1979, Report 11.07.
39. H. Singer. Numerische Feldberechnung mit Hilfe von Multipolen. *Arch. f. Elektrot.* **59** (1977), pp. 191–195.
40. H. Singer. Feldberechnung mit Oberflächenleitschichten und Volumenfähigkeit. *ETZ Archiv* **3** (1981), pp. 265–267.
41. H. Singer and P. Grafoner. Optimization of electrode and insulator contours. 2nd Int. Symp. on High Voltage Engg., Zurich, 1975, Report 1.3-03, pp. 111–116.
42. D. Metz. Optimization of high voltage fields. 3rd Int. Symp. on High Voltage Engg., Milan, 1979, Report 11.12.
43. H. Singer. Flächenladungen zur Feldberechnung von Hochspannungssystemen. *Bull. SEV* **65** (1974), pp. 739–746.
44. J. H. McWhirter and J. J. Oravec. Three-dimensional electrostatic field solutions in a rod gap by a Fredholm integral equation. 3rd Int. Symp. on High Voltage Engg., Milan, 1979, Report 11.14.
45. S. Sato *et al.* High speed charge simulation method. *Trans. IEE Japan*, **101** A (1981), pp. 1–8 (in Japanese).
46. A. Knecht. Development of surface charges on epoxy resin spacers stressed with direct applied voltages. *Proc. 3rd Int. Symp. on Gaseous Diel.*, Knoxville, 1982. (Gaseous Dielectrics III, 1982, pp. 356–364.)

Chapter 5

ELECTRICAL BREAKDOWN IN GASES, SOLIDS AND LIQUIDS

Before proceeding to discuss breakdown in gases it is appropriate to review these fundamental principles of kinetic theory of gases which are pertinent to the study of gaseous ionization and breakdown. A brief review of the classical gas laws will therefore be presented, followed by the ionization and decay processes which lead to conduction of current through a gas and ultimately to a complete breakdown or spark formation.

5.1 CLASSICAL GAS LAWS

In the absence of electric or magnetic fields charged particles in weakly ionized gases participate in molecular collisions. Their motions follow closely the classical kinetic gas theory.

The oldest gas law established experimentally by Boyle and Mariotte states that for a given amount of enclosed gas at a constant temperature the product of pressure (p) and volume (V) is constant or

$$pV = C = \text{const.} \tag{5.1}$$

In the same system, if the pressure is kept constant, then the volumes V and V_0 are related to their absolute temperatures T and T_0 (in $^\circ$K) by Gay-Lussac's Law:

$$\frac{V}{V_0} = \frac{T}{T_0}. \tag{5.2}$$

When temperatures are expressed in degrees Celsius, eqn. (5.2) becomes

$$\frac{V}{V_0} = \frac{273 + \theta}{273}.$$ (5.3)

Equation (5.3) suggests that as we approach $\theta = -273°C$ the volume of gas shrinks to zero. In reality, all gases liquefy before reaching this value.

According to eqn. (5.2) the constant C in eqn. (5.1) is related to a given temperature T_0 for the volume V_0:

$$pV_0 = C_0.$$ (5.4)

Substituting V_0 from eqn. (5.2) gives

$$pV = \left(\frac{C_0}{T_0}\right)T.$$ (5.5)

The ratio (C_0/T_0) is called the universal gas constant and is denoted by R. Equation (5.5) then becomes

$$pV = RT = C.$$ (5.6)

Numerically R is equal to 8.314 joules/°K mol. If we take the mass of the gas in the system considered equal to 1 kilogram molecule (1 kilomole), then for the general case eqn. (5.1) takes the form

$$pV = nC = nRT,$$ (5.7)

where n is the number of kilomoles of gas. Equation (5.7) then describes the state of an ideal gas, since we assumed that R is a constant independent of the nature of the gas. Equation (5.7) may be written in terms of gas density N in volume V containing N_1 molecules. Putting $N = N_0$ where $N_0 = 6.02 \times 10^{23}$ molecules/mole, N_0 is known as the Avogadro's number. Then eqn. (5.7) becomes

$$\frac{N_1}{V} = N = \frac{N_0}{R}\frac{p}{T}$$

or

$$p = N\frac{R}{N_0}T = NkT.$$ (5.8)

The constant $k = R/N_0$ is the universal Boltzmann's constant ($= 1.3804 \times 10^{-23}$ joules/°K).

If two gases with initial volumes V_1 and V_2 are combined at the same temperature and pressure, then the new volume will be given by

$$V = V_1 + V_2$$

or in general

$$V = V_1 + V_2 + \ldots V_n. \qquad (5.9)$$

Combining eqns. (5.7) and (5.9) gives

$$V = \frac{n_1 RT}{p} + \frac{n_2 RT}{p} + \ldots + \frac{n_n RT}{p}$$

rearranging

$$p = \frac{n_1 RT}{V} + \frac{n_2 RT}{V} + \ldots + \frac{n_n RT}{V}$$

or

$$p = p_1 + p_2 + \ldots p_n \qquad (5.10)$$

where $p_1, p_2 \ldots p_n$ denote the partial pressures of gases $1, 2 \ldots n$. Equation (5.10) is generally referred to as the law of partial pressures.

Equations (5.1) to (5.10) can be derived directly from the kinetic theory of gases developed by Maxwell in the middle of last century. A brief derivation will be presented.

The fundamental equation for the kinetic theory of gas is derived with the following assumed conditions:

1. Gas consists of molecules of the same mass which are assumed spheres.
2. Molecules are in continuous random motion.
3. Collisions are elastic—simple mechanical.
4. Mean distance between molecules is much greater than their diameter.
5. Forces between molecules and the walls of the container are negligible.

Consider a cubical container of side $l = 1$ m as shown in Fig. 5.1 with N_1 molecules, each of mass m and r.m.s. velocity u. Let us resolve the velocity into components, u_x, u_y, u_z where $u^2 = u_x^2 + u_y^2 + u_z^2$. Suppose a molecule of mass m is moving in the x-direction with velocity u_x. As it strikes the wall of container plane YZ it rebounces the velocity $-u_x$. The change in

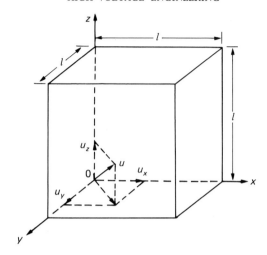

Fig. 5.1. Resolution of molecular forces.

momentum, therefore, is

$$\Delta m = mu_x - (-mu_x) = 2mu_x.$$

For the cube of side l the number of collisions per second with the right-hand wall is $u_x/2l$, therefore

$$\Delta m/\text{sec}/\text{molecule} = \frac{2mu_x u_x}{2l} = \frac{mu_x^2}{l},$$

but the same molecule will experience the same change in momentum at opposite wall. Hence $\Delta m/\text{sec}/\text{molecule}$ in the x-direction $= 2mu_x^2/l$. For the three-dimensional cube with total change in momentum per second per molecule (which is the force) we obtain the force per particle as

$$F = \frac{2m}{l}(u_x^2 + u_y^2 + u_z^2) = \frac{2mu^2}{l}. \tag{5.11}$$

As kinetic energy for a particle $W = \frac{1}{2}mu^2$, therefore,

$$F = 4\frac{W}{l}.$$

For N_1 particles the energy due to different velocities u of particles will become the mean energy, and therefore

$$F = 4\frac{N_1\bar{W}}{l}.$$

Force leads to pressure p, taking into account the total area of the cube $(A = 6l^2)$

$$p = \frac{F}{A} = \frac{4N_1\bar{W}}{6l\cdot l^2} = \frac{2}{3}\frac{N_1\bar{W}}{l^3} \tag{5.12}$$

with $l^3 = V$ = volume. Comparing eqns. (5.8) and (5.12) leads to:

$$pV = \tfrac{2}{3}N_1\bar{W}.$$

Comparing eqn. (5.12) with eqn. (5.1) we note that these equations are identical for constant temperature. Using eqn. (5.8) gives

$$p = \frac{2}{3}\frac{N_1}{V}\bar{W} = \frac{2}{3}N\bar{W} = NkT$$

which leads to the expression for mean energy per molecule:

$$\bar{W} = \tfrac{3}{2}kT. \tag{5.13}$$

Velocity Distribution of a Swarm of Molecules

It has been shown using probability consideration that the distribution of molecular velocities depends both on the temperature and the molecular weight of the gas. The mathematical analysis shows the most probable velocity is neither the average nor the r.m.s. velocity of all the molecules.

The velocity u of gas molecules or particles has a statistical distribution and follows the Boltzmann–Maxwell distribution given by the expression[1]*

$$f(u) = \frac{dN_u}{N} = \frac{4}{\sqrt{\pi}}\left(\frac{u}{u_p}\right)^2 [e^{(-u/u_p)^2}]\frac{du}{u_p}. \tag{5.14}$$

where u_p is the most probable velocity and dN_u/N the relative number of particles whose instantaneous velocities lie in the range u/u_p and $(u+du)/u_p$.

*Superscript numbers are to References at the end of the chapter.

Let

$$f\left(\frac{u}{u_p}\right) = \frac{dN_u}{N} \bigg/ \frac{du}{u_p}$$

and

$$u_r = \frac{u}{u_p} \text{ (relative velocity).}$$

Introducing this dimensionless variable into eqn. (5.14) gives the function representing velocity distribution

$$f(u_r) = \frac{4}{\sqrt{\pi}} u_r^2 \, e^{-u_r^2} \tag{5.14a}$$

with

$$\frac{dN_u}{N} = f(u_r) \, du_r.$$

The distribution function corresponding to eqn. (5.14a) is shown in Fig. 5.2. It should be noted that the function is assymetrical about the most probable velocity u_p. A greater number of particles has a velocity higher than u_p. The average velocity $\bar{u}$ is obtained from integrating u_r from 0 to ∞.

$$\bar{u}_r = \int_{u_r=0}^{\infty} u_r f(u_r) \, du_r = \frac{4}{\sqrt{\pi}} \underbrace{\int_0^{\infty} u_r^3 \, e^{-u_r^2} \, du_r}_{1/2} = \frac{2}{\sqrt{\pi}};$$

or

$$\bar{u} = \bar{u}_r u_p = 1.128 u_p. \tag{5.15}$$

The r.m.s. or effective value of velocity is obtained by squaring u_r and obtaining the average square value

$$(u_r)_{\text{eff}}^2 = \int_{u_r=0}^{\infty} u_r^2 f(u_r) \, du_r = \frac{4}{\sqrt{\pi}} \underbrace{\int_0^{\infty} u_r^4 \, e^{-u_r^2} \, du_r}_{3/8\sqrt{\pi}} = \frac{3}{2}$$

$$u_{\text{eff}} = u_{r\text{eff}} u_p = \sqrt{\tfrac{3}{2}} u_p = 1.224 u_p. \tag{5.16}$$

The mean kinetic energy of the particle given by eqn. (5.13) relates its

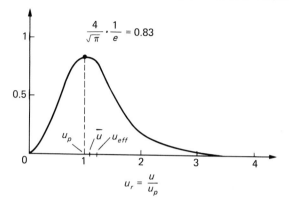

FIG. 5.2. Distribution of velocities (u_p most probable; $\bar{u}$ average; u_{eff} effective of r.m.s.).

effective velocity to the temperature ($\frac{1}{2}mu_{\text{eff}}^2 = \frac{3}{2}kT$) and we obtain

$$u_{\text{eff}} = \sqrt{\frac{3kT}{m}}; \quad \bar{u} = \sqrt{\frac{8kT}{\pi m}}; \quad u_p = \sqrt{\frac{2KT}{m}}. \tag{5.17}$$

Hence the respective velocities remain in the ratio $u_p : \bar{u} : u_{\text{eff}} = 1 : 1.128 : 1.224$.

It should be noted that the foregoing considerations apply only when the molecules or particles remain in thermal equilibrium, and in the absence of particle acceleration by external fields, diffusion, etc. If the gas contains electrons or ions or other atoms that are at the same temperature, the average particle energy of such mixture is

$$\frac{1}{2}mu_{\text{eff}}^2 = \frac{1}{2}m_e u_{e\text{eff}}^2 = \frac{1}{2}m_i u_{i\text{eff}}^2 = \ldots = \frac{3}{2}kT \tag{5.18}$$

where m, m_i, m_e are the respective masses of gas molecules, ions, electron, and u_{eff}, $u_{i\text{eff}}$, $u_{e\text{eff}}$ are their corresponding velocities.

The values of the mean molecular velocities calculated for 20°C and 760 Torr for several of the common gases are included in Table 5.1.

TABLE 5.1
Mean Molecular Velocities at 20°C and 760 Torr[2]

Gas	Electron	H_2	O_2	N_2	Air	CO_2	H_2O (vapour)	SF_6
$\bar{u}$ (m/sec)	100×10^3	1760	441	470	465	375	556	199

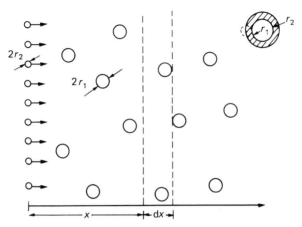

FIG. 5.3. Model for determining free paths.

The Free Path λ of Molecules and Electrons

Knowledge of dependency and distribution of free paths (λ) may explain (with restrictions) dependency of $\alpha = f(E, N)$ discussed later, even assuming a simple "ballistic" model. For this reason a short treatment of free paths will be presented. The free path (λ) is defined as the distance molecules or particles travel between collisions. The free path is a random quantity and as we shall see its mean value depends upon the concentration of particles or the density of the gas.

To derive the mean free path $(\bar{\lambda})$ assume an assembly of stationary molecules of radius r_1, and a moving layer of smaller particles of radius r_2 as shown in Fig. 5.3. As the smaller particles move, their density will decrease due to scattering caused by collisions with gas molecules. If we assume that the moving particles and molecules behave as solid spheres, then a collision will occur every time the centres of two particles come within a distance $r_1 + r_2$. The area for collision presented by a molecule is then $\pi(r_1 + r_2)^2$ and in a unit volume it is $N\pi(r_1 + r_2)^2$. This is often called the effective area for interception where N = number of particles per unit volume of gas.

If we consider a layer of thickness dx, distant x from the origin (Fig. 5.3) and $n(x)$ the number of particles that survived the distance x, then the decrease in the moving particles due to scattering in layer dx is

$$dn = -n(x)N\pi(r_1 + r_2)^2 \, dx.$$

Assuming the number of particles entering (at $x = 0$) is n_0, integration gives

$$n(x) = n_0 \, e^{-N\pi(r_1 + r_2)^2 x}. \tag{5.19}$$

The probability of free path of length x is equal to the probability of collisions between x and $x + dx$. The mean free path $\bar{\lambda} = \bar{x}$ is obtained as follows. Differentiating eqn. (5.19) we obtain

$$f(x) = \frac{dn}{n_0} = N\pi(r_1 + r_2)^2 \, e^{-N\pi(r_1 + r_2)^2 x} \, dx.$$

For the mean free path

$$\bar{x} = \bar{\lambda} = \int_{x=0}^{\infty} x f(x) \, dx$$

$$= N\pi(r_1 + r_2)^2 \int_{x=0}^{\infty} x \, e^{-N\pi(r_1 + r_2)^2 x} \, dx$$

$$= \frac{1}{N\pi(r_1 + r_2)^2}. \tag{5.20}$$

The denominator in eqn. (5.20) has the dimensions of area and the value $\pi(r_1 + r_2)^2$ is usually called the cross-section for interception or simply collision cross-section and is denoted by σ:

$$\sigma = \frac{1}{N\bar{\lambda}}. \tag{5.21}$$

We shall see later that the collisions between the incoming particles and the stationary molecules may lead to processes such as ionization, excitation, attachment, etc.

If we put in eqn. (5.21) $Q = N\sigma$, then Q will represent the effective cross-section presented by molecules or particles in unit volume of gas for all collisions for density of N molecules/volume. If, for example, only a fraction P_i of collisions between the incoming particles and the gas particles leads to ionization then P_i is the probability of ionization. Thus if only ionizing collisions are counted, the molecules present an effective area of only $P_iQ = Q_i$; Q_i is the effective cross-section for ionization. Similarly for other processes, excitation (Q_e), photoionization Q_{ph} attachment (Q_a), etc., including elastic collisions

$$Q = Q_{\text{elastic}} + Q_i + Q_e + Q_a + \dots \tag{5.22}$$

Atomic cross-sections (σ) for different processes vary over a wide range. For ionization they can rise to some 2×10^{-16} cm^2, but for collisions resulting in nuclear reactions they may be 10^{-24} cm^2 or less.

In deriving the expression (5.20) it was assumed that the struck molecules were stationary, i.e. the molecules of gas 2 had no thermal velocity. In reality this is not true. It can be shown that the expression giving the collisional cross-section must be still multiplied by a factor

$$\eta = \sqrt{1 + \frac{m_1}{m_2}}$$

with m_1 and m_2 the mass of each gas component. In a gas mixture the collisional cross-section of particles of type 1 of gas (m_1, r_1, N_1) becomes equal to the sum of all collisional cross-sections of the other particles of types of gas $(m_2, m_3, \ldots, r_2, r_3, \ldots, N_2, N_3, \ldots)$. Thus the mean free path of particles of type 1 is

$$\bar{\lambda}_1 = \frac{1}{\pi \sum\limits_{i=1}^{n} N_i (r_1 + r_i)^2 \sqrt{1 + \frac{m_1}{m_i}}} \qquad (5.23)$$

For an atom in its own gas $r_1 = r_2 = r$; $u_1 = u_2$. Then

$$\bar{\lambda}_a = \frac{1}{4\sqrt{2}\pi r^2 N}. \qquad (5.24)$$

For an electron in a gas $r_1 \ll r_2$ and $m_1 \ll m_2$ eqn. (5.23) gives

$$\bar{\lambda}_e = \frac{1}{\pi r_2^2 N} \qquad (5.25)$$

or

$$\bar{\lambda}_e = 4\sqrt{2}\bar{\lambda}_a = 5.66\bar{\lambda}_a. \qquad (5.25)$$

Table 5.2 shows examples of mean free path (gas) for gases of different molecular weight.

From eqn. (5.8), $N = p/kT$, it follows that the mean free path is directly proportional to temperature and inversely as the gas pressure

$$\lambda(p, T) = \lambda_0 \frac{p_0}{p} \frac{T}{T_0}. \qquad (5.26)$$

TABLE 5.2
Mean Free Paths Measured at 15°C and 760 Torr[2]

Type of gas	H_2	O_2	N_2	CO_2	H_2O	Dimensions
λ	11.77	6.79	6.28	4.19	4.18	10^{-8} m
Molecular weight	2.016	32.00	28.020	44.00	18.00	

Considering a typical practical case with values for average velocity of gas $\bar{u} \approx 500$ m/sec and the mean free path $\bar{\lambda} \approx 10^{-7}$ m we obtain the number of collisions per second:

$$v = \frac{\bar{u}}{\bar{\lambda}} = 5 \times 10^9 \frac{1}{\text{sec}} \approx 5 \text{ collisions/nsec.}$$

The average time between two collisions

$$\Delta t = \frac{1}{v} = \frac{1}{5 \times 10^9} = 0.2 \text{ nsec.}$$

Distribution of Free Paths

In the earlier sections it was shown that molecular collisions are random events and these determine free paths. Hence, free path is a random quantity and will have a distribution about a mean value. For the system in Fig. 5.3 the mean free path is given by eqn. (5.20)

$$\bar{\lambda} = \frac{1}{N\pi(r_1 + r_2)^2},$$

N being the gas density, r_1 and r_2 the radii of the two types of particles.
The distribution function of free paths is obtained from eqn. (5.19)

$$\int_{n_0}^{n} dn = -\int_{x=0}^{x} \ln \frac{dx}{\bar{\lambda}}$$

or

$$n(x) = n_0 \, e^{-x/\bar{\lambda}} \tag{5.27}$$

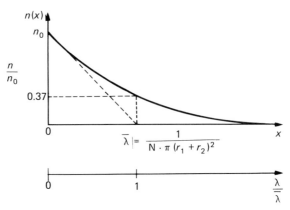

FIG. 5.4. Distribution of free paths.

where $n(x)$ = number of molecules reaching a distance x without collision, dn = number of molecules colliding thereafter within a distance dx, n_0 = total number of molecules just after collision. Equation (5.27) is plotted in Fig. 5.4.

It is seen that the percentage of molecules that survive collisions at $\lambda = \bar{\lambda}$ is only 37%. The exponent in eqn. (5.27) may also be written in terms of collision cross-sections defined by eqn. (5.21), to represent absorption or decay of particles along the path x or

$$n = n_0\, e^{-N\sigma x} \tag{5.28}$$

where σ may include photoabsorption, attachment, etc.

Collision—Energy Transfer

The collisions between gas particles are of two types: (i) elastic or simple mechanical collisions in which the energy exchange is always kinetic, and (ii) inelastic in which some of the kinetic energy of the colliding particles is transferred into potential energy of the struck particle or vice versa. Examples of the second type of collisions include excitation, ionization, attachment, etc., which will be discussed later.

To derive an expression for energy transfer between two colliding particles, let us consider first the case of an elastic collision between two particles[2] of masses m and M. Assume that before collision the particle of

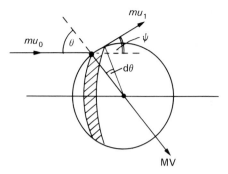

FIG. 5.5. Energy transfer during elastic collision.

large mass M was at rest and the velocity of the smaller particle was u_0 in the direction shown in Fig. 5.5. After collision let the corresponding velocities be u_1 and V the latter along line of centres as shown. θ is the incidence angle and ϕ the scattering angle.

The fractional energy loss by the incoming particle during a collision at an angle θ is then given by

$$\Delta(\theta) = \left(\frac{u_0^2 - u_1^2}{u_0^2}\right). \tag{5.29}$$

Since the collision is assumed to be kinetic, the equations for conservation of momentum and energy are

$$mu_0 - mu_1 \cos\phi = MV \cos\theta \tag{5.30}$$

$$mu_1 \sin\phi = MV \sin\theta \tag{5.31}$$

$$\tfrac{1}{2}mu_0^2 - \tfrac{1}{2}mu_1^2 = \tfrac{1}{2}MV^2. \tag{5.32}$$

Squaring eqns. (5.30) and (5.31) and adding and combining with eqn. (5.32) we obtain

$$V = \frac{2mu_0 \cos\theta}{M+m}.$$

Rearranging eqn. (5.32) and combining with eqn. (5.29) gives

$$\Delta(\theta) = \frac{MV^2}{mu_0^2} = \frac{4mM \cos^2\theta}{(m+M)^2}. \tag{5.33}$$

To obtain the mean fractional energy loss per collision, let $P(\theta)$ be the probability of a collision at an angle of incidence between θ and $\theta + d\theta$. The total area presented for collision is $\pi(r_1 + r_2)^2$. The probability of a collision taking place between θ and $\theta + d\theta$ is the ratio of the projected area (Fig. 5.5) to the whole area or

$$P(\theta)\,d\theta = \begin{cases} \dfrac{2\pi(r_1+r_2)^2 \sin\theta \cos\theta \, d\theta}{\pi(r_1+r_2)^2} = \sin 2\theta \, d\theta & \begin{cases} \text{for } 0 \leqslant \theta \\ \text{for } \pi/2 \leqslant \theta \leqslant \pi \end{cases} \end{cases}.$$

The mean fractional loss of energy per collision allowing for collisions at all angles is

$$\overline{\Delta(\theta)} = \int_0^{\pi/2} P(\theta)\Delta(\theta)\,d\theta \Big/ \int_0^{\pi/2} P(\theta)\,d\theta. \tag{5.34}$$

Using eqns. (5.33) and (5.34), we obtain

$$\overline{\Delta(\theta)} = \frac{2mM}{(m+M)^2}. \tag{5.35}$$

If we consider the case when the incoming particle is an ion of the same mass as the struck particle, then $m = M$ and eqn. (5.35) gives $\overline{\Delta(\theta)} = \frac{1}{2}$, which indicates a high rate of energy loss in each elastic collision. On the other hand, if the incoming particle is an electron, then $m \ll M$ and eqn. (5.35) gives $\overline{\Delta(\theta)} = 2m/M$. The average fraction of energy lost by an electron in an elastic collision is therefore very small. For example, if we consider the case of electrons colliding with He gas atoms, the average fractional energy loss per collision $\overline{\Delta(\theta)}$ is 2.7×10^{-4} and in argon it is 2.7×10^{-5}. Thus electrons will not readily lose energy in elastic collisions whereas ions will.

Let us now consider the case when part of the kinetic energy of the incoming particle is converted into potential energy of the struck particle. Then applying the laws of energy and momentum conservation we obtain

$$\tfrac{1}{2}mu_0^2 = \tfrac{1}{2}mu_1^2 + \tfrac{1}{2}MV^2 + W_p \tag{5.36}$$

$$mu_0 = mu_1 + MV \tag{5.37}$$

where W_p is the increase in potential energy of the particle of mass M initially at rest. Substituting eqn. (5.37) into eqn. (5.36) and rearranging we obtain

$$W_p = \frac{1}{2}\left[m(u_0^2 - u_1^2) - \frac{m^2}{M}(u_0 - u_1)^2 \right]. \tag{5.38}$$

For the conditions of constant kinetic energy of the incoming particles, differentiation of eqn. (5.38) with respect to u_1 gives the maximum energy transfer when

$$\frac{dW_{pmax}}{du} = 0$$

or

$$\frac{u_1}{u_0} = \frac{m}{m+M}. \tag{5.39}$$

Equation (5.39) shows that the potential energy gained from the incident particle reaches a maximum value when the ratio of its final to initial velocity equals the ratio of its mass to the sum of masses of the individual particles.

When the colliding particles are identical, the maximum kinetic to potential energy transfer occurs when $u_1 = u_0/2$. On the other hand, if the colliding particle is an electron of mass $m \ll M$ the maximum energy transfer corresponds to $u_1 - (m/M)u_0$ which means that the new velocity u_1 becomes only a small fraction of the original velocity.

For the case when the target particle was initially at rest, the maximum amount of potential energy gained will be given by the expression obtained by inserting the value of velocity u_1 from eqn. (5.39) into eqn. (5.38) or

$$W_{pmax} = \frac{M}{m+M} \frac{mu_0^2}{2}. \tag{5.40}$$

For an electron $m \ll M$, eqn. (5.40) becomes

$$W_{pmax} \cong \tfrac{1}{2}mu_0^2 \tag{5.41}$$

or almost all its kinetic energy is converted into potential energy. Thus we shall see later that electrons are good ionizers of gas, while ions are not. To cause ionization the incoming electron must have a kinetic energy of at least $\tfrac{1}{2}mu_0^2 \geqslant eV_i$ where V_i is the ionization potential of the atom or molecule.

5.2. IONIZATION AND DECAY PROCESSES

At normal temperature and pressure gases are excellent insulators. The conduction in air at low field is in the region 10^{-16}–10^{-17} A/cm^2.[*] This

---

[*] The figure 10^{-16}–10^{-17} A correlates with the current flowing to the whole surface of earth (due to natural electric field). This current is 1000–1200 A. With earth surface of about 5×10^{19} cm^2, we get

$$j = \frac{I}{\text{surface}} = \frac{1000}{5 \times 10^{19}} = 0.2 \times 10^{-16} \text{ A/cm}^2.$$

current results from cosmic radiations and radioactive substances present in earth and the atmosphere. At higher fields charged particles may gain sufficient energy between collisions to cause ionization on impact with neutral molecules. It was shown in the previous section that electrons on the average lose little energy in elastic collisions and readily build up their kinetic energy which may be supplied by an external source, e.g. an applied field. On the other hand, during elastic collisions a large fraction of their kinetic energy is transferred into potential energy, causing, for example, ionization of the struck molecule. Ionization by electron impact is for higher field strength the most important process leading to breakdown of gases. The effectiveness of ionization by electron impact depends upon the energy that an electron can gain along the mean free path in direction of field.

If $\bar{\lambda}_e$ is the mean free path in field direction of strength E then the average energy gained over a distance $\bar{\lambda}$ is $\Delta W = eE\bar{\lambda}_e$. This quantity is proportional to E/p since $\bar{\lambda}_e \propto 1/p$ [eqn. (5.26)]. To cause ionization on impact the energy ΔW must be at least equal to the ionization energy of the molecule (eV_i). Electrons with lower energy than eV_i may excite particles and the excited particles on collision with electrons of low energy may become ionized. Furthermore, not all electrons having gained energy $\Delta W \geqslant eV_i$

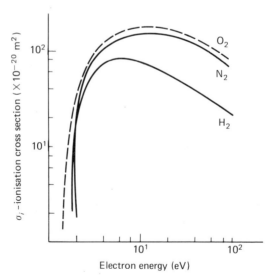

FIG. 5.6. Variation of ionization cross-sections for O_2, N_2, H_2 with electron energy.

upon collision will cause ionization. This simple model is not applicable for quantitative calculations, because ionization by collision, as are all other processes in gas discharges, is a probability phenomenon, and is generally expressed in terms of cross-section for ionization defined as the product $P_i\sigma$ $= \sigma_i$ where P_i is the probability of ionization on impact and σ is the molecular or atomic cross-sectional area for interception defined earlier. The cross-section σ_i is measured using monoenergetic electron beams of different energy. The variation of ionization cross-sections for H_2, O_2 and N_2 with electron energy is shown in Fig. 5.6.[3] It is seen that the cross-section is strongly dependent upon the electron energy. At energies below ionization potential the collision may lead to excitation of the struck atom or molecule which on collision with another slow moving electron may become ionized. This process becomes significant only when densities of electrons are high. Very fast moving electrons may pass near an atom without ejecting an electron from it. For every gas there exists an optimum electron energy range which gives a maximum ionization probability.

Townsend First Ionization Coefficient

In the absence of electric field the rate of electron and positive ion generation in an ordinary gas is counterbalanced by decay processes and a state of equilibrium exists. This state of equilibrium will be upset upon the application of a sufficiently high field. The variation of the gas current measured between two parallel plate electrodes was first studied as function of the applied voltage by Townsend.[4]

Townsend found that the current at first increased proportionately with the applied voltage and then remained nearly constant at a value i_0 which corresponded to the background current (saturation current), or if the cathode was irradiated with an u.v. light, i_0 gave the emitted photocurrent. At still higher voltage the current increased above the value i_0 at an exponential rate. The general pattern of the current–voltage relationship is shown schematically in Fig. 5.7.

The increase in current beyond V_2 Townsend ascribed to ionization of the gas by electron collision. As the field increases, electrons leaving the cathode are accelerated more and more between collisions until they gain enough energy to cause ionization on collision with gas molecules or atoms.

To explain this current increase Townsend introduced a quantity α,

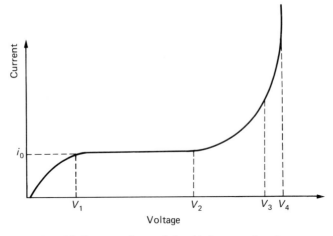

Fig. 5.7. Current–voltage relationship in prespark region.

known as Townsend's first ionization coefficient, defined as the number of electrons produced by an electron per unit length of path in the direction of the field.

Thus if we assume that n is the number of electrons at a distance x from the cathode in field direction (Fig. 5.8) the increase in electrons dn in additional distance dx is given by

$$dn = \alpha n \, dx.$$

Integration over the distance (d) from cathode to anode gives

$$n = n_0 \, e^{\alpha d} \qquad (5.42)$$

where n_0 is the number of primary electrons generated at the cathode. In terms of current, with I_0 the current leaving the cathode, eqn. (5.42)

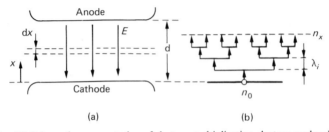

(a)   (b)

Fig. 5.8. Schematic representation of electron multiplication electron avalanche.

becomes

$$I = I_0 \, e^{\alpha d}.$$ (5.43)

The term $e^{\alpha d}$ in eqn. (5.42) is called the electron avalanche and it represents the number of electrons produced by one electron in travelling from cathode to anode. The electron multiplication within the avalanche is shown diagrammatically in Fig. 5.8.

The increase of current (avalanche growth) shown in the diagram (Fig. 5.8(b)) would be $I = I_0 \, e^k$, with $k = $ number of ionizing steps ($k = x/\lambda_i$). The transition for infinitely small values of

$$dx \left(\begin{array}{c} \lim \lambda_i \\ \lambda_i \to dx \end{array} \right)$$

leads to the expression $e^{\alpha x}$.

The quantity α, although a basic quantity describing the rate of ionization by electron collision, cannot be readily calculated from the measured cross-section for ionization (σ_i). The latter is determined for monoenergetic electrons and calculation of α from value of σ_i is only possible when the electron energy distribution in the gas is known. For "swarm" conditions Raether[5] derived a relationship between α, σ_i, which is of the form

$$\frac{\alpha}{N} = \frac{1}{W_e} \int_0^\infty v\sigma_i(v)f(v) \, dv$$

with N the concentration, molecules/atoms, $f(v_{th})$ the distribution of velocities of electrons, and W_e the drift velocity of electrons in the field direction. A simple derivation is possible for simple gases (non-attaching) using the Clausius distribution of free paths (Fig. 5.4) and applying it to electrons.

We have seen that at a constant temperature for a given gas the energy distribution ΔW depends only on the value E/p. Also for a given energy distribution the probability of an ionization occurring will depend on the gas density or pressure.

Therefore, we can write

$$\alpha = pf\left(\frac{E}{p}\right)$$

or

$$\frac{\alpha}{p} = f\left(\frac{E}{p}\right). \tag{5.44}$$

Equation (5.44) describes a general dependence of α/p upon E/p which has been confirmed experimentally.

A derivation of expression for this dependence is possible for simple gases, using the Clausius distribution [eqn. (5.27)] for free paths applied to electrons. This means that we assume that this distribution will not be altered by the additional velocity of electrons in field direction. Then all electrons which acquire energy $\Delta W \geqslant eV_i$, where V_i is the ionization potential, will ionize the gas. These electrons have travelled a distance x, and using eqn. (5.27) the fraction of electrons with paths exceeding a given value x is

$$f'(x) = e^{-x/\bar{\lambda}}.$$

Therefore, only with a very small probability electrons can gain high energies if they reach long distances.

The number of successful collisions—the ionization coefficient α—is clearly related to this distribution, and is certainly directly proportional to the decay of collisions in the intervals between x and $(x + dx)$, or

$$\alpha = \frac{df'(x)}{dx} = \frac{1}{\bar{\lambda}} e^{-(\lambda_i/\bar{\lambda})} \tag{5.44a}$$

where $\lambda_i = x$ is the ionizing free path. The above treatment assumes $\bar{\lambda}_E = \bar{\lambda}$, i.e. the velocity distribution is not altered by the additional velocity of electrons in the field direction. In reality there is a difference between $\bar{\lambda}$ and $\bar{\lambda}_E$ as shown below.

Hence

$$\frac{\bar{v}}{\bar{\lambda}} = \frac{v}{\lambda_E} \quad \text{and} \quad \bar{\lambda}_E = \frac{1}{n_E}$$

v being the electron drift velocity.

Then eqn. (5.44) when corrected for field drift velocity becomes

$$\alpha = n_E \, e^{-\lambda_i/\bar{\lambda}_E} = \frac{1}{\bar{\lambda}_E} \, e^{-\lambda_i/\bar{\lambda}_E} \ldots \tag{5.45}$$

Using eqn. (5.21), with σ_i as true cross-section for ionization and N the gas density, we obtain

$$\bar{\lambda} = \frac{1}{N\sigma_i}.$$

Introducing from eqn. (5.8) $N = p/kT$, for a gas pressure p the mean free path becomes

$$\bar{\lambda} = \frac{kT}{p\sigma_i}.$$

If in addition we put $\lambda_i = V_i/E$, then

$$\alpha = \frac{df'(x)}{dx} = \frac{p\sigma_i}{kT} \, e^{-(V_i/E)(p\sigma_i/kT)}, \tag{5.46}$$

or

$$\frac{\alpha}{p} = \frac{\sigma_i}{kT} \, e^{-(\sigma_i/kT)[V_i/(E/p)]} = A_{(T)} \, e^{-[B_{(T)}/(E/p)]} \tag{5.47}$$

where

$$A_{(T)} = \frac{\sigma_i}{kT}; \quad B_{(T)} = \frac{V_i\sigma_i}{kT}. \tag{5.47a}$$

It cannot be expected that the real dependence of α/p upon E/p agrees with measured values within the whole range of E/p, because phenomena which have not been taken into account are influencing the ionization rate. However, even with constant values of A and B, eqn. (5.47) determines the ionization process within certain ranges of E/p. Therefore, for various gases the "constants" A and B have been determined experimentally and can be found in the literature.[6]

Some of these experimental values for several of the more common gases are listed in Table 5.3.

The constants A and B in eqn. (5.47a), as derived from kinetic theory,

TABLE 5.3
Ionization Constants A and B (T = 20°C)

Gas	A ion pairs cm^{-1} $Torr^{-1}$	B $V\ cm^{-1}$ $Torr^{-1}$	E/p range $V\ cm^{-1}\ Torr^{-1}$	V_i volts
H_2	5	130	150–600	15.4
N_2	12	342	100–600	15.5
air	15	365	100–800	—
CO_2	20	466	500–1000	12.6
He	3	34	20–150	24.5
Hg	20	370	200–600	—

rarely agree with the experimentally determined values. The reasons for this disagreement lies in the assumptions made in our derivations. We assumed that every electron whose energy exceeds eV_i will automatically lead to ionization. In reality the probability of ionization for electrons with energy just above the ionization threshold is small and it rises slowly to a maximum value of about 0.5 at 4 to 6 times the ionization energy. Beyond that it decreases. We have also assumed that the mean free path is independent of electron energy which is not necessarily true. A rigorous treatment would require taking account of the dependence of the ionization cross-section upon the electron energy.

Using the experimental values for the constants A and B for N_2 and H_2 in

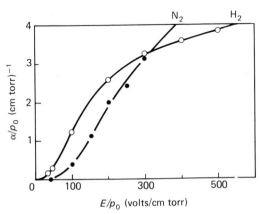

FIG. 5.9. Dependence of α/p on E/p in N_2 and H_2, reduced to 0°C.

eqn. (5.47), the graphical relationship between the parameters α/p and E/p has been plotted in Fig. 5.9. The values have been corrected to $T = 0°C$.

It should be noted that theoretically α/p begins at zero value of E/p, which follows from the distribution of free paths which have values from 0 to ∞. In practice in many gases attachment η will also be present, and at low values of E/p it is difficult to obtain the values for "real" α and for "real" η. Experimental measurements yield the "effective" ionization coefficient $(\bar{\alpha} = \alpha - \eta)$. In this case $\bar{\alpha}p$ begins at a finite value of E/p corresponding to the lowest breakdown strength.

Numerous measurements of α in various gases have been made by Townsend[4] and subsequent workers and the data can be found in the literature.[7–9] The Geballe and Harrison's data are included in Table 5.5.

Photoionization

Electrons of lower energy than the ionization energy eV_i may on collision excite the gas atoms to higher states. The reaction may be symbolically represented as $A + e + K$ energy $\rightarrow A^* + e$; $A^* \rightarrow A + hv$; A^* represents the atom in an excited state. On recovering from the excited state in some 10^{-7}–10^{-10} sec, the atom radiates a quantum of energy of photon (hv) which in turn may ionize another atom whose ionization potential energy is equal to or less than the photon energy. The process is known as photoionization and may be represented as $A + hv \rightarrow A^+ + e$, where A represents a neutral atom or molecule in the gas and hv the photon energy. For ionization to occur $hv \geqslant eV_i$ or the photon wavelength $\lambda \leqslant c_0 h/eV_i$, c_0 being the velocity of light and h Planck's constant. Therefore, only very short wavelength light quanta can cause photoionization of gas. For example, the shortest wavelength radiated from an u.v. light with quartz envelope is 145 nm, which corresponds to $eV_i = 8.5$ eV, lower than the ionization potential of most gases.

The probability of photon ionizing a gas or molecule is maximum when $(hv - eV_i)$ is small (0.1–1 eV). Photoionization is a secondary ionization process and may be acting in the Townsend breakdown mechanism and is essential in the streamer breakdown mechanism and in some corona discharges. If the photon energy is less than eV_i it may still be absorbed by the atom and raise the atom to a higher energy level. This process is known as photoexcitation.

Ionization by Interaction of Metastables with Atoms

In certain elements the lifetime in some of the excited electronic states extends to seconds. These states are known as metastable states and the atoms in these states are simply referred to as metastables represented by A^m. Metastables have a relatively high potential energy and are therefore able to ionize neutral particles. If V^m, the energy of a metastable A^m, exceeds V_i, the ionization of another atom B, then on collision ionization may result according to the reaction

$$A^m + B \rightarrow A^+ + B + e.$$

For V^m of an atom $A^m < V_i$ of an atom B the reaction may lead to the exciting of the atom B which may be represented by $A^m + B \rightarrow A + B^*$.

Another possibility for ionization by metastables is when $2V^m$ for A^m is greater than V_i for A. Then the reaction may proceed as

$$A^m + A^m \rightarrow A^+ + A + e + \text{K.E.}$$

This last reaction is important only when the density of metastables is high. Another reaction may follow as

$$A^m + 2A \rightarrow A_2^* + A$$
$$A_2^* \rightarrow A + A + h\nu.$$

The photon released in the last reaction is of too low energy to cause ionization in pure gas, but it may release electron from the cathode.

Ionization by metastable interactions comes into operation long after excitation, and it has been shown that these reactions are responsible for long time lags observed in some gases.[10] It is effective in gas mixtures.

Thermal Ionization

The term thermal ionization, in general, applies to the ionizing actions of molecular collisions, radiation and electron collisions occurring in gases at high temperature. If a gas is heated to sufficiently high temperature many of the gas atoms or molecules acquire sufficiently high velocity to cause ionization on collision with other atoms or molecules. Thermal ionization is the principal source of ionization in flames and high-pressure arcs.

In analysing the process of thermal ionization, the recombination between positive ions and electrons must be taken into account. Under thermodynamic equilibrium conditions the rate of new ion formation must be equal to the rate of recombination. Using this assumption Saha[11] derived an expression for the degree of ionization θ in terms of the gas pressure and absolute temperature as follows:

$$\frac{\theta^2}{1-\theta^2} = \frac{1}{p}\frac{(2\pi m_e)^{3/2}}{h}(kT)^{5/2}\,e^{-W_i/kT}$$

or

$$\frac{\theta^2}{1-\theta^2} = \frac{2.4 \times 10^{-4}}{p}\,T^{5/2}\,e^{-W_i/kT} \tag{5.48}$$

where p is the pressure in Torr, W_i the ionization energy of the gas, k Boltzmann's constant, θ the ratio of n_i/n, and n_i the number of ionized particles of total n particles. The strong dependence of θ on temperature in eqn. (5.48) shows that the degree of ionization is negligible at room temperature. On substitution of values W_i, kT, p and T in eqn. (5.48) we find that thermal ionization becomes significant for temperatures above $1000°K$.

Deionization by Recombination

Whenever there are positively and negatively charged particles present, recombination takes place. The potential energy and the relative kinetic energy of the recombining electron–ion is released as quantum of radiation. Symbolically the reaction may be represented as

or

$$\left.\begin{array}{l} A^+ + e \to A + h\nu \\ A^+ + e \to A^m + h\nu \end{array}\right\} \begin{array}{l} \text{radiation} \\ \text{recombination.} \end{array}$$

Alternatively a third body C may be involved and may absorb the excess energy released in the recombination. The third body C may be another heavy particle or electron. Symbolically

or

$$A^+ + C + e \to A^* + C \to A + C + h\nu$$

$$A^+ + e + e \to A^* + e \to A + e + h\nu.$$

At high pressures, ion-ion recombination takes place. The rate of recombination in either case is directly proportional to the concentration of both positive ions and negative ions. For equal concentrations of positive ions n_+ and negative ions n_- the rate of recombination

$$\frac{dn_+}{dt} = \frac{dn_-}{dt} = -\beta n_+ n_- \qquad (5.49)$$

where β is a constant known as recombination rate coefficient.

Since $n_+ \approx n_- = n_i$ and if we assume at time $t = 0$ $n_i = n_{i0}$ and at time t $n_i = n_i(t)$, then eqn. (5.49) becomes

$$\frac{dn_i}{dt} = -\beta n_i^2.$$

Integration gives

$$\int_{n_{i0}}^{n_i} \frac{dn_i}{n_i^2} = -\beta \int_0^t dt$$

or

$$n_i(t) = \frac{n_{i0}}{1 + n_{i0}\beta t}. \qquad (5.50)$$

The half-time duration, during which time the concentration of ions has decreased to half its original value, is given by

$$t_n = \frac{1}{n_{i0}\beta}. \qquad (5.51)$$

The variation of the recombination rate coefficient β with pressure in air is shown in Fig. 5.10. The recombination process is particularly important at high pressures for which diffusion is relatively unimportant.

Deionization by Attachment—Negative Ion Formation

Electron affinity. Certain atoms or molecules in their gaseous state can readily acquire a free electron to form a stable negative ion. Gases, whether atomic or molecular, that have this tendency are those that are lacking one or two electrons in their outer shell and are known as electronegative gases.

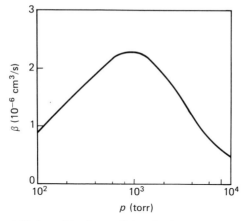

FIG. 5.10. Recombination coefficient (ion-ion) in air at 20°C.

Examples include the halogens (F, Cl, Br, I and At) with one electron missing in their outer shell O, S, Se with two electrons deficient in the outer shell.

For a negative ion to remain stable for some time, the total energy must be lower than that of an atom in the ground state. The change in energy that occurs when an electron is added to a gaseous atom or molecule is called the electron affinity of the atom and is designated by W_a. This energy is released as a quantum or kinetic energy upon attachment. Table 5.4 shows electron affinities of some elements.

There are several processes of negative ion formation.

(1) The simplest mechanism is one in which the excess energy upon attachment is released as quantum known as radiative attachment. This process is reversible, that is the captured electron can be released by

TABLE 5.4
Electron Affinities of Some Elements

Element	Ion formed	W_a (kJ/mole)
H	H –	-72
O	O –	-135
F	F –	-330
Cl	Cl –	-350
Br	Br –	-325
I	I –	-295

absorption of a photon known as photodetachment. Symbolically the process is represented as:

$$A + e \rightleftharpoons A^- + hv \quad (W_a = hv).$$

(2) The excess energy upon attachment can be acquired as kinetic energy of a third body upon collision and is known as a third body collision attachment, represented symbolically as:

$$e + A + B \rightarrow A^- + (B + W_k) \quad (W_a = W_k).$$

(3) A third process known as dissociative attachment which is predominant in molecular gases. Here the excess energy is used to separate the molecule into a neutral particle and an atomic negative ion, symbolically expressed as:

$$e + AB \rightleftharpoons (AB^-)^* \rightleftharpoons A^- + B.$$

(4) In process (3) in the intermediate stage the molecular ion is at a higher potential level and upon collision with a different particle this excitation energy may be lost to the colliding particle as potential and/or kinetic energy. The two stages of the process here are:

$$e + AB \rightleftharpoons (AB^-)^*$$

$$(AB^-)^* + A \rightleftharpoons (AB)^- + A + W_k + W_p.$$

Other processes of negative ion formation include splitting of a molecule into positive and negative ions upon impact of an electron without attaching the electron:

$$e + AB \rightleftharpoons A^+ + B^- + e$$

and a charge transfer following heavy particle collision, yielding an ion pair according to:

$$A + B \rightarrow A^+ + B^-.$$

All the above electron attachment processes are reversible, leading to electron detachment.

The process of electron attachment may be expressed by cross-section for negative ion formation σ_A in an analogous way to ionization by electron impact. Typical examples of the variation of attachment cross-section with electron energy for processes (2) and (3) measured in SF_6 and CO_2 are shown in Figs. 5.11 and 5.12 respectively.

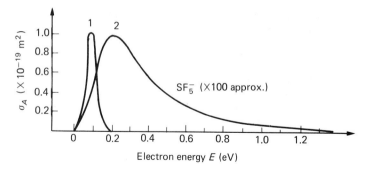

FIG. 5.11. Variation of attachment cross-section with electron energy in SF_6. 1. Radiative attachment. 2. Dissociative attachment.

Cumulatively the process of electron attachment describing the removal of electrons by attachment from ionized gas by any of the above processes may be expressed by a relation analogous to the expression (5.43) which defines electron multiplication in a gas. If η is the attachment coefficient defined by analogy with the first Townsend ionization coefficient α, as the number of attachments produced in a path of a single electron travelling a distance of 1 cm in the direction of field, then the loss of electron current in a distance dx due to this cause is

$$dI = -\eta I dx$$

or for a gap of length d with electron current I_0 starting at cathode

$$I = I_0 \, e^{-\eta d}. \tag{5.52}$$

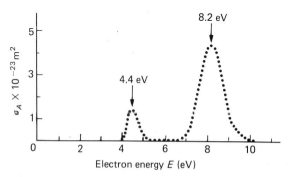

FIG. 5.12. Variation of electron attachment cross-section with electron energy in CO_2 (both peaks O^-).

Several methods for the measurements of the attachment coefficient have been described in the literature.[12] Methods for the determination of attachment coefficient utilizing eqn. (5.52) rely on the measurement of the surviving electronic current[13] at grids distance d apart inserted at two points along the path of the current between the electrodes. Such methods are applicable only at relatively low values of E/p when ionization by electron collision can be neglected. At higher values of E/p it becomes necessary to measure both the ionization coefficient α and the attachment coefficient η simultaneously.

If the processes of electron multiplication by electron collision and electron loss by attachment are considered to operate simultaneously, then neglecting other processes the number of electrons produced by collision in distance dx is

$$dn_i = n\alpha \, dx$$

where x is the distance from the cathode. At the same time the number of electrons lost in dx by attachment is

$$dn_a = -n\eta \, dx$$

so that the number of electrons still free is

$$dn = dn_i + dn_a = n(\alpha - \eta) \, dx.$$

Integration from $x = 0$ to x with n_0 electrons starting from the cathode gives the number of electrons at any point x in the gap as

$$n = n_0 \, e^{(\alpha - \eta)x}. \tag{5.53}$$

The steady-state current under such conditions will have two components, one resulting from the flow of electrons and the other from negative ions. To determine the total current we must find the negative current component. We note that the increase in negative ions in distance dx is

$$dn_- = n\eta \, dx = n_0\eta \, e^{(\alpha - \eta)x} \, dx.$$

Integration from 0 to x gives

$$n_- = \frac{n_0\eta}{\alpha - \eta} [e^{(\alpha - \eta)x} - 1].$$

The total current equals the sum of the two components or

$$\frac{n + n_-}{n_0} = \frac{\alpha}{\alpha - \eta} e^{(\alpha - \eta)d} - \frac{\eta}{\alpha - \eta} \tag{5.54}$$

and the expression for current becomes

$$I = I_0 \left[\frac{\alpha}{\alpha - \eta} e^{(\alpha - \eta)d} - \frac{\eta}{\alpha - \eta} \right]. \tag{5.55}$$

In the absence of attachment when η is zero the expression (5.55) reduces to the form $i = i_0 \, e^{\alpha d}$ and the log $i - d$ plot of eqn. (5.55) gives a straight line, with α representing the slope. When the value of η is appreciable, there may be a decrease in currents, especially at large values of d, such that the log i against d curve drops below the straight line relation. The departure from linearity in plotting log i against d gives a measure of the attachment coefficient. Several workers[9] have used this method for determining the α and η coefficients. The results obtained by this method by Geballe and Harrison for ionization α and attachment η in oxygen and in air are included in Table 5.5. It is convenient to represent the observed ionization coefficient by a single coefficient $\bar{\alpha} = \alpha - \eta$ defined as the effective ionization coefficient.

As electron attachment reduces electron amplification in a gas, gases with

TABLE 5.5
Geballe and Harrison's Values for α/p and η/p in Oxygen and Air

E/p V	Oxygen			Air		
cm. Torr	α/p	η/p	$\alpha/p - \eta/p$	α/p	η/p	$\alpha/p - \eta/p$
25.0	0.0215	0.0945	−0.0730	0.00120	0.00495	−0.00375
27.5	0.0293	0.0900	−0.0607	0.00205	0.00473	−0.00268
30.0	0.0400	0.0851	−0.0451	0.00340	0.00460	−0.00120
32.5	0.0532	0.0795	−0.0263	0.00560	0.00460	+0.00100
35.0	0.0697	0.0735	−0.0038	0.00880	0.00475	+0.00405
37.5	0.0862	0.0685	+0.0177	0.0130	0.00497	+0.0080
40.0	0.107	0.0645	+0.043	0.0190	0.00530	+0.0137
42.5	0.128	0.0605	+0.068	0.0260	0.00575	+0.0203
45.0	0.152	0.0570	+0.095	0.0340	0.00635	+0.0227
47.5	0.179	0.0535	+0.126	0.0460	0.00700	+0.0390
50.0	0.206	0.052	+0.154	0.057	0.00780	+0.049
52.5	0.234	0.049	+0.185	0.070	0.00870	+0.061
55.0	0.263	0.047	+0.216	0.087	0.00967	+0.077
57.5	0.292	0.045	+0.247	0.102	0.0108	+0.091
60.0	0.323	0.043	+0.280	0.120	0.0119	+0.108
62.5	0.355	0.0415	+0.314	0.140	—	—
65.0	0.383	0.040	+0.343	0.170	—	—
70.0	0.450	—	—	—	—	—
72.5	0.480	—	—	—	—	—
75.0	0.518	—	—	—	—	—

a high attachment coefficient such as sulphur hexafluoride or Freon have much higher dielectric strength than air or nitrogen. The most recent measured data for ionization and attachment coefficients for SF_6 are included in Table 5.6. These gases are technically important and are widely used as insulating medium in compact h.v. apparatus including totally enclosed substations and h.v. cables.

TABLE 5.6
Experimental Values of the Ionization and Attachment Coefficients in SF_6 (temp. $= 20°C$)

$\dfrac{E/p_{20}}{\text{V}}$ cm. Torr	p Torr	$\bar{\alpha}/p \times 10^3$ cm^{-1} $Torr^{-1}$	α/p cm^{-1} $Torr^{-1}$	η/p cm^{-1} $Torr^{-1}$	$\gamma \times 10^7$
115.0	5.2	-90	1.05	1.14	
125.0	5.2	200	1.32	1.12	
135.0	5.2	480.	1.52	1.04	
145.0	5.2	760	1.73	0.97	
154.0	5.2	1000			
155.0	5.2	1050			
165.0	5.2	1300			
175.0	5.2	1550			
185.0	5.2	1850			
200.0	5.2	2250			
115.0	19.5	90	1.04	1.13	
120.0	19.5	50	1.18	1.13	
125.0	19.5	200	1.30	1.10	
135.0	19.5	505			1
116.0	50.2	-25			
118.0	50.2	8	1.15	1.14	
120.0	50.2	60	1.18	1.12	
122.0	50.2	115			
125.0	50.2	225			
126.0	50.2	240			3
116.0	99.1	-38			
118.0	99.1	10			
119.0	99.1	33			
120.0	99.1	56			
122.0	99.1	120			
115.0	202.0	75			
117.0	202.0	-16			
118.0	202.0	8			
119.0	202.0	29			
119.25	202.0	36			60
122.0	202.0	110			6
117.0	402.4	-30			
118.0	402.4	5			
118.5	402.4	16			75

Mobility of Gaseous Ions and Deionization by Diffusion

Mobility. In the presence of an electric field charged particles in a gas will experience a force causing them to drift with a velocity that varies directly with the field and inversely with the density of the gas through which it moves. The drift velocity component in the field direction of unit strength is defined as the mobility (K) or symbolically

$$K = \frac{u}{E} \text{ (m}^2/\text{V sec)},$$

where u is the average drift velocity in field direction and E is the electric field strength. The mobility (K) is mainly a characteristic of the gas through which the ion moves and is independent of E/p over a wide range of E/p so long as the velocity gained by the ion from the field is considerably less than the average thermal velocity of the gas through which the ion moves.

To derive an expression for mobility of ions in a gas under an influence of electric field in the region of low values of E/p we assume that the ions are in thermal equilibrium with the gas molecules. Their drift velocity is small compared to the thermal velocity. If τ, the time interval between two successive collisions, is independent of E, then

$$\tau = \frac{\bar{\lambda}_i}{\bar{c}}$$

where $\bar{\lambda}_i$ is the ionic mean free path and $\bar{c}$ is the mean thermal velocity of the ion. During time τ the ion is accelerated by the field E with an acceleration $a = eE/m$, where m is the ionic mass and e is its charge. Therefore, in time τ it moves a distance

$$s = \frac{eE}{2m}\tau^2$$

and the drift velocity becomes

$$u = \frac{eE}{2m}\tau = \left(\frac{e\tau}{2m}\right)E = \left(\frac{e\bar{\lambda}_i}{2m\bar{c}}\right)E$$

and

$$K = \frac{u}{E} = \frac{e\bar{\lambda}_i}{2m\bar{c}}. \tag{5.56}$$

In deriving eqn. (5.56) we assumed that $\bar{\lambda}_i$ is uneffected by the drift motion, that is all ions are moving with the same random velocity and all ions have the same mean free path $\bar{\lambda}_i$. To take the statistical distribution of mean free paths $\bar{\lambda}_i$ into account, let us assume that the ions are moving with an average velocity $\bar{c}$ in zig-zag projections of lengths which are distributed about the mean free path $\bar{\lambda}_i$. Then if a is the acceleration caused by the field E, the distance between two collisions is

$$s = \frac{1}{2}at^2 = \frac{1}{2}\frac{eE}{m}\left(\frac{x^2}{\bar{c}^2}\right).$$

x denotes the total distance travelled between these collisions. The average value of s is obtained by averaging x^2 over the distribution of free paths

$$\bar{s} = \frac{eE}{2m}\frac{1}{\bar{c}^2}\int_0^\infty x^2\, e^{-x/\bar{\lambda}_i}\frac{dx}{\bar{\lambda}_i}\bigg/\int_0^\infty e^{-x/\bar{\lambda}_i}\frac{dx}{\bar{\lambda}_i}$$

$$= \frac{eE}{m\bar{c}^2}\bar{\lambda}_i^2.$$

If the mean free time $\bar{\tau} = \lambda_i/\bar{c}$

$$\bar{s} = \frac{eE}{m}\bar{\tau}^2,$$

the drift velocity

$$u = \frac{\bar{s}}{\bar{\tau}} = \frac{eE}{m\bar{c}}\bar{\lambda}_i,$$

and

$$K = \frac{u}{E} = \frac{e\bar{\lambda}_i}{m\bar{c}}. \tag{5.57}$$

Thus when the distribution of free paths is taken into account the expression for mobility is increased by a factor of 2. The expression (5.57) ignores the fact that after collision the ions may have initial velocities in the direction of field. Langevin[14] deduced a more exact expression which takes into account this effect of "persistence of motion" and for an ion of mass m moving through a gas consisting of molecules of mass M the expression becomes

$$K = \frac{0.815e\bar{\lambda}}{Mc}\sqrt{\frac{m+M}{m}} \tag{5.58}$$

where c is the r.m.s. velocity of agitation of the gas molecules and $\bar{\lambda}$ is an approximation to the ionic mean free path ($\bar{\lambda} \approx \bar{\lambda}_i$). For condition of thermal equilibrium

$$\frac{mc_1^2}{2} = \frac{Mc^2}{2} = \frac{3}{2}kT.$$

With c_1 the r.m.s. velocity of the ions, k Boltzmann's constant and T absolute temperature, expression (5.58) can be written in the form

$$K = 0.815 \frac{e\bar{\lambda}_i}{mc_1} \sqrt{\frac{m+M}{M}}. \qquad (5.59)$$

For an electron $m \ll M$ this expression reduces to

$$K = 0.815 \frac{e}{m} \frac{\bar{\lambda}_e}{c_1}. \qquad (5.60)$$

Table 5.7 gives some experimentally determined mobilities for negative and positive ions. The presence of impurities is found to have a profound effect on the measured mobility. The effect is particularly large in the case of negative ions when measured in non-attaching gases such as helium or hydrogen for which the electrons are free if the gases are extremely pure. The ion and electron mobilities can be used for the determination of conductivity or resistivity of an ionized gas. In the simplest case when the

TABLE 5.7
Mobility of Singly Charged Gaseous Ions at $0°C$ and 760 Hg (in cm/sec/volts/cm) (taken from Cobine[4])

Gas	K^-	K^+	Gas	K^-	K^+
Air (dry)	2.1	1.36	H_2 (very pure)	7900.0	
Air (very pure)	2.5	1.8	HCl	0.95	1.1
A	1.7	1.37	H_2S	0.56	0.62
A (very pure)	206.0	1.31	He	6.3	5.09
Cl_2	0.74	0.74	He (very pure)	500.0	5.09
CCl_4	0.31	0.30	N_2	1.84	1.27
C_2H_2	0.83	0.78	N_2 (very pure)	145.0	1.28
C_2H_5Cl	0.38	0.36	NH_3	0.66	0.56
C_2H_5OH	0.37	0.36	N_2O	0.90	0.82
CO	1.14	1.10	Ne		9.9
CO_2	0.98	0.84	O_2	1.80	1.31
H_2	8.15	5.9	SO_2	0.41	0.41

concentrations of positive ions and electrons are equal

$$n_+ = n_e = n,$$

then the total current density

$$j = j_i + j_e = n(u_i + u_e)e$$

where u_i and u_e are the drift velocities of the ions and electrons respectively. In terms of mobilities, the current density (j) and the conductivity (σ) become

$$j = neE(K_e + K_i)$$

and

$$\sigma = \frac{j}{E} = n(K_e + K_i). \qquad (5.61)$$

Since $K_e \gg K_i$, the conductivity is given approximately by

$$\sigma = nK_e. \qquad (5.62)$$

In the presence of appreciable space charge $n_e \neq n_i$ the conductivity components must be considered separately.

Diffusion. In electrical discharges whenever there is a non-uniform concentration of ions there will be movement of ions from regions of higher concentration to regions of lower concentration. The process by which equilibrium is achieved is called diffusion. This process will cause a deionizing effect in the regions of higher concentrations and an ionizing effect in regions of lower concentrations. The presence of walls confining a given volume augments the deionizing effect as the ions reaching the walls will lose their charge. The flow of particles along the ion concentration gradient constitutes a drift velocity similar to that of charged particles in an electric field. Both diffusion and mobility result in mass motion described by drift velocity caused in one case by the net effect of unbalanced collision forces (ion concentration gradient) and in the other case by the electric field.

If we consider a container with gas in which the concentration varies in the x-direction, then taking a layer of unit area and thickness dx placed perpendicularly to the direction x, the number of particles crossing this area is proportional to the ion concentration gradient dn/dx. The flow of particles or flux in the x-direction is

$$\Gamma = -D\frac{dn}{dx}. \qquad (5.63)$$

The negative sign indicates that n increases and the rate of flow (Γ) must decrease in the direction of flow. The constant D is known as the diffusion coefficient. From kinetic theory it can be shown that $D = \bar{u} \cdot \bar{\lambda}/3$. With $\bar{u}$ being the mean thermal velocity, the rate of change of concentration in the layer dx is

$$\frac{d}{dt}(n\,dx) = \Gamma - \left(\Gamma + \frac{d\Gamma}{dx}\,dx\right)$$

$$\frac{dn}{dt} = D\frac{d^2n}{dx^2}. \tag{5.64}$$

For the three-dimensional case eqn. (5.64) becomes

$$\frac{\partial n}{\partial t} = D\nabla^2 n \tag{6.65}$$

which is the general equation for diffusion.

Relation Between Diffusion and Mobility

In most transport phenomena, both diffusion and mobility will be acting together. It is therefore important to establish a relation between the diffusion coefficient and mobility. Consider a cloud of singly charged particles diffusing through the gas. For simplicity let us take again the unidirectional case with particles diffusing in the x-direction at a rate of flow given by eqn. (5.63). Then the ion velocity is equal to

$$u_i = \frac{\Gamma}{n_i} = -\frac{D}{n_i}\frac{dn_i}{dx}$$

where n_i is the ion concentration. Because n_i is directly proportional to p_i

$$u_i = -\frac{D}{p_i}\frac{dp_i}{dx} = f_i,$$

the force acting on the ions in this volume.

Since there are N ions per unit volume, the force exerted on one ion is

$$f_i = \frac{1}{N}\frac{dp_i}{dx} = -\frac{p_i}{DN}u_i.$$

An ion subjected to E, the force acting on it opposite to drift motion is

$$f_e = eE = \frac{eu}{K}, \quad u\text{-drift velocity of ion.}$$

In order that there is no net flow in the x-direction the force f_i must be balanced by f_e (oppointly diverted, $u_i = u$) and $f_i = -f_e$:

$$\frac{D}{K} = \frac{p_i}{eN} = \frac{kTn_i}{en_i} = \frac{kT}{e} \quad \left(n_i = \frac{p_i}{kT}\right) \tag{5.66}$$

In general the mobilities of negatively charged ions are higher than those of positive ones (Table 5.7) and consequently the negative ions will diffuse more rapidly. If the concentration of the diffusing particles is significant, the differential rate of diffusion will cause charge separation which will give rise to an electric field. The action of the field is such that it will tend to augment the drift velocity of the positive ions and retard that of negative ions, and the charge separation reaches a state of equilibrium in which the position and negative ions diffuse with the same velocity. This process is known as ambipolar diffusion. The average velocity of the diffusing ions may be obtained by considering the ion motion to be governed by the combined action of diffusion and mobility in the induced field E.

Then the velocity of the positive ions is given by

$$u^+ = -\frac{D^+}{n^-} \frac{dn^+}{dx} + K^+ E. \tag{5.67}$$

Similarly the velocity of negative ions is

$$u^- = -\frac{D^-}{n^-} \frac{dn^-}{dx} - K^- E. \tag{5.68}$$

Eliminating E between eqns. (5.67) and (5.68), and assuming $n^+ = n^- = n$,

$$\frac{dn^+}{dx} = \frac{dn^-}{dx} = \frac{dn}{dx} \quad \text{and} \quad u^+ = u^- = u.$$

The average velocity of the ions then becomes

$$\bar{u} = -\frac{D^+ K^- + D^- K^+}{n(K^+ + K^-)} \frac{dn}{dx} \tag{5.69}$$

and the ambipolar diffusion coefficient for mixed ions may be written as

$$D_a = -\frac{D^+K^- + D^-K^+}{K^+ + K^-} \tag{5.70}$$

and since from eqn. (5.66)

$$\frac{K^+}{D^+} = \frac{e}{kT^+} \quad \text{and} \quad \frac{K^-}{D^-} = \frac{e}{kT^-}$$

therefore, for the cases when $T_e = T^- \gg T^+$ and when $K_e = K^- \gg K^+$ we have

$$D_a \simeq D^+\frac{T_e}{T^+} \simeq D^-\frac{K^+}{K_e} \simeq D_e\frac{K^+}{K_e} \simeq \frac{kT_e}{e}. \tag{5.71}$$

If the electrons and ions are in equilibrium with the gas, that is all particles are at the same temperature, then we may put $D_eK_i = D_iK_e$ and the ambipolar diffusion coefficient becomes

$$D_a \approx \frac{2D_iK_e}{K_e} \approx 2D_i, \tag{5.72}$$

since $K_e \gg K_i$.

Finally, the field E between the space charges can be obtained by eliminating u from eqns. (5.66) and (5.67), giving

$$E = -\frac{D^- - D^+}{K^- + K^+}\frac{1}{n}\frac{dn}{dx}. \tag{5.73}$$

Equations (5.71) and (5.72) are commonly used, although both are only approximated, but they demonstrate that D_a increases with T_e, that is with the random electron energy and that if electrons are at the same temperature as the gas, D_a is of the same order as D_i so that electrons are slowed much more than positive ions are accelerated. Diffusion processes are of particular importance in studying streamer discharge and spark channels.

5.3. CATHODE PROCESSES—SECONDARY EFFECTS

Electrodes, in particular the cathode, play a very important role in gas discharges by supplying electrons for the initiation, for sustaining and for the completion of a discharge. Under normal conditions electrons are prevented from leaving the solid electrode by the electrostatic forces between the electrons and the ions in the lattice. The energy required to remove an electron from a Fermi level is known as the work function (W_a) and is a characteristic of a given material. There are several ways in which the required energy may be supplied to release the electrons.

Photoelectric Emission

Photons incident upon cathode surface whose energy exceeds the work function ($hv > W_a$) may eject electrons from the surface. For most metals the critical frequency v_0 lies in the u.v. range. When the photon energy exceeds the work function, the excess energy may be transferred to electron kinetic energy according to the Einstein relation:

$$\tfrac{1}{2}mu_e^2 = hv - hv_0 \qquad (5.74)$$

where m is the electron mass, u_e its velocity and hv_0 is the critical energy required to remove the electron and $hv_0 = W_a$ the work function.

Table 5.8 gives the work functions for several elements. The work function is sensitive to contamination which is indicated by the spread in the measured values shown in Table 5.8.

The spread is particularly large in the case of aluminium and metals which readily oxidize. In the presence of a thin oxide film, it has been shown by Malter[16] that positive ions may gather at the oxide layer without being neutralized, giving rise to a high field strength leading to augmented secondary emission. The effect is known as the *Malter effect*.

Electron Emission by Positive Ion and Excited Atom Impact

Electrons may be emitted from metal surfaces by bombardment of positive ions or metastable atoms. To cause a secondary emission of an

TABLE 5.8
Work Function for Typical Elements[15]

Element	Ag	Al	Cu	Fe	W
W_a (eV)	4.74	2.98–4.43	4.07–4.7	3.91–4.6	4.35–4.6

electron the impinging ion must release two electrons, one of which is utilized to neutralize the ion charge. The minimum energy required for a positive ion electron emission is twice the work function $W_K + W_p \geqslant 2W_a$, since the ion is neutralized by one electron and the other electron is ejected. W_K and W_p are the respective kinetic and potential energies of the incident ion. The electron emission by positive ions is the principal secondary process in the Townsend spark discharge mechanism.

Neutral excited (metastable) atoms or molecules incident upon the electrode surface are also capable of ejecting electrons from the surface.

Thermionic Emission

In metals at room temperature the conduction electrons will not have sufficient thermal energy to leave the surface. If we consider the electrons as a gas at room temperature, then their average thermal energy is

$$\frac{mu_e^2}{2} = \frac{3kT}{2} = 3.8 \times 10^{-2} \text{ eV},$$

which is much lower than the work function (Table 5.8). If, however, the metal temperature is increased to some 1500–2500°K, the electrons will receive energy from the violent thermal lattice vibrations sufficient to cross the surface barrier and leave the metal. The emission current is related to the temperature of the emitter by the Richardson[17] relation for thermionically emitted saturation current density:

$$J_s = \frac{4\pi m e k^2}{h^3} T^2 \exp\left[-\frac{W_a}{kT}\right] \text{ A/m}^2 \qquad (5.75)$$

where e and m are the electronic charge and mass respectively, h is Planck's constant, k Boltzmann's constant, T the absolute temperature and W_a the surface work function.

Putting

$$A = \frac{4\pi m e k^2}{h^3},$$

the above expression becomes

$$J_s = AT^2 \exp\left[-\frac{W_a}{kT}\right] \qquad (5.76)$$

which shows that the saturation current density increases with decreasing work function and increasing temperature. On substitution of the constants m, e, k and h, $A = 120 \times 10^4$ A m^{-2} degr^{-2}. The experimentally obtained values are lower than predicted by eqn. (5.76). This discrepancy is attributed to the wave nature of the electrons. Although electrons may possess the required escape energy, some of them may be reflected back into the solid from the surface atoms or surface contaminants such as adsorbed gases. The effect may be taken into account by inserting the effective value $A_{eff} = A(1-R)$ in the current density expression (5.76), where R is the reflection coefficient. In the presence of a strong electric field there will be a reduction in the work function as the Schottky[18] effect discussed in the next section, and the thermionic emission will be enhanced.

Field Emission

Electrons may be drawn out of a metal surface by very high electrostatic fields. It will be shown that a strong electric field at the surface of a metal may modify the potential barrier at the metal surface to such an extent that electrons in the upper level close to Fermi level will have a definite probability of passing through the barrier. The effect is known as "tunnel effect". The fields required to produce emission currents of a few microamperes are of the order of 10^7–10^8 V/cm. Such fields are observed at fine wires, sharp points and submicroscopic irregularities with an average applied voltage quite low (2–5 kV). These fields are much higher than the breakdown stress even in compressed gases.

To derive an expression for the emission current let us consider an electron as it leaves the surface in the direction x as shown in Fig. 5.13. Its electric field can be approximated as that between a point charge and the equipotential planar surface. The field lines here are identical to those existing when an image charge of $+e$ is thought to exist at a normal distance of $-x$ on the other side of the equipotential metal surface. Applying Coulomb's Law, the force on the electron in the x-direction is given by

$$F(x) = \frac{-e^2}{4\pi\varepsilon_0(2x)^2} = \frac{-e^2}{16\pi\varepsilon_0 x^2}.$$

The potential energy at any distance x is obtained by integrating the above

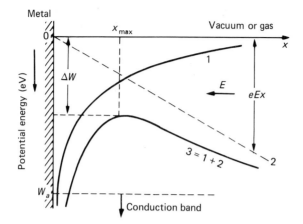

FIG. 5.13. Lowering of the potential barrier by an external field. 1. Energy with no field. 2. Energy due to field. 3. Resultant energy.

equation from ∞ to x.

$$W_{e1} = \frac{-e^2}{16\pi\varepsilon_0 x} \tag{5.77}$$

which gives a parabola shown by curve 1 of Fig. 5.13. The effect of the accelerating external field when applied at right angles to the cathode surface gives electron a potential energy

$$W_E = -eEx \tag{5.78}$$

which is a straight line shown by Fig. 5.13 (curve 2). The total energy is then

$$W = W_a + W_E = -\left(\frac{e^2}{16\pi\varepsilon_0 x}\right) - eEx \tag{5.79}$$

which is shown by the resultant curve 3 (Fig. 5.13). Thus a marked reduction ΔW in the potential barrier is obtained. The maximum reduction at x_m is obtained by differentiating eqn. (5.79) or

$$\frac{dW}{dx} = \frac{e^2}{16\pi\varepsilon_0 x_m^2} - eE = 0$$

$$x_m = \sqrt{\frac{e}{16\pi\varepsilon_0 E}}.$$

Inserting this value into eqn. (5.79) the lowering in the work function becomes

$$\Delta W = -e \sqrt{\frac{eE}{4\pi\varepsilon_0}}.$$ (5.80)

Hence, the effective value of the work function is

$$W_{\mathrm{eff}} = W_a - \sqrt{\frac{eE}{4\pi\varepsilon_0}}$$ (5.81)

and the saturation current due to electron emission using eqn. (5.76) in the presence of field E becomes

$$J_s = AT^2 \exp\left[-\frac{e}{kT}\left(W_a - \sqrt{\frac{eE}{4\pi\varepsilon_0}}\right)\right]$$ (5.81)

which is known as the Schottky's equation. If the current density in the absence of external field is J_0 [eqn. (5.76)] then rearranging (5.81) we obtain

$$J_s = J_0 \exp\left[\frac{e}{kT}\sqrt{\frac{eE}{4\pi\varepsilon_0}}\right] = J_0 \exp\left[\frac{B\sqrt{E}}{T}\right].$$ (5.82)

To obtain emission current J significantly higher than J_0, E must be of the magnitude of 10 MV/cm or higher. In practice a significant field emission current may be observed at somewhat lower fields. The effect has been explained by Fowler and Nordheim[19] who derived an expression for field emission on the basis of wave mechanics. These authors have shown that a few electrons in a metal will have an energy slightly above the Fermi level and thus will have a greater probability to penetrate the potential barrier "tunnel effect". The Fowler–Nordheim equation has the form.

$$j = CE^2 \exp\left[-\frac{D}{E}\right]$$ (5.83)

where C and D are constants involving atomic constants. Equation (5.83) shows that field emission is independent of temperature, but this is valid only at low temperatures. At higher temperatures both thermionic and field emission will occur simultaneously.

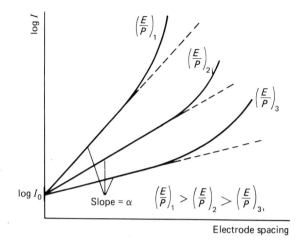

FIG. 5.14. Variation of gap current with electrode spacing in uniform field gaps.

Townsend Second Ionization Coefficient γ

According to eqn. (5.43) a graph of log I against gap length should yield a straight line of slope α if for a given pressure of p, E is kept constant. In his early measurements of current in parallel plate gaps Townsend[4] observed that at higher voltages the current increased at a more rapid rate than given by eqns. (5.43) or (5.55). Figure 5.14 shows the kind of curves obtained by plotting log I against electrode separation at a constant pressure. To explain this departure from linearity Townsend postulated that a second mechanism must be affecting the current. He first considered liberation of electrons in the gas by collision of positive ions, and later the liberation of electrons from the cathode by positive ion bombardment according to the mechanism discussed earlier. On these assumptions he deduced the equation for the current in the self-sustained discharge. Other processes responsible for the upcurving of the (log $I-d$) graph Fig. 5.14 include the secondary electron emission at the cathode by photon impact and photoionization in the gas itself.

Following Townsend's procedure we consider the case for a self-sustained discharge where the electrons are produced at the cathode by positive ion bombardment.

Let n = number of electrons reaching the anode per second, n_0 =

number of electrons emitted from cathode by (say) u.v. illumination, $n_+ =$ number of electrons released from cathode by positive ion bombardment, γ = number of electrons released from cathode per incident positive ion.

Then

$$n = (n_0 + n_+) \, e^{\alpha d}$$

and

$$n_+ = \gamma [n - (n_0 + n_+)].$$

Eliminating n_+

$$n = \frac{n_0 \, e^{\alpha d}}{1 - \gamma(e^{\alpha d} - 1)}$$

or for steady-state current

$$I = I_0 \frac{e^{\alpha d}}{1 - \gamma(e^{\alpha d} - 1)}. \tag{5.84}$$

Townsend's original expression was of the form

$$I = I_0 \frac{(\alpha - \beta) \, e^{(\alpha - \beta)d}}{\alpha - \beta \, e^{(\alpha - \beta)d}} \tag{5.85}$$

where β represents the number of ion pairs produced by a positive ion travelling a 1-cm path in the field direction and α, d, I and I_0 have the same significance as in eqn. (5.84). Townsend's original suggestion for secondary ionization in the gas by positive ion impact does not work, because ions rapidly lose energy in elastic collisions according to eqn. (5.35) and ordinarily are unable to gain sufficient energy from the field to cause ionization on collision with neutral atoms or molecules.

Secondary Electron Emission by Photon Impact

The case where the secondary emission arises from photon impact at the cathode may be expressed by the equation:[12]

$$I = I_0 \frac{\alpha \, e^{\alpha d}}{\alpha - \theta \eta g \, e^{(\alpha - \mu)d}} \tag{5.86}$$

where θ is the number of photons produced by an electron in advancing 1 cm in the direction of the field, μ is the average absorption coefficient for photons in the gas, g is a geometrical factor representing the fraction of photons that reach the cathode, and η is the fraction of the photons producing electrons at the cathode capable of leaving the surface.

In practice both positive ions and photons may be active at the same time in producing electrons at the cathode. Furthermore, metastable atoms may contribute to the secondary emission at the cathode. Which of the particular secondary mechanisms is predominant depends largely upon the experimental conditions in question. There may be more than one mechanism operating in producing the secondary ionization in the discharge gap and it is customary to express the secondary ionization by a single coefficient γ and represent the current by eqn. (5.84), bearing in mind that γ may represent one or more of the several possible mechanisms $(\gamma = \gamma_i + \gamma_{ph} + \ldots)$.

Experimental values of γ can be determined from eqn. (5.84) by measurement of the current in the gap for various pressures, field strength and gap length and using the corresponding values of α. As would be expected from the considerations of the electron emission processes, the value of γ is greatly affected by the nature of the cathode surface. Low work function materials under the same experimental conditions will produce higher emission. The value of γ is relatively small at low values of E/p and will increase with E/p. This is because at higher values of E/p there will be a larger number of positive ions and photons of sufficiently high energy to eject electrons upon impact on the cathode surface.

TABLE 5.9

Gas	Cathode	V_m (volts)	E/p V —— cm. Torr	γ
Air contaminated	Copper amalgam	460	720	0.004
with Hg vapour	Mercury film on aluminium	390	885	0.014
	Mercury film on nickel	390	885	0.014
	Mercury film on staybrite steel	390	585	0.006
Air	Oxidized aluminium	416	905	0.01
	Oxidized nickel	421	957	0.01
Hydrogen	Aluminium	243	200	0.1
(electrode treated	Aluminium deposited on nickel	212	200	0.15
by glow discharge)	Nickel	289	180	0.075
	Nickel deposited on aluminium	390	245	0.015
	Commercial aluminium	225	200	0.125
	Aluminium on staybrite steel	205	210	0.15
	Staybrite steel	274	190	0.075
	Steel deposited on aluminium	282	190	0.075

Llewellyn Jones and Davies[20] have studied the influence of cathode surface layers on the breakdown characteristic of air and on the corresponding values of γ. Their data are included in Table 5.9 which shows a wide variation in the minimum breakdown voltage V_m and the accompanying variation in the values of γ. Influence of γ to breakdown strength is restricted to the "Townsend breakdown mechanism", i.e. to low-pressure breakdown only as can be shown by the various breakdown criteria to be discussed in the next section.

5.4 TRANSITION FROM SELF-SUSTAINED DISCHARGES TO BREAKDOWN

The Townsend Mechanism

As the voltage between electrodes in a gas with small or negligible electron attachment increases, the electrode current at the anode increases in accordance with eqn. (5.84)

$$I = I_0 \frac{e^{\alpha d}}{1 - \gamma(e^{\alpha d} - 1)}$$

or, introducing eqn. (5.44) and $E = V/d$

$$\frac{I}{I_0} = \frac{e^{(pd)} \cdot f\left(\dfrac{V}{pd}\right)}{1 - \gamma \left[e^{(pd)} \cdot f\left(\dfrac{V}{pd}\right) - 1 \right]}$$

until at some point there is a sudden transition from the dark current I_0 to a self-sustaining discharge. At this point the current (I) becomes indeterminate and the denominator in the above equation vanishes, i.e.

$$\gamma(e^{\alpha d} - 1) = 1.$$

If the electron attachment is taken into account (section 5.10), this equation becomes

$$\frac{\alpha \gamma}{\alpha - \eta} \left[e^{(\alpha - \eta)d} - 1 \right] = 1$$

or approximately

$$\gamma\, e^{(\alpha-\eta)\cdot d} = \gamma\, e^{\bar{\alpha}d} = 1 \qquad (5.87)$$

since

$$e^{\bar{\alpha}d} \gg 1 \quad \text{and} \quad \alpha \gg \eta$$

where $\bar{\alpha} = \alpha - \eta$ represents the effective ionization coefficient defined earlier in this chapter. The electron current at the anode equals the current in the external circuit. Theoretically the value of the current becomes infinitely large, but in practice it is limited by the external circuitry and, to a small extent, by the voltage drop within the arc. Equation (5.87) defines the conditions for onset of spark[20] and is called the Townsend criterion for spark formation or Townsend breakdown criterion. When $\gamma(e^{\bar{\alpha}d} - 1) = 1$ the number of ion pairs produced in the gap by the passage of one electron avalanche is sufficiently large that the resulting positive ions, on bombarding the cathode, are able to release one secondary electron and so cause a repetition of the avalanche process. The secondary electron may also come from a photoemission process [see eqn. (5.86)]. In either case electron avalanche will have a successor. The discharge is then self-sustaining and can continue in the absence of the source producing I_0, so that the criterion $\gamma(e^{\bar{\alpha}d} - 1) = 1$ can be said to define the sparking threshold. For $\gamma(e^{\bar{\alpha}d} - 1) > 1$ the ionization produced by successive avalanches is cumulative. The spark discharge grows more rapidly the more $\gamma(e^{\bar{\alpha}d} - 1)$ exceeds unity.

For $\gamma(e^{\bar{\alpha}d} - 1) < 1$ the current I is not self-sustained, i.e. on removal of source producing the primary current I_0 it ceases to flow (see Fig. 5.14).

An alternative expression for the Townsend breakdown criterion is obtained by rewriting expression (5.87) in the form

$$\bar{\alpha}d = \ln\left(\frac{1}{\gamma} + 1\right) = K. \qquad (5.88)$$

The right-hand side of this equation, K, can often be treated as being constant, due to the following phenomena. As mentioned earlier, the electron emission processes characterized by γ are greatly affected by cathode surface, also by gas pressure. However, γ is of very small value ($<10^{-2}$–10^{-3}) and therefore $1/\gamma$ is quite a high number. Therefore, $K = \ln(1/\gamma + 1)$ does not change too much and is for a Townsend discharge of the order of 8–10. As α is often very strongly dependent upon gas pressure p or field strength E, the exact value of K is of minor importance and may be treated as a constant for many conditions of p and E.

5.5 THE STREAMER OR "KANAL" MECHANISM OF SPARK

The growth of charge carriers in an avalanche in a uniform field $E_0 = V_0/d$ is described by the exponent $e^{\alpha d}$. This is valid only as long as the electrical field of the space charges of electrons and ions can be neglected compared to the external field E_0. In his studies of the effect of space charge of an avalanche on its own growth, Raether observed that when the charge concentration was higher than 10^6 but lower than 10^8 the growth of an avalanche was weakened

$$\left(\frac{dn}{dx} < e^{\alpha d}\right).$$

When the ion concentration exceeded 10^8 the avalanche current was followed by a steep rise in current and breakdown of the gap followed. Both the 'underexponential growth" at the lower concentration and rapid growth in the presence of the high concentration have been attributed to the modification of the originally uniform field (E_0) by the space charge field. Figure 5.15 shows diagramatically the electric field around an avalanche as it progresses along the gap and the resulting modification to the original field (E_0). For simplicity the space charge at the head of the avalanche is assumed concentrated within a spherical volume, with the negative charge ahead because of the higher electron mobility. The field is enhanced in front of the head of the avalanche with field lines from the anode terminating at the head. Further back in the avalanche, the field betwen the electrons and the ions left behind reduced the applied field (E_0). Still further back the field between the cathode and the positive ions is enhanced again. The field distortion becomes noticeable with a carrier number $n > 10^6$. For instance, in nitrogen with $d = 2$ cm, $p = 760$ Torr, $\alpha \approx 7$ and $E_0/p \approx 40$ V/Torr cm, the field distortion is about 1%, leading to 5% change in α. If the distortion of $\simeq 1\%$ prevailed in the entire gap it would lead to a doubling of the avalanche size, but as the distortion is only significant in the immediate vicinity of the avalanche head it has still an insignificant effect. However, if the carrier number in the avalanche reaches $n \approx 10^8$ the space charge field becomes of the same magnitude as the applied field and may lead to the initiation of a streamer. The space charge fields play an important role in the mechanism of corona and spark discharges in non-uniform field gaps. For analytical treatment of space charge field distortion the reader is referred to reference 12.

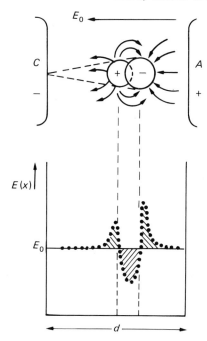

F_{IG}. 5.15. Diagrammatic representation of field distortion in a gap caused by space charge of an electron avalanche.

In the Townsend spark mechanism discussed in the previous section the gap current grows as a result of ionization by electron impact in the gas and electron emission at the cathode by positive ion impact. According to this theory, formative time lag of the spark should be at best equal to the electron transit time t_i. At pressures around atmospheric and above ($pd > 10^3$ Torr cm) the experimentally determined time lags have been found to be much shorter than t_i. Furthermore, cloud chamber photographs of avalanche development have shown[22] that under certain conditions the space charge developed in an avalanche is capable of transforming the avalanche into channels of ionization known as streamers that lead to rapid development of breakdown. From measurements of the prebreakdown current growth[23] and the minimum breakdown strength it has been found that the transformation from avalanche to streamer generally occurs when the charge within the avalanche head (Fig. 5.15) reaches a critical value of $n_0 \exp [\alpha x_c] \approx 10^8$ or $\alpha x_c \approx 18\text{–}20$, where x_c is the length of the avalanche path in field direction when it reaches the critical size. If x_c is larger than the gap length ($x_c > d$) then the initiation of streamers is unlikely. Typical cloud chamber photographs of electron avalanche and streamer development are shown in Fig. 5.16 (a) to (d). In (a) the discharge has been arrested before reaching the critical size ($\sim 10^8$), giving the avalanche the classical "carrot" shape. In (b) the avalanche has grown beyond the critical size, its head has opened up indicating ionization around the original avalanche head and a cathod directed streamer starts. This continues (c, d) till a plasma channel connects cathode and anode. The early cloud chamber results have led Raether[22] to postulate the development of two types of streamers: (1) the "anode directed streamer" describing the apparent growth of ionization and of the avalanche head, and (2) the "cathod directed streamer" describing the additional discharge growth from the avalanche tail.

More recently Wagner[24] has obtained streak photographs of "avalanche streamer" development using an image intensifier. In these experiments the time and space resolved in radiation density which corresponds to the electron density is monitored. The observed radiation pattern together with the photocurrent growth is sketched in Fig. 5.17 (a) and (b). Region (a)–(b) corresponds to the development of avalanche with an approximate velocity of 10^8 cm/sec. The current growth is exponential. Beyond (b), after the avalanche has reached the critical size, there is an increase in the velocity of the avalanche head by about a factor of 10. In

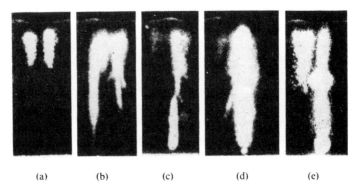

(a)   (b)   (c)   (d)   (e)

FIG. 5.16. Cloud chamber photographs showing development of the cathode directed streamers (with increasing pulse length): (a) avalanche near anode; (b) and (c) cathode directed streamer starts; (d) and (e) time period for plasma channel to connect cathode and anode.[22]

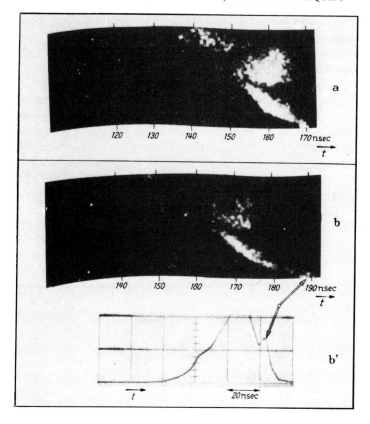

FIG. 5.17. Image intensifier photographs, and a photocurrent oscillogram showing the development of cathode directed streamers in N_2 (20% CH_4) $p = 88.5$ Torr. (a) and (b) progress of streamers after switching off external voltage; (c) photocurrent oscillogram corresponding to (b).[24]

many cases almost simultaneously a second luminous front is observed proceeding towards the cathode with the same velocity as the anode directed growth. The current growth in this region is faster than exponential.

The observed short time lags together with the observations of discharge development have led Raether and independently Meek[25] and Meek and Loeb[26] to the advancement of the "streamer" or "Kanal" mechanism for spark formation, in which the secondary mechanism results from photo-ionization of gas molecules and is independent of the electrodes.

In the models developed by Raether and Meek it has been proposed that when the avalanche in the gap reaches a certain critical size the combined space charge field and externally applied field lead to intense ionization and excitation of the gas particles in front of the avalanche head. Instantaneous recombination between positive ions and electrons releases photons which in turn generate secondary electrons by the photoionization process. These electrons under the influence of the electric field in the gap develop into secondary avalanches as shown in Fig. 5.18. Since photons travel with the velocity of light, the process leads to a rapid development of conduction channel across the gap.

On the basis of his experimental observations and some simple assumptions Raether[33] developed an empirical expression for the streamer spark criterion of the form

$$\alpha x_c = 17.7 + \ln x_c + \ln \frac{E_r}{E} \qquad (5.89)$$

where F_i is the space charge field strength directed radially at the head of avalanche as shown in Fig. 5.19, E is the externally applied field strength at the head of the avalanche $(E + E_r)$ while in the positive ion region just behind the head the field is reduced to a value $(E - E_r)$. It is also evident that the space charge increases with the avalanche length $(e^{\alpha x})$.

The condition for the transition from avalanche to streamer assumes that space charge field E_r approaches the externally applied field $(E_r \approx E)$, hence

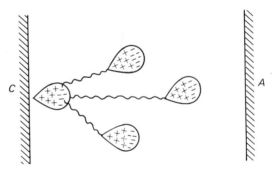

FIG. 5.18. Secondary avalanche formation by photoelectrons.

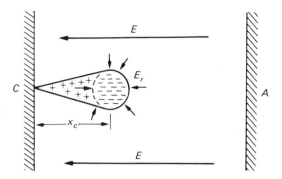

FIG. 5.19. Space charge field (E_r) around avalanche head.

the breakdown criterion [eqn. (5.89)] becomes

$$\alpha x_c = 17.7 + \ln x_c. \tag{5.90}$$

The minimum breakdown value for a uniform field gap by streamer mechanism is obtained on the assumption that the transition from avalanche to streamer occurs when the avalanche has just crossed the gap (d). Then Raether's empirical expression for this condition takes the form

$$\alpha d = 17.7 + \ln d. \tag{5.91}$$

Therefore the minimum breakdown by streamer mechanism is brought about only when the critical length $x_c \geqslant d$. The condition $x_c = d$ gives the smallest value of α to produce streamer breakdown.

A similar criterion equation for the transition from avalanche to streamer has been developed by Meek.[25] As in Raether's case the transition is assumed to take place when the radial field about the positive space charge in an electron avalanche attains a value of the order of the externally applied field. Meek[25] has shown that the radial field produced by positive ions immediately behind the head of the avalanche can be calculated from the expression

$$E_r = 5.3 \times 10^{-7} \frac{\alpha \, e^{\alpha x}}{\left(\dfrac{x}{p}\right)^{1/2}} \text{ volts/cm} \tag{5.92}$$

where x is the distance (in cm) which the avalanche has progressed, p is the gas pressure in Torr and α is the Townsend coefficient of ionization by electrons corresponding to the applied field E. As in Raether's model the minimum breakdown voltage is assumed to correspond to the condition when the avalanche has crossed the gap of length d and the space charge field E_r approaches the externally applied field. Substituting into eqn. (5.92) $E_r = E$ and $x = d$ and rearranging gives

$$\alpha d + \ln \frac{\alpha}{p} = 14.5 + \ln \frac{E}{p} + \frac{1}{2} \ln \frac{d}{p}. \tag{5.93}$$

This equation is solved by trial and error using the experimentally determined relation between α/p and E/p. Values of α/p corresponding to E/p at a given pressure are chosen until the equation is satisfied.

Table 5.10 compares Meek's calculated and the measured values V_b for air according to eqn. (5.93). At small d, the calculated values V_b are higher than the measured ones. The reverse is true at large d. In general, however, the deviation between theory and experiment should be regarded as not very large, in view of the various simplifying assumptions made by Meek,[25] especially those in order to determine the charge density and the tip radius of the avalanche. The avalanche radius was calculated on the basis of thermal diffusion using the relationship $r = \sqrt{3Dt}$ where D is thermal diffusion coefficient, t the time. The charge was assumed to be concentrated in a spherical volume which is only approximately correct. At the charge densities in question, ambipolar diffusion is likely to be important, but so far has been neglected.

In section 5.4 we have seen that the Townsend criterion for spark formation is satisfied when the product $\bar{\alpha}d$ reaches a value of 8–10 ($\bar{\alpha}d = \ln (1/\gamma + 1) = 8$–10). The streamer criterion for spark formation,

TABLE 5.10

Comparison of Calculated and Measured V_b Values for Air according to Meek's Model

Gap length cm	E/p V/cm Torr	αd	V_b calculated kV	V_b measured kV
0.1	68.4	15.7	5.19	4.6
0.5	48.1	17.7	18.25	17.1
1.0	42.4	18.6	32.20	31.6
2.5	37	19.7	70.50	73
10	32.8	21.5	249	265
20	31.2	22.4	474	510

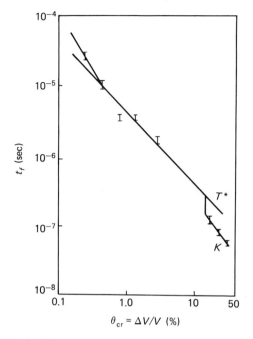

FIG. 5.20. Formative time lag in N_2 as function of overvoltage. $p = 500$ Torr, $d = 2$ cm. T^* Townsend mechanism, K streamer mechanism.

however, requires a value of 18–20, $\bar{\alpha}d = (\bar{\alpha}x_c) = \ln\ 10^8 \approx 20$ with $x_c \leqslant d$. Therefore under certain experimental conditions there will be a transition from the Townsend to streamer mechanism. This transition is brought about by increased pressure and gap length and in practice it occurs in the region of $pd \geqslant 1$–2 bar cm. The transition is indicated by a discontinuity in the formative time lag discussed in section 5.10. The streamer mechanism which relies on photoionization in the gas requires a much shorter formative time than the Townsend mechanism in which the secondary mechanism is cathode dependent and is affected by the transit time of positive ions. Figure 5.20 compares the formative time lag[20] in nitrogen at $p = 500$ Torr and $d = 2$ cm with the measured values, plotted as function of percentage overvoltage ($\theta = \Delta V/V\%$). At lower overvoltages the formative time lag follows the Townsend mechanism up to a critical value $\theta_{crit} = \Delta V_{crit}/V$ at which the electron amplification within the avalanche reaches a value $e^{\alpha d} \geqslant 10^8$. Curve K has been calculated from the

TABLE 5.11
Critical Overvoltages for Various Gases[27]

Gas	p (Torr)	d (cm)	pd (Torr cm)	θ_{crit} (%)
H_2	500	2	1000	16.6
N_2	500	2	1000	18.2
N_2	400	3	1200	17
Air	760	1	760	4.5

time (t_A) required to reach the critical size at various overvoltages,

$$t_A = \frac{x_{crit}}{v_-} = \frac{18}{\alpha v_-} \qquad (5.94)$$

where v_- is the electron drift velocity. Curve T is obtained from the Townsend mechanism. No discontinuity is observed and the curve gives a too long formative time lag for the higher overvoltages.

Table 5.11 gives the critical overvoltages for several of the commonly used gases together with the corresponding pd values. The sudden change in the formative time lag usually takes place for values of some 10^{-7} sec.

5.6 THE SPARKING VOLTAGE—PASCHEN'S LAW

The Townsend criterion, eqn. (5.87), enables the breakdown voltage of the gap to be determined by the use of appropriate values $\bar{\alpha}/p$ and γ corresponding to the values E/p without ever taking the gap currents to high values, that is keeping them below 10^{-7} A, so that space charge distortions are kept to minimum, and more importantly so that no damage to electrodes occurs. Good agreement has been found[28] between calculated and experimentally determined breakdown voltages for short or long gaps and relatively low pressures for which this criterion is applicable.

An analytical expression for breakdown voltage for uniform field gaps as function of gap length and gas pressure can be derived from the threshold eqn. (5.87) by expressing the ionization coefficient $\bar{\alpha}/p$ as a function of field strength and gas pressure. If we put $\bar{\alpha}/p = f(E/p)$ in the criterion equation we obtain

$$e^{f(E/p)pd} = \frac{1}{\gamma} + 1$$

or

$$f(E/p)pd = \ln\left(1+\frac{1}{\gamma}\right) = K. \tag{5.95}$$

For uniform field $V_b = Ed$, where V_b is the breakdown voltage,

$$e^{f(V_b/pd)pd} = K \tag{5.96}$$

or

$$V_b = F(pd)$$

which means that the breakdown voltage of a uniform field gap is a unique function of the product of pressure and the electrode separation for a particular gas and electrode material. Equation (5.96) is known as Paschen's Law, and was established experimentally in 1889. Equation (5.96) does not imply that the sparking voltage increases linearly with the product pd, although it is found in practice to be nearly linear over certain regions. The relation between the sparking voltage and the product pd takes the form shown in Fig. 5.21 (solid curve). The breakdown voltage goes through a minimum value (V_{bmin}) at a particular value of the product (pd_{min}).

Let us now examine graphically the relation of the Paschen's curve (Fig. 5.21) with the spark criterion eqn. (5.88). If the experimental relationship

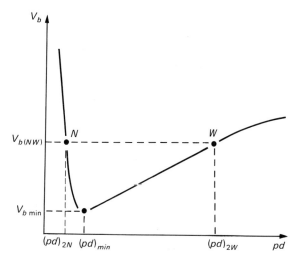

Fig. 5.21. The sparking voltage–pd relationship (Paschen's curve).

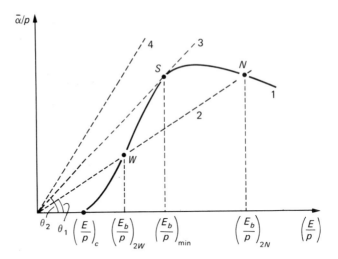

FIG. 5.22. Relation between the Townsend criterion for spark ($\alpha d = k$) and the function of α/p
$= f(E/p)$.

between the ionization coefficient and the field strength ($\bar{\alpha}/p = f(E/p)$) for a
given gas is plotted we obtain a curve as shown in Fig. 5.22 (curve 1) with a
limiting value $(E/p)_c$ corresponding to the onset of ionization. Rearranging
the Townsend criterion, eqn. (5.88), and remembering that in uniform field
$V = Ed$, where V is the applied voltage, gives

$$\frac{\bar{\alpha}}{p} = \frac{K}{V}\frac{E}{p}$$

and

$$\tan \theta = \frac{\bar{\alpha}/p}{E/p} = \frac{K}{V}. \tag{5.97}$$

Equation (5.97) gives for constant values of K straight lines of a slope ($\tan \theta$)
depending upon the value of the applied voltage (V), curves (2, 3, 4) Fig. 5.22.
At low values of V there is no intersection between the line (curve 4) and the
curve ($\bar{\alpha}/p$) $= f(E/p)$. No breakdown therefore results with small voltages
below Paschen's minimum irrespective of the value pd in eqn. (5.96). At the
higher applied voltage (V), there must exist two breakdown values at a
constant pressure, one corresponding to the small value of gap length (d_1)
and intersection at N and the other to the longer gap (d_2) intersection at W.

The point S (tangent) gives the lowest breakdown value or the minimum sparking voltage. The breakdown voltages corresponding to the points W, N and S are indicated in the Paschen's curve in Fig. 5.21.

The existence of the minimum value in the breakdown voltage–gap length relation may be explained qualitatively by considering the efficiency of the ionization of electrons traversing the gap with different electron energies. Neglecting the secondary coefficient γ for values $pd > (pd)_{min}$, electrons crossing the gap make more frequent collisions with the gas molecules than at $(pd)_{min}$, but the energy gained between collisions is lower than at (pd). Hence, the probability of ionization is lower unless the voltage is increased. For $pd < (pd)_{min}$ electrons cross the gap without making many collisions. The point $(pd)_{min}$ corresponds to the highest ionization efficiency.

An analytical expression for the minimum values of V_{bmin} and $(pd)_{min}$ may be obtained by inserting in the criterion eqn. (5.87) for $\bar{\alpha}/p$ the expression (5.47)

$$\bar{\alpha} = AP \exp\left(-\frac{Bp}{E}\right)\left[= Ap \exp\left(-\frac{Bpd}{V}\right)\right]$$

and determining the minimum value of V.

Assuming that the coefficient γ remains constant, then

$$d = \frac{e^{Bpd/V_b}}{Ap} \ln\left(1 + \frac{1}{\gamma}\right).$$

Rearranging we obtain

$$V_b = \frac{Bpd}{\ln \dfrac{Apd}{\ln(1 + 1/\gamma)}}. \tag{5.98}$$

Differentiating with respect to (pd) and equating the derivative to zero

$$\frac{dV_b}{d(pd)} = \frac{B}{\ln \dfrac{Apd}{\ln(1 + 1/\gamma)}} - \frac{B}{\left[\ln \dfrac{Apd}{\ln(1 + 1/\gamma)}\right]^2} = 0.$$

Therefore

$$\ln \frac{Apd}{\ln(1 + 1/\gamma)} = 1$$

and

$$(pd)_{min} = \frac{e^1}{A} \ln \left(1 + \frac{1}{\gamma} \right). \tag{5.99}$$

Substitution into eqn. (5.98) gives

$$V_{b(min)} = 2.718 \frac{B}{A} \ln \left(\frac{1}{\gamma} + 1 \right). \tag{5.100}$$

This equation could be used for the calculation of the minimum sparking constants (V_{bmin}, $(pd)_{min}$) if the correct values of A and B are used for the simulation of the real dependency of $\bar{\alpha}/p = f(E/p)$ in the vicinity of

$$\frac{d^2(\alpha/p)}{d(E/p)^2} = 0.$$

In practice, the sparking constants (V_{bmin} and $(pd)_{min}$) are measured values, and some of these values for the more common gases are shown in Table 5.12. For example, by inserting in eqn. (5.100) the values for the constants $A = 12$, $B = 365$ and $\gamma = 0.02$ that are commonly quoted in the literature, we obtain for the minimum breakdown voltage for air $V_{bmin} = 325$ V which agrees well with the experimental value quoted in Table 5.12. It should be noted, however, that these values are sometimes strongly dependent upon the cathode material and cathode conditions, according to eqns. (5.94) and (5.95), in which the real value of γ is significant.

The measured minimum sparking voltage in any gas is dependent upon the work function of the cathode material. A minimum sparking voltage as

TABLE 5.12
Minimum Sparking Constants for Various Gases[29]

Gas	$(pd)_{min}$ Torr cm	V_{bmin} volts
Air	0.55	352
Nitrogen	0.65	240
Hydrogen	1.05	230
Oxygen	0.7	450
Sulphur hexafluoride	0.26	507
Carbon dioxide	0.57	420
Neon	4.0	245
Helium	4.0	155

low as 64 V has been observed by Cueilleron[30] in neon between caesium coated electrodes at a gas pressure of 26 Torr.

The breakdown voltage for uniform field gaps in air over a wide range of pressures and gap lengths may be calculated by combining the Schumann's relation with the criterion eqn. (5.88). Schumann[31] has shown that over a wide but restricted range of E/p, α/p may be expressed as

$$\frac{\bar{\alpha}}{p} = C\left[\left(\frac{E}{p}\right) - \left(\frac{E}{p}\right)_c\right]^2 \tag{5.101}$$

where E and E_c are field strengths, E_c being the limiting value of E at which effective ionization starts. p is pressure and C is a constant.

Dividing eqn. (5.88) by pd and combining with eqn. (5.101) we obtain

$$\frac{K}{pd} = C\left[\frac{E}{p} - \left(\frac{E}{p}\right)_c\right]^2$$

or

$$\frac{E}{p} = \left(\frac{E}{p}\right)_c + \sqrt{\frac{K/C}{pd}}$$

and the expression for the breakdown voltage V_b becomes

$$V_b = \left(\frac{E}{p}\right)_c pd + \sqrt{\frac{K}{C}}\sqrt{pd}. \tag{5.102}$$

Inserting the values for the constants E_c and K/c which were determined by Sohst[32] and Schröder[33] for homogeneous field gaps at $p = 1$ bar; 20°C $E_c = 24.36$ (kV/cm), $(K/C) = 45.16$ (kV)^2/cm, eqn. (5.102) becomes

$$V_b = 6.72\sqrt{pd} + 24.36(pd)\,\text{kV}. \tag{5.103}$$

The calculated breakdown voltages, using eqn. (5.103) for uniform field gaps in air for a range of the product pd from 10^{-2} to 5×10^2 (bar cm), are compared with the available experimental data in Fig. 5.23. The calculated and the measured data agree well except at the very low values of the product pd. In this region in which the E/p values are high the Schumann's quadratic relationship [eqn. (5.102)] no longer holds, but this region is of little practical interest.

It is often more convenient to use the gas density δ instead of the gas pressure p in the Paschen's eqn. (5.96), since in the former case account is taken for the effect of temperature at constant pressure on the mean free

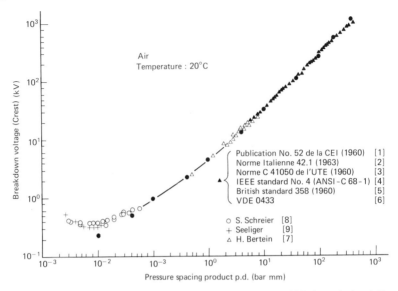

FIG. 5.23. Paschen curve for air in log-log scale. Temperature 20°C. (● calculated $V_B =$ $6.72\sqrt{pd} + 24.4(pd)$).[74]

path in the gas. The number of collisions by an electron in crossing the gap is proportional to the product δd and γ.

Atmospheric air provides the basic insulation for many practical h.v. installations (transmission lines, switchyards, etc.). Since the atmospheric conditions (temperature and pressure) vary considerably in time and locations, the breakdown characteristics of various apparatus will be affected accordingly. For practical purposes, therefore, the breakdown characteristics can be converted to standard atmospheric conditions ($p = 760$ Torr $= 1.01$ bar and $t = 20°C = 293°K$). Correction for the variation in the ambient conditions is made by introducing the relative density defined as

$$\delta = \frac{p}{760} \frac{293}{273+t} = 0.386 \frac{p}{273+t}. \qquad (5.104)$$

The breakdown voltage at standard conditions multiplied by this factor gives the breakdown voltage corresponding to the given ambient conditions approximately

$$V_b(\delta) = \delta V_b(\delta = 1). \qquad (5.105)$$

Paschen's Law is found to apply over a wide range of the parameter values up to 1000–2000 Torr cm. At higher products, however, the breakdown voltage (in non-attaching gases) is found to be somewhat higher than at smaller spacing for the same values of pd. This departure is probably associated with the transition from Townsend breakdown mechanism to the streamer mechanism, as the product pd is increased above a certain value. We have seen that the streamer breakdown criterion is satisfied at higher values of $\bar{\alpha}d$ than the Townsend criterion, i.e. the value of the constant K in eqn. (5.88) will increase from about 8–10 to 18–20. At very low pressure deviations from Paschen's Law are observed when the breakdown mechanism ceases to be influenced by the gas particles and becomes electrode dominated (vacuum breakdown).

5.7 PENNING EFFECT

Paschen's Law is not applicable in many gaseous mixtures. The outstanding example is the neon–argon mixture. A small admixture of argon in neon reduces the breakdown strength below that of pure argon or neon as shown in Fig. 5.24. The reason[34] for this lowering in the

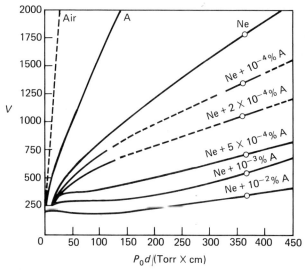

FIG. 5.24. Breakdown voltage curves in neon–argon mixtures between parallel plates at 2-cm spacing at 0°C.

breakdown voltage is that the lowest excited state of neon is metastable and its excitation potential (16 eV) is about 0.9 eV greater than the ionization potential of argon. The metastable atoms have a long life in neon gas, and on hitting argon atoms there is a very high probability of ionizing them. The phenomenon is known as the *Penning effect*.

5.8 THE BREAKDOWN FIELD STRENGTH (E_b)

For uniform field gaps the breakdown field strength in a gas may be obtained from eqn. (5.98) by dividing both sides of this equation by (pd), then

$$\frac{V_b}{(pd)} = \frac{E_b}{p} = \frac{B}{\ln \dfrac{Apd}{\ln (1 + 1/\gamma)}}. \tag{5.106}$$

We note that for a constant gas pressure p the breakdown field strength (E_b) decreases steadily with the gap length (d). Furthermore, the field strength to pressure ratio (E_b/p) is only dependent upon the product of (pd). Equation (5.106) also shows that the breakdown field strength (E_b) for a constant gap length increases with the gap pressures but at a rate slightly lower than directly proportional, as the pressure also affects the denominator in the expression.

Qualitatively the decrease in the pressure related breakdown field strength (E_b/p) with increasing pd may easily be understood by considering the relationship between the ionization coefficient $\bar{\alpha}$ and the field strength

$$\frac{\bar{\alpha}}{p} = f\left(\frac{E}{p}\right)$$

plotted in Fig. 5.25 and applying the Townsend criterion equation to different values of (pd) as shown. The breakdown criterion of eqn. (5.88) can be written as

$$\frac{\bar{\alpha}}{p}(pd) = K.$$

Assuming first that this equation is satisfied for a small product $(pd)_2$ at

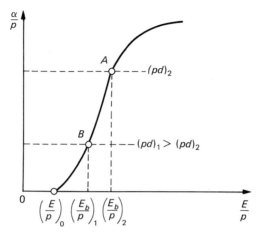

FIG. 5.25. Functional relationship between ionization coefficient α and breakdown field strength at different values of pd.

$(E_b/p)_2$ when $\bar{\alpha}/p$ reaches the point A (Fig. 5.25) and then increasing in value of the product to $(pd)_1$, the criterion equation will now be satisfied at a lower value of $\bar{\alpha}/p(B)$ giving a reduced breakdown strength $(E_b/p)_1$. By repeating this procedure for other values of pd we obtain a functional relationship between the breakdown strength E_b/p and the product pd as shown in

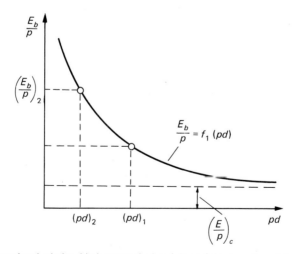

FIG. 5.26. Functional relationship between the breakdown field strength and the product pd.

Fig. 5.26. Thus, the curve obtained in Fig. 5.26 is in qualitative agreement with experimental data.

Calculations of the breakdown strength (E_b) and the pressure related breakdown field strength (E/p) using eqn. (5.106) yields data that are in agreement with the experimental values over a limited range of pressures and gap length. For air a much closer agreement with the experimental data may be obtained using the Schumann's eqn. (5.103). Dividing both sides of eqn. (5.103) by the product pd gives

$$\frac{V_b}{pd} = \frac{E_b}{p} = \frac{6.72}{\sqrt{pd}} + 24.36 \frac{kV}{cm\ bar}. \qquad (5.107)$$

The breakdown field strength (E_b), when calculated for air at standard temperature and pressure for gap lengths extending from 1 mm to 100 mm using eqn. (5.107), agrees well with experimental values.

5.9 BREAKDOWN IN NON-UNIFORM FIELDS

In non-uniform fields, e.g. in point-plane, sphere-plane gaps or coaxial cylinders, the field strength and hence the eff. ionisation coefficient $\bar{\alpha}$ vary across the gap. The electron multiplication is governed by the integral of $\bar{\alpha}$ over the path $(\int \bar{\alpha}\, dx)$. At low pressures the Townsend criterion for spark takes the form

$$\gamma \left[\exp\left(\int_0^d \bar{\alpha}\, dx \right) - 1 \right] = 1 \qquad (5.108)$$

where d is the gap length. The integration must be taken along the line of the highest field strength. The expression is valid also for higher pressures if the field is only slightly non-uniform. In strongly divergent fields there will be at first a region of high values of E/p over which $\alpha/p > 0$. When the field falls below a given strength E_c the integral $\int \alpha\, dx$ ceases to exist. The Townsend mechanism then loses its validity when the criterion relies solely on the γ effect, especially when the field strength at the cathode is low.

In reality breakdown (or inception of discharge) is still possible if one takes into account photoionization processes.

The criterion condition for breakdown (or inception of discharge) for the general case may be represented by modifying the expression (5.90) to take

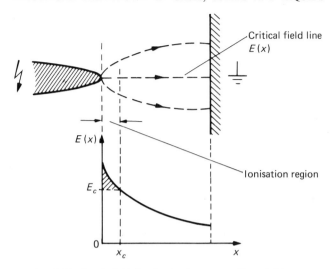

FIG. 5.27. Electric field distribution in a non-uniform field gap.

into account the non-uniform distribution of $\bar{\alpha}$ or

$$\exp \int_0^{x_c < d} \bar{\alpha}\,dx = N_{cr} \qquad (5.109)$$

where N_{cr} is the critical electron concentration in an avalanche giving rise to initiation of a streamer (it was shown to be approx. 10^8, p. 353), x_c is the path of avalanche to reach this size and d the gap length. Hence eqn. (5.109) can be written as

$$\int_0^{x_c < d} \bar{\alpha}\,dx = \ln N_{cr} \approx 18\text{--}20. \qquad (5.109a)$$

Figure 5.27 illustrates the case of a strongly divergent field in a positive point-plane gap. Equation (5.109a) is applicable to the calculation of breakdown or discharge inception voltage, depending on whether direct breakdown occurs or only corona. The difference between direct breakdown and corona inception will be discussed in detail in the next section.

For the special case of a coaxial cylindrical geometry in air, an empirical relation based on many measurements of the critical field strength E_c (corona inception) for different diameters of the inner conductor $(2r)$ and relative air density δ was developed by Peek[35] of the form:

$$\frac{E_c}{\delta} = 31.53 + \frac{9.63}{\sqrt{\delta r}} \qquad (5.110)$$

where E_c is in kV/cm; r in cm and δ is the relative air density defined by eqn. (5.104). For values of $(\delta r) > 1$ cm this expression gives higher values than experimentally observed. Recently Zaengl et al.[36] have developed an analytical expression based upon eqns. (5.109) and (5.101) replacing the Peek's eqn. (5.110) for calculating the corona inception voltage given as

$$\left(\frac{E_c}{\delta}\right)^2 - 2\left(\frac{E_c}{\delta}\right) E_0 \ln\left[\frac{1}{E_0}\left(\frac{E_c}{\delta}\right)\right] - E_0^2 = \frac{K/C}{(\delta r)}. \qquad (5.111)$$

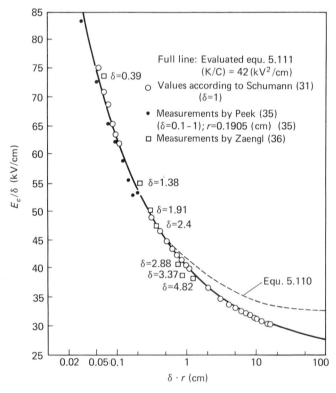

FIG. 5.28. Variation of corona inception field strength (E_c/δ) with δr for coaxial cylindrical geometry in air.

In this expression the constants E_c and K/C have the same significance as in the Schumann's eqn. (5.103), but the best agreement of the calculated values with many of the known measured values (a.c. and d.c.) of positive polarity is obtained with the constant $K/C = 42$ (kV/cm)^2 as compared to $K/C = 45.16$ (kV/cm)^2 used in eqn. (5.103). Figure 5.28 compares the calculated values (E_c/δ) plotted as function of the product (δr) using eqn. (5.111) (solid curve), with the measured values by Peek and those measured by Schumann. The dotted curve indicates the calculated values obtained using the original empirical expression of Peek [eqn. (5.110)]. It is seen that for the product less than $\delta r < 1$ the values obtained from the Peek's empirical expression are in good agreement with experimental observations, but a deviation is observed for conductors of larger radius, due to the fact that the original expression was based on measurements on conductors of small size.

Equation (5.111) also shows that the critical field strength E_c for a coaxial arrangement is independent of the radius of the outer cylinder (R). This is true as long as the field strength $E(R)$ does not exceed (δE_0).

5.10 EFFECT OF ELECTRON ATTACHMENT ON THE BREAKDOWN CRITERIA

In section 5.2 it was shown that there are a number of gases in which the molecules readily attach free electrons forming negative ions, having a similar mass as the neutral gas molecules. They are, therefore, unable to ionize neutral particles under field conditions in which electrons will readily ionize. The ionization by electron collision is then represented by the effective ionization coefficient $(\bar{\alpha} = \alpha - \eta)$.

In the presence of attachment, the growth of current in a gap when the secondary coefficient γ is included in eqn. (5.84) is given by the relation[37]

$$I = I_0 \frac{\dfrac{\alpha}{\alpha - \eta}[\exp{(\alpha - \eta)d - (\eta/\alpha)}]}{\left\{1 - \dfrac{\alpha\gamma}{\alpha - \eta}[\exp{(\alpha - \eta)d - 1}]\right\}} \tag{5.112}$$

where α and γ are the primary and secondary ionization coefficients and η is the attachment coefficient as defined earlier in this chapter. It was also shown that in a given gas both coefficients α and η are dependent only on the field strength E and the gas pressure

$$\left[\frac{\alpha}{p} = f\left(\frac{E}{p}\right)\right], \quad \left[\frac{\eta}{p} = f\left(\frac{E}{p}\right)\right].$$

For a self-sustained discharge in an attaching gas the denominator in eqn. (5.112) will tend to zero, and as a result we obtain the Townsend criterion for attaching gases

$$(\alpha - \eta)d = \ln\left[\frac{(\alpha - \eta)}{\alpha}\frac{1}{\gamma} + 1\right]. \tag{5.113}$$

As the difference of $(\alpha - \eta)/p$ for low values of E/p becomes negative, eqn. (5.113) can only be fulfilled for values $\alpha > \eta$. This means that a critical value of a pressure-dependent field strength exists for which $\alpha = \eta$ and $(E/p) \to (E/p)_0$. Therefore, in the presence of attachment no breakdown can take place in accordance with processes so far considered for this or lower values of E/p.

However, for SF_6, which has been most widely studied because of its practical applications, the breakdown criterion of eqn. (5.113) could experimentally be verified up to now for low values of pressure and gap spacings (pd) only. For high values of this product the reported data are contradictory. This disagreement between the values given by this "Townsend criterion" and the experimental results is principally not due to the necessity to modify eqn. (5.113) to a "streamer criterion" but, as shown by Zaengl,[38] may be associated with the strong dependence of the coefficient γ upon the gas pressure, but mainly depend upon electrode effects.

As all secondary feedback processes represented by the coefficient γ can be quite sensitive to gas pressure,[38] as shown in Fig. 5.29, to electrode surface conditions, or even impurities, the right-hand side of eqn. (5.113) will increase with higher values of gas pressure. Furthermore, since at higher (pd) values the streamer theory applies, which is based upon the space charge field at the head of the avalanche producing secondary electrons and thus secondary avalanches by photoionization, the breakdown criteria for higher gas pressures or products pd are based upon a critical number of electrons N_{cr} produced in an avalanche. For this case the critical number N_{cr} ($\approx 10^8$ electrons) is reached along a path of critical length x_c which is shorter than the gap length d. Counting of x_c starts from the cathode in homogeneous fields, but in inhomogeneous fields the integration of the discharge criterion according to the streamer theory has

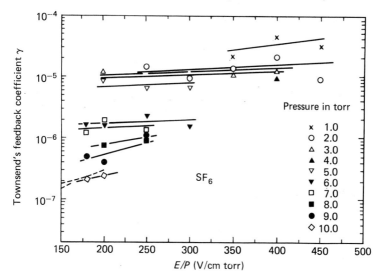

FIG. 5.29. Values of Townsend's feedback coefficient as a function of E/p, with pressure as a parameter.[38]

to be extended over any part of the discharge gap where $\alpha - \eta = \bar{\alpha}$ is appreciable and the spark criterion is given by eqn. (5.109).

For SF_6 most of the experimentally determined values for α and η fit well into a linear relationship

$$\frac{\bar{\alpha}}{p} = \frac{\alpha - \eta}{p} = k\left[\frac{E}{p} - \left(\frac{E}{p}\right)_0\right]. \tag{5.114}$$

The relationship of eqn. (5.114) is plotted in Fig. 5.30. The constants k and $(E/p)_0$ determined from the graph (Fig. 5.30) become $k = 27.7$ (kV)$^{-1}$ or 2.27×10^{-2} (V)$^{-1}$ and $(E/p_0) = 88.5$ kV/cm bar or 118 V/cm Torr. Experiments show that eqn. (5.114) remains valid within the range $75 < E/p < 200$ kV/cm bar.

The steep increase in $\bar{\alpha}/p$ ($= \alpha - \eta/p$) with the pressure-dependent field strength accounts for strong influence of local field distortions upon the breakdown strength (or corona inception) observed in SF_6.

Equation (5.114) can be used for the calculation of the breakdown field strength in SF_6 in uniform or quasi-uniform field gaps. By combining eqn. (5.114) with the criterion eqn. (5.88) we obtain for a homogeneous field

$$\frac{E_b}{p} = (E/p)_0 + \frac{K}{k(pd)} \text{ (kV/cm)}. \tag{5.115}$$

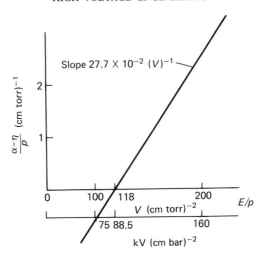

FIG. 5.30. $(\alpha - \eta)/p - (E/p)$ relationship in SF_6.

For a pressure of 760 Torr, using $K = 18$ and the values for k and $(E/p)_0$ from the graph (Fig. 5.30), eqn. (5.115) reduces to approximately

$$E_b = 88.5 + \frac{0.65}{d}\,(kV/cm) \qquad (5.116)$$

and for the breakdown voltage at standard temperature we obtain an expression

$$V_b = 0.65 + 88.5(pd)\,(kV). \qquad (5.117)$$

Equation (5.117) gives good agreement with measured values for the approximate range $1\ kV \leqslant V_b \leqslant 250\ kV$ corresponding to the range of values $4 \times 10^{-2} \leqslant pd \leqslant 3$ bar cm. At higher values of pd the measured values of V_b are lower than predicted by eqn. (5.117) and are found to follow closely the empirical relationship

$$V_b = 40 + 68(pd)\,(kV) \qquad (5.118)$$

$$(pd - bar\ cm).$$

It can be shown, however, that such a reduction of the breakdown voltage has to be related to "microscopic field effects" generated by protrusions at the electrodes, which have not been taken into account in eqn. (5.115).[38]

5.11 PARTIAL BREAKDOWN, CORONA DISCHARGES

In uniform field and quasi-uniform field gaps the onset of measurable ionization usually leads to complete breakdown of the gap. In non-uniform fields various manifestations of luminous and audible discharges are observed long before the complete breakdown occurs. These discharges may be transient or steady state and are known as "coronas". An excellent review of the subject may be found in a book by Loeb.[40] The phenomenon is of particular importance in h.v. engineering where non-uniform fields are unavoidable. It is responsible for considerable power losses from h.v. transmission lines and often leads to deterioration of insulation by the combined action of the discharge ions bombarding the surface and the action of chemical compounds that are formed by the discharge. It may give rise to inteference in communication systems. On the other hand, it has various industrial applications such as high-speed printing devices, electrostatic precipitators, paint sprayers, Geiger counters, etc.

The voltage gradient at the surface of the conductor in air required to produce a visual a.c. corona in air is given approximately by the Peek's expression (5.110).[35]

There is a distinct difference in the visual appearance of corona at wires under different polarity of the applied voltage. Under positive voltage, corona appears in the form of a uniform bluish-white sheath over the entire surface of the wire. On negative wires the corona appears as reddish glowing spots distributed along the wire. The number of spots increases with the current. Stroboscopic studies show that with alternating voltages corona has about the same appearance as with direct voltages. Because of the distinctly different properties of coronas under the different voltage polarities it is convenient to discuss separately positive and negative coronas.

In this section a brief review of the main features of corona discharges and their effect on breakdown characteristics will be included. For detailed treatment of the basic fundamentals of this subject the reader is referred to other literature sources.[40]

Positive or Anode Coronas

The most convenient electrode configurations for the study of the physical mechanism of corona are hemispherically capped rod-plane or point-plane gaps. In the former arragement, by varying the radius of the electrode tip, different degrees of field non-uniformity can be readily achieved. The point-plane arrangement is particularly suitable for obtaining a high localized stress and for localization of dense space charge.

In discussing the corona characteristics and their relation to the breakdown characteristics it is convenient to distinguish between the phenomena that occur under pulsed voltage of short duration (impulse corona), where no space charge is permitted to drift and accumulate, and under long lasting (d.c.) voltages (static field corona).

Under impulse voltages at a level just above ionization threshold, because of the transient development of ionization, the growth of discharge is difficult to monitor precisely. However, with the use of "Lichtenberg figures" techniques,[44] and more recently with high-speed photographic techniques, it has been possible to achieve some understanding of the various discharge stages preceding breakdown under impulse voltages.

The observations have shown that when a positive voltage pulse is applied to a point electrode, the first detectable ionization is of filamentary branch, nature as shown diagrammatically in Fig. 5.31(a). This discharge is called streamer and is analogous to the case of uniform field gaps at higher pd values. As the impulse voltage level is increased, the streamers grow both in length and their number of branches as indicated in Fig. 5.31(b) and (c). One of the interesting characteristics is their large number of branches which never cross each other. The velocity of the streamers decreases rapidly as they penetrate the low field region. Figure 5.32 shows velocities of impulse streamers recorded in air in a 2.5-cm gap under two different values

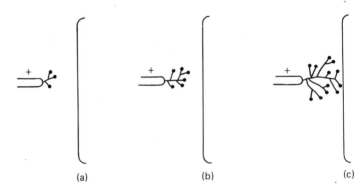

(a)   (b)   (c)

FIG. 5.31. Schematic illustration of the formation of streamers under impulse voltage—progressive growth with increasing pulse duration—positive rod-plane gap.

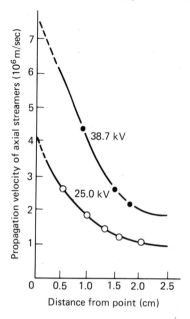

FIG. 5.32. Streamer velocity in a gap of 2.5 cm under two different voltages of fast rise in air.[43]

of voltage. The actual mechanism of the transition from streamer to final breakdown is complex, and several models have been developed[4] to explain this transition, but for space limitation reasons will not be discussed here.

When the voltage is applied for an infinitely long time (e.g. under d.c. or 60 Hz) the ionization products will have sufficient time to wander in the gap and accumulate in space, causing a distortion in the original field.

To study this phenomenon, let us choose the rod-plane gap with the rod tip of radius of (say) 1 cm as shown in Fig. 5.33 and study the various discharge modes together with the breakdown characteristics for this arrangement in atmospheric air. Then if the gap length is small (less than about 2 cm) and the voltage is gradually raised no appreciable ionization is detected up to breakdown. As the gap is increased, the field distribution becomes more inhomogeneous, and on increasing the voltage at first a transient slightly branched filamentary discharge appears. These discharges have been shown to be identical with those observed under impulse voltages and are also called streamers. Under steady state the streamer

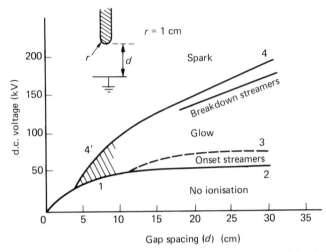

FIG. 5.33. Threshold curves for various modes of anode corona and for spark breakdown for a unispherically capped anode and plate cathode.

develops with varying frequencies, giving rise to currents that are proportional to their physical length. These streamers are somtimes called onset streamers or burst pulses.

When the voltage is increased further, the streamers become more frequent, until the transient activity stops, the discharge becomes self-sustained and a steady glow appears close to the anode. This glow gives rise to continuous but fluctuating current. Further increase in voltage increases the luminosity of the glow both in area and in the intensity. It should be noted that glow corona develops only in the presence of negative ions. On increasing the voltage still further, new and more rigorous streamers appear which ultimately lead to complete breakdown of the gap.

The onsets of the various discharge modes observed, as the gap length is increased, is illustrated schematically in Fig. 5.33 together with the corresponding discharge characteristics. At the smaller spacing when the voltage is still reasonably uniform the streamer is capable of penetrating the weaker field, reaching the cathode and initiating breakdown in the same manner as in uniform field gaps. This condition is shown by curve 1 of Fig. 5.33. With the larger spacing above 10 cm, streamers appear that do not cross the gap (shown by curve 2). Curve 3 represents transition from streamers to steady glow corona without sparking. At the larger spacings there is a considerable spread in the voltage at which breakdown streamers develop preceding the complete breakdown of the gap. The dashed area represents the region of uncertain transitions; portion 1 indicates the onset of streamers followed immediately by transition to spark. If, however, the gap is increased to a point where glow is established and then reduced keeping the voltage constant, the glow discharge will have stabilized the gap against breakdown at a voltage that otherwise would have broken down. If the voltage is then raised, a spark is induced by glow corona (curve 4), but if it is lowered, a streamer breakdown is induced. By decreasing the gap further to lower values and increasing the voltage at the various points the glow-corona sparking voltage characteristic can be projected backwards as shown by curve 4. Thus if a steady corona glow is established, the sparking voltage is raised and the lower breakdown by streamer is suppressed.

Negative or Cathode Corona

With a negative polarity point-plane gap under static conditions above the onset voltage the current flows in very regular pulses as shown in Fig. 5.34(b), which indicates the nature of a single pulse and the regularity with which the pulses are repeated. The pulses were studied in detail by Trichel[44] and are named after their discoverer as "Trichel pulses". The onset voltage is practically independent of the gap length and in value is close to the onset of streamers under positive voltage for the same arrangement. The pulse frequency increases with the voltage and depends upon the radius of the cathode, the gap length and the pressure. The relationship between the pulse frequency and the gap voltage for different gap lengths and a cathode point of 0.75 mm radius in atmospheric air is shown in Fig. 5.34(a). A decrease in pressure decreases the frequency of the Trichel pulses.

Figure 5.35 illustrates the onset voltage of different negative coronas plotted as a function of electrode separation for a typical example of cathode of 0.06 mm radius. The lowest curve gives the onset voltage for Trichel pulses not greatly affected by the gap length. Raising the voltage does not change the mode of the pulses over a wide voltage range. Eventually at a much higher voltage a steady glow discharge is observed, but the transition from Trichel pulses to glow discharge is not sharply defined and is therefore shown as broad transition region in Fig. 5.35. On

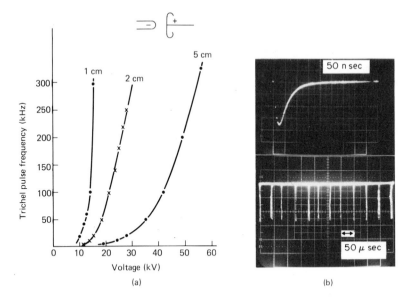

FIG. 5.34. Trichel pulse frequency–voltage relationship for different gap lengths in air (r = 0.75 mm).

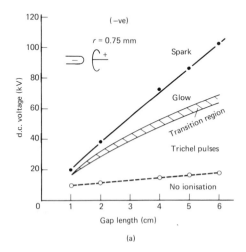

FIG. 5.35. Negative rod-plane breakdown and corona characteristics in atmospheric air.

increasing the voltage further, the glow discharge persists until breakdown occurs. It should be noted that breakdown under negative polarity occurs at considerably higher voltage than under positive voltage, except at low pressures; therefore, under alternating power frequency voltage the breakdown of non-uniform field gap invariably takes place during the positive half-cycle of the voltage wave.

5.12 POLARITY EFFECT—INFLUENCE OF SPACE CHARGE

It was shown in Fig. 5.33 that in non-uniform field gaps the appearance of first streamer may lead to breakdown or it may lead to the establishment of a steady-state corona discharge which stabilizes the gap against breakdown. Accordingly we may have a corona stabilized or direct breakdown. Whether direct or corona stabilized breakdown occurs depends on factors such as the degree of field non-uniformity, gas pressure, voltage polarity and the nature of the gas. For example, in air the corona stabilized breakdown will extend to higher pressures than in SF_6 due to the relatively immobile SF_6^- ions (Figs. 5.36 and 5.37).

Figure 5.36 compares the positive and negative point-plane gap breakdown characteristics measured in air as a function of gas pressure. At very small spacing the breakdown characteristics for the two polarities nearly coincide and no corona stabilized region is observed. As the spacing is increased, the positive characteristics display the distinct high corona breakdown up to a pressure of approximately 7 bar, followed by a sudden drop in breakdown strengths. Under the negative polarity the corona stabilized region extends to much higher pressures.

Experiments carried out in SF_6 show that the region of corona stabilized breakdown under positive voltage is limited to pressures below approximately 1.5 bar. Typical set of breakdown (V_b) and corona onset (V_i) characteristics for a rod-plane gap is included in Fig. 5.37.

From their recent extensive studies of breakdown and corona inception in highly divergent fields in SF_6 Sangkasaad[45] and Hazel[46] have shown that while the corona stabilized voltage increases rapidly as the field becomes more divergent, the critical pressure beyond which the breakdown strength fall abruptly is little affected by the field non-uniformity and for all geometries studies it is limited to pressures below 2 bar.

A practical non-uniform field geometry that is frequently used in the

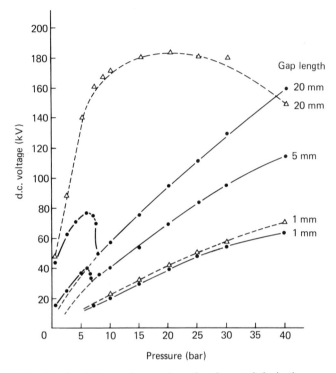

Fɪɢ. 5.36. Point-plane breakdown and corona inception characteristics in air : ——— positive point, — — — negative point (radius of curvature of point $r = 1$ mm).

construction of h.v. apparatus is the coaxial cylindrical arrangement. By properly choosing the radial dimensions for the cylinders it is possible to optimize such a system for the maximum corona free breakdown.

Let us consider a system of two coaxial cylinders with inner and outer radii r_i and r_o respectively. Then it can be readily shown that in the interelectrode space at radial distance r the field strength is given by

$$E_r = \frac{V}{r \ln \dfrac{r_o}{r}}$$

where V is the applied voltage. Since breakdown or corona onset will follow when the voltage stress at the smaller wire reaches the breakdown stress (E_b)

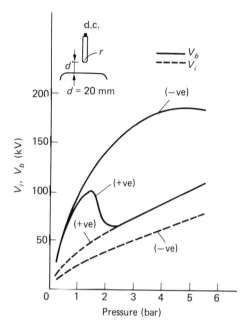

FIG. 5.37. D.C. corona inception and breakdown voltage in SF_6–rod-plane gap $d = 20$ mm; $r = 1$ mm.

we can write the above equation as

$$V_b = E_b r_i \ln \frac{r_o}{r_i}. \tag{5.119}$$

The maximum breakdown voltage for the system is obtained by differentiating eqn. (5.119) with respect to r_i. In eqn. (5.119) E_b is the breakdown (or corona inception) field strength of the system. It was shown earlier that this field strength depends upon the gas density as well as the radius $r = r_i$ of the inner conductor. Neglecting this dependency, which would hold approximately for not too small radii r_i and/or strongly attaching gases (with a steep increase of $\bar{\alpha}/p - f(E/p)$), we may assume that E_b is a constant value. Then, keeping r_o constant this condition gives the optimal design for the system.

$$\frac{dV_b}{dr_i} = E_b \left(\ln \frac{r_o}{r_i} - 1 \right) = 0$$

or

$$\frac{r_o}{r_i} = e$$

and

$$(V_b)_{\text{max}} = E_b r_i. \qquad (5.120)$$

Figure 5.38 shows the functional relationship between the breakdown voltage and the radius of the inner cylinder for a fixed radius r_o of the outer cylinder. The maximum breakdown voltage is also indicated. The dotted curve indicates quantitively the corona onset voltage and the solid curve the breakdown voltage.

At low pressures the breakdown voltage is usually *lower* when the smaller electrode is negative. The effect is due to the higher field at the cathode so that γ is greater and therefore a lower value is needed for $\exp\left(\int_o^d \alpha\, dx\right)$ to satisfy the sparking criterion equation. Figure 5.39 shows the direct breakdown voltage characteristics for nitrogen at low pressures between a wire and coaxial cylinder. At higher pressures the order of the characteristics is reversed. The large polarity effect at the higher pressure can be

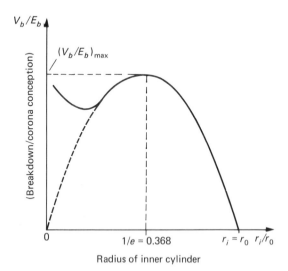

FIG. 5.38. Relationship between breakdown voltage and inner radius in a coaxial cylinder system.

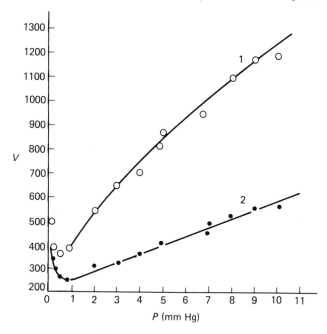

Fig. 5.39. Breakdown voltage curves for nitrogen between a wire and a coaxial cylinder (radii 0.083 and 2.3 cm respectively); curve 1 refers to a positive wire, curve 2 to a negative wire.

qualitatively explained by considering the role of the space charge of the prebreakdown current.

If we consider the case of a positive point-plane gap shown in Fig. 5.40(a) then an ionization by electron collision takes place in the high field region close to the point. Electrons because of their higher mobility will be readily drawn into the anode, leaving the positive space charge behind. The space charge will cause a reduction in the field strength close to the anode and at the same time will increase the field further away from it. The field distortion caused by the positive space charge is illustrated in Fig. 5.40(b). The dotted curve represents the original undistorted field distribution across the gap while the solid curve shows the distorted field. The high field region is in time moving further into the gap extending the region for ionization. The field strength at the tip of the space charge may be high enough for the initiation of a cathode-directed streamer which subsequently may lead to complete breakdown. With the negative point (Fig. 5.41) the electrons are repelled into the low field region and in the case of

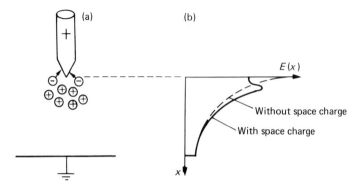

FIG. 5.40. (a) Space charge build-up in positive point-plane gap. (b) Field distortion by space charge.

attaching gases become attached to the gas molecules and tend to hold back the positive space charge which remains in the space between the negative charge and the point. In the vicinity of the point the field is grossly enhanced, but the ionization region is drastically reduced. The effect is to terminate ionization. Once ionization ceases, the applied field sweeps away the negative and positive ion space charge from the vicinity of the point and the cycle starts again after the clearing time for the space charge. To overcome this retarding action of the ions a higher voltage is required, and hence negative breakdown voltage is higher than the positive breakdown voltage in gaps with marked asymmetrical fields.

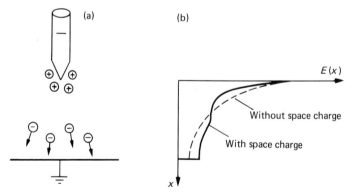

FIG. 5.41. (a) Space charge build-up in negative point-plane gap. (b) Field distortion by space charge.

Mathematically at any given time the voltage across the gap is given by the field integral $\int E(x)\,dx = V$. Integration of the space charge distorted field in Figs. 5.40 and 5.41 respectively shows immediately that

$$V_b(+\text{point}) < V_b(-\text{point}).$$

5.13 SURGE BREAKDOWN VOLTAGE—TIME LAG

For the initiation of breakdown an electron must be available to start the avalanche. With slowly rising voltages (d.c. and a.c.) there are usually sufficient initiatory electrons created by cosmic rays and naturally occurring radioactive sources. Under surge voltages and pulses of short duration, however, the gap may not break down as the peak voltage reaches the lowest breakdown value (V_s) unless the presence of initiatory electrons is ensured by using artificial irradiation. V_s is a voltage which leads to breakdown of the gap after a long time of application. With weak irradiation the peak value may have to be greatly increased so that the voltage remains above the d.c. value (V_s) for long intervals of time. Figure 5.42 illustrates the breakdown on a step-function voltage pulse; V_p represents the peak value of a step voltage applied at time $t = 0$ to a gap that breaks down under V_s after a long time.

The time which elapses between the application of voltage to a gap

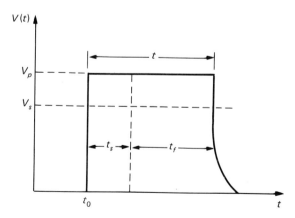

FIG. 5.42. Time lag components under a step voltage. V_s minimum static breakdown voltage; V_p peak voltage; t_s statistical time lag; t_f formative time lag.

sufficient to cause breakdown and the breakdown is called the time lag (t). It consists of two components: one is the time which elapses during the voltage application until a primary electron appears to initiate the discharge and is known as the statistical time lag (t_s); and the other is the time required for the breakdown to develop once initiated and is known as the formative time lag (t_f).

The statistical time lag depends upon the amount of preionization in the gap. This in turn depends upon the size of the gap and the radiation producing the primary electrons. The appearance of such electrons is usually statistically distributed. The techniques generally used for irradiating gaps artificially, and thereby reducing the statistical time lag, include the use of u.v. light, radioactive materials and illumination by auxiliary sparks. The statistical time will also be greatly reduced by the application of an overvoltage $(V_p - V_s)$ to the gap.

The formative time lag (t_f) depends essentially upon the mechanism of spark growth in question. In cases when the secondary electrons arise entirely from electron emission at the cathode by positive ions, the transit time from anode to cathode will be the dominant factor determining the formative time. The formative time lag increases with the gap length and the field non-uniformity, but it decreases with the applied overvoltage.

Breakdown Probability under Impulse Voltages

An impulse voltage is a unidirectional voltage which rises rapidly to a maximum value and then decays slowly to zero. The exact definition of a standard impulse voltage was presented in Chapter 2.

When an impulse voltage of a peak value higher than V_s is applied to a gap, as shown in Fig. 5.43, there is a certain probability but not a certainty that breakdown will follow. For breakdown it is essential that the spark develops during the interval of overvoltage $[V(t) - V_s]$ duration, i.e. the overvoltage duration must exceed the time lag $[t < (t_2 - t_1)]$. For a given impulse voltage waveshape the overvoltage duration will increase with the voltage amplitude (V_p).

Because of the statistical nature of the time lags, when a given number of impulses of an amplitude V_p, exceeding the static value V_s, is applied to a gap only a certain percentage will lead to breakdown. We therefore obtain a breakdown probability P for each given applied maximum impulse voltage

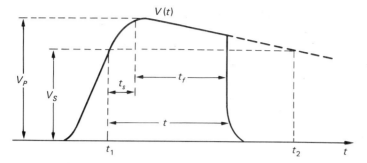

Fig. 5.43. Breakdown under impulse voltage.

V_p as a function of V_p. The breakdown probability for a given impulse voltage is obtained by applying a larger number of identical impulses (e.g. 100) and taking the ratio of the number of impulses that lead to breakdown to the total number applied. Figure 5.44 illustrates an example of the breakdown probability distribution function for impulse voltages of amplitude V_p. $V_{b\text{-}100}$ represents the 100% breakdown voltage, i.e. each voltage application of this magnitude leads to breakdown. This voltage is of particular importance in determining "protective levels".

$V_{b\text{-}50}$ is the 50% breakdown voltage, i.e. one-half of the applied voltages at this level lead to breakdown.

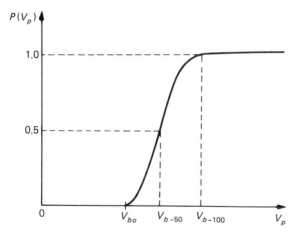

Fig. 5.44. Breakdown probability under impulse voltage. V_{bc} impulse withstand level; $V_{b\text{-}50}$ 50% impulse breakdown; $V_{b\text{-}100}$ 100% breakdown-protective level.

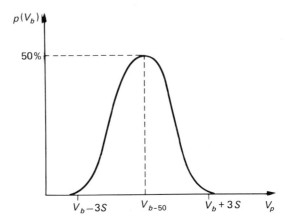

FIG. 5.45. Gaussian probability distribution curve.

V_{b-0} represents the highest impulse voltage that does not lead to break-down. It is known as the "impulse withstand level" and is important in the design of insulations. In practice it is convenient to present the $P(V_p) -$ V_p data on a logarithmic scale known as Gaussian probability scale which gives a linear relationship. The distribution function can also be presented by the normal (Gaussian) distribution shown in Fig. 5.45. Because of the asymptotic approach of the curve to the values V_{b-0} and V_{b-100} the exact values (V_{b-0} and V_{b-100}) can only be obtained from a very large number of experimental observations. These values, however, can be approx. obtained from the distribution of breakdown values about the middle value enclosed between the limits of standard deviation S. For example, if we count all breakdown enclosed between $\pm 3S$, i.e.

$$V_{b-0} = V_{b-50} - 3S$$

$$V_{b-100} = V_{b-50} + 3S$$

the range includes the breakdown probability from 0.15% to 99.85%.

Volt-Time Characteristics

When an impulse voltage of a value V_{b-100} or higher is applied to a gap, breakdown will result on each voltage application. The time required for

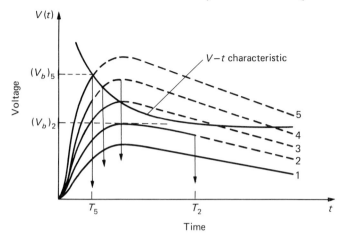

FIG. 5.46. Impulse-time-volt characteristics.

the spark development (time lag) will depend upon the rate of rise of voltage and the field geometry. Therefore, for each gap geometry it is possible to construct a volt-time characteristic by applying a number of impulses of increasing amplitude and noting oscillographically the time lag. A schematic plot of such a characteristic is shown in Fig. 5.46. In uniform and quasi-uniform field gaps the characteristic is usually sharply defined and it rises steeply with increasing the rate of rise of the applied voltage. In non-uniform field gaps, however, due to larger scatter in the results, the data fall into a dispersion band as shown in Fig. 5.47. The time to breakdown is less sensitive to the rate of voltage rise. Hence, quasi-uniform field gaps (sphere-sphere) have often been used as protective devices against overvoltages in electric power systems. The volt-time characteristic is an important practical property of any insulating device or structure. It provides the basis for establishing the impulse strength of the insulation as well as for the design of the protection level against overvoltages and will be discussed in Chapter 7.

Experimental Studies of Time Lags

Numerous investigators have studied time lags in the past. In the techniques generally used either a constant voltage is applied to an

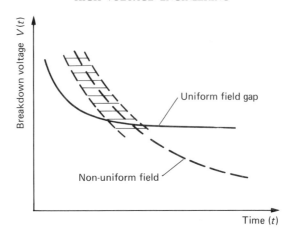

FIG. 5.47. Schematic diagram of volt-time characteristics for uniform and non-uniform field gaps.

irradiated gap and a spark is initiated by a sudden illumination of the gap from a nearby spark, or an overvoltage is suddenly applied to a gap already illuminated.

In the former case the time lag is measured from the flash until breakdown occurs, while in the latter the time lag is measured between the voltage application and the gap breakdown. The overvolted conditions may be obtained either by superimposing a step voltage pulse upon a direct voltage already applied to the gap or by using an impulse voltage of a suitably short front duration. The measured time lags for given experimental conditions are usually presented graphically by plotting the average time lags against the overvoltage. The latter is defined as the percentage ratio of the voltage in question to the minimum direct voltage which will cause breakdown. In the case when an impulse voltage is used on its own, the time lags are plotted against the impulse ratio defined as the ratio of the applied impulse voltage to the minimum direct breakdown voltage.

The measured values are affected by factors such as the intensity of the background irradiation, the nature and the condition of the electrode surface, the gap length, the electron affinity of the gas, etc.

With a gap illuminated from an intense u.v. source, time lags down to 10^{-8} sec and shorter have been recorded in highly overvolted gaps.[47]

Figure 5.48 shows time lags of spark breakdown for short gaps with the

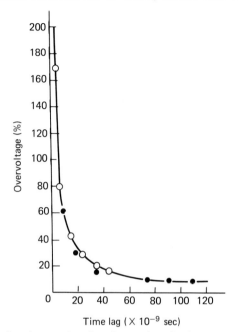

FIG. 5.48. Time lag of spark gap as function of overvoltage for short gap between spheres with intense u.v. illumination of the cathode in air.

cathode irradiated by a quartz mercury lamp, obtained by Brayant and Newman[47] between spheres in air. Fisher and Benderson[48] studied time lags in air between uniform field electrodes in slightly overvolted conditions and the results obtained for four gap lengths are shown in Fig. 5.49. These authors used different gas pressures and found that in the range of pressure from 760 Torr down to about 200 Torr the results were independent of the gas pressure.

Long and highly scattered time lags have been observed in strongly electronegative gases under irradiated conditions. Figure 5.50 compares time lags observed in SF_6 with those obtained in air under similar experimental conditions. It was impossible[49] to attribute these long time lags to the shortage of initiatory electrons. It was suggested that the long time lags are associated with the complex nature of the growth of spark in the highly electron attaching gases.

An alternative method for presenting time lags has been developed by Laue[50] and Zuber.[51] These authors showed that the time lag in spark

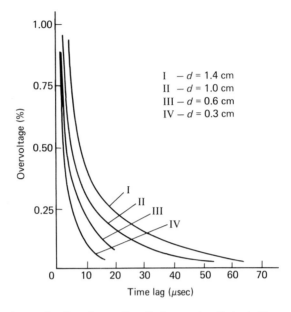

FIG. 5.49. Time lag as a function of overvoltage for four gap lengths in air. The curves represent the average data for all pressures between atmospheric and 200 mm Hg.

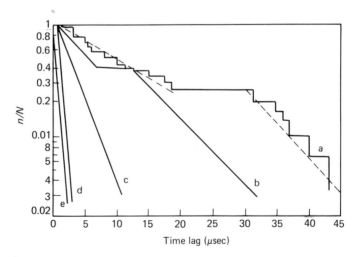

FIG. 5.50. Time lag distribution in SF_6 and air. Overvoltages: (a) 10%; (b) 10%; (c) 20%; (d) 25% for SF_6; (e) 5.3% for air.

gaps may be represented in the form

$$\frac{n}{N} = e^{-\int_0^t \rho_1 \rho_2 \beta \, dt} \tag{5.121}$$

where N represents the total number of time lags observed, n is the number of time lags of length greater than t, β the rate at which electrons are produced in the gap by irradiation, ρ_1 the probability of an electron appearing in a region of the gap where it can initiate a spark, and ρ_2 the probability that an electron at a given field strength will lead to the development of the spark. The factor ρ_1 is a function of the gap length and the gas density, while ρ_2 is a function of the applied field. The factor β is dependent on the source of irradiation. Providing that the primary current in the gap is constant and the applied field remains constant with respect to time, eqn. (5.121) can be written as:

$$\frac{n}{N} = e^{-kt}. \tag{5.122}$$

Equation (5.122) gives a linear relation between $\ln \dfrac{n}{N}$ and time t. The method gives a truer representation of the results in the case of highly scattered results.

5.14 BREAKDOWN IN SOLID AND LIQUID DIELECTRICS

5.14.1 Breakdown in Solids

Solid insulations form an integral part of h.v. structures. The solid materials provide the mechanical support for conducting parts and at the same time insulate the conductors from one another. Frequently practical insulation structures consist of combinations of solids with liquid and/or gaseous media. Therefore, a knowledge of failure mechanisms of solid dielectrics under electric stress is of great practical importance.

In gases the transport of electricity is limited to positive and negative charge carriers, and the destruction of insulating properties involves a rapid growth of current through formation of electron avalanches. The mechanism of electrical failure in gases is now understood reasonably clearly. This is not the case for solid insulations. Although numerous investigators have studied the breakdown of solids for nearly a century now, and a number of detailed theories have been put forward which aimed to explain quantitatively the breakdown processes in solids, the state of knowledge in this area is still very crude and inconclusive.

Electrical conduction studies in solids are obscured by the fact that the transport phenomena besides electronic and ionic carriers include also currents due to the slower polarization processes such as slow moving dipoles (orientation polarization) and interfacial polarization. Electrical methods are unable to distinguish between the conduction currents and the currents due to polarization having a longer time constant than the duration of a particular experiment. At low stresses and normal temperatures conduction by free electrons and ions in solids is exceptional. Examples in which the conduction is believed to be of the simple electrolytic type at room temperature and above are glasses. In this case the conduction–temperature relation is found to be of the form

$$\sigma = A \exp \left[-\frac{u}{kT} \right]$$

where A and u are empirical constants. Ceramics also develop a significant conductivity at higher temperatures that may be electronic or ionic.

As the stress in solids is increased and approaches the breakdown stress, the current is found to increase exponentially, but does not vary so markedly with time for steady voltage.[52] This increased current at high stresses is generally believed to result from the injection of carriers from an electrode or from electron multiplication in the bulk of the material or both. In addition, if impurities or structural defects are present they may cause local allowed energy levels (traps) in the forbidden band, and electrons may pass through the insulator by jumping from one trap to another (hopping effect).

From the electrodes the electrons are believed to be ejected by either the "Schottky's emission effect" or "the field emission effect" (tunelling) discussed earlier in this chapter. Once injected into the material the electron multiplication is thought to be analogous to that in a gas discharge. Under certain strictly controlled experimental conditions the breakdown of solids may therefore be accomplished by a process similar to gas breakdown. Under normal industrial conditions, however, the same solid materials are found to exhibit a wide range of dielectric strength, depending upon the conditions of the environment and the method of testing. The measured

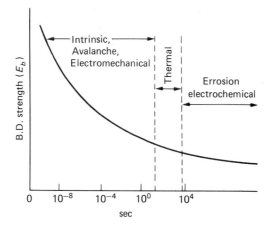

FIG. 5.51. Variation of breakdown strength in solids with time of stressing.

breakdown voltage is influenced by a large number of external factors such as temperature, humidity, duration of test, whether a.c., d.c., or impulse voltage is applied, pressure applied to the electrodes, discharges in the ambient medium, discharges in cavities and many other factors. The fundamental mechanisms of breakdown in solids are understood much less clearly than in gases; nevertheless, several distinct mechanisms have been identified and treated theoretically.[53–55]

In this section the presently accepted breakdown mechanisms will be discussed briefly in a qualitative manner. No conduction mechanism will be discussed here and the reader is referred to reference 57. Broadly speaking the mechanism of failure and the breakdown strength changes with the time of voltage application and for discussion purposes it is convenient to divide the time scale of voltage application into regions in which different mechanisms operate as shown in Fig. 5.51.

Intrinsic Breakdown

If the material under test is pure and homogeneous, the temperature and environmental conditions are carefully controlled, and the sample is so stressed that there are no external discharges. Then under voltages applied for short time the electric strength increases up to an upper limit which is called the *Intrinsic Electric Strength*. The intrinsic strength is a property of the material and temperature only. Experimentally the intrinsic strength is rarely reached, but numerous attempts have been made to measure it for various materials. To achieve the highest strength the sample is so designed that there is a high stress in the centre of the solid under test and too low stress at the edges to cause discharge in the medium as shown in Fig. 5.52.

The intrinsic breakdown is accomplished in times of the order of 10^{-8} sec and has therefore been postulated to be electronic in nature. The stresses required for an intrinsic breakdown are well in excess of 10^6 V/cm. The intrinsic strength is generally assumed to be reached when electrons in the insulator gain sufficient energy from the applied field to cross the forbidden energy gap from the valence to the conduction band. The criterion condition is formulated by solving an equation for the energy balance between the gain of energy by conduction electrons from the applied field and its loss to the lattice. Several models have been proposed in an attempt to predict the critical value of the field which causes intrinsic breakdown, but no completely satisfactory solution has yet been obtained. The models used by various workers differ from each other in the proposed mechanisms of energy transfer from conduction electrons to the lattice, and also by the assumptions made concerning the distribution of conduction electrons. In pure homogenous dielectric materials the conduction and the valence bands are separated by a large energy gap, and at room temperature the electrons cannot acquire sufficient thermal energy to make transitions from valence to conduction band. The conductivity in perfect dielectrics should therefore be zero. In practice, however, all crystals contain some imperfections in their structures due to missing atoms, and more frequently due to the presence of foreign atoms (impurities). The impurity atoms may act as traps for free electrons in energy levels that lie just below the conduction band, as illustrated schematically in Fig. 5.53.

At low temperatures the trap levels will be mostly filled with electrons

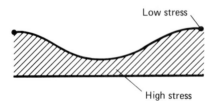

FIG. 5.52. Electrode arrangement used for measuring intrinsic breakdown in solids.

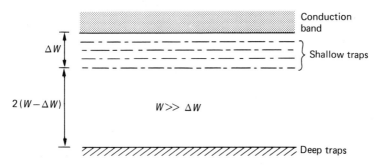

FIG. 5.53. Schematic energy level diagram for an amorphous dielectric.

caught there as the crystal was cooled down during its manufacturing. At room temperature some of the trapped electrons will be excited thermally into the conduction band, because of the small energy gap between the trapping levels and the conduction level. An amorphous crystal will therefore have some free conduction electrons.

When a field is applied to a crystal the conduction electrons gain energy from it, and due to collisions between them the energy is shared by all electrons. For a stable condition this energy must be somehow dissipated. If there are relatively few electrons such as in pure crystals, most of the energy will be transferred to the lattice by electron-lattice interaction. In steady-state conditions the electron temperature (T_e) will be then nearly equal to the lattice temperature (T).

In amorphous dielectrics the electron interactions predominate, the field raises the energy of the electrons more rapidly than they can transfer it to the lattice, and the electron temperature T_e will exceed the lattice temperature T. The effect of the increased electron temperature will be a rise in the number of trapped electrons reaching the conduction band. This increases the material's conduction and as the electron temperature continues to increases a complete breakdown is eventually reached known as "high-temperature breakdown".

Neglecting for the moment the details of the mechanism of energy transfer and assuming electronic conduction in solids, then for an applied field E the rate of energy gained by electrons from the field will be a function of the field strength E and the lattice temperature T. The rate at which this energy is transferred to the lattice will depend only on T. In addition, both rates will depend on parameters describing the conduction electrons. If we denote these parameters collectively by α, then for the steady-state

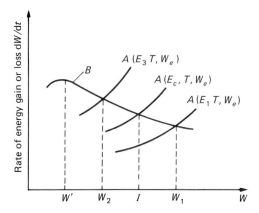

FIG. 5.54. The average rate of energy gain $A(E, T, W_e)$ from an applied field for various field strengths and the average rate of energy loss to lattice $B(W_L, T)$.

conditions the energy equation for conduction electrons may be written as

$$A(E, T, \alpha) = B(T, \alpha) \qquad (5.122)$$

where the l.h.s. represents the rate of energy gain by electrons from the field and the r.h.s. the rate of energy transfer from electrons to lattice. Equation (5.122) can be physically satisfied for values of E below a certain critical value E_c, and this value has been considered by several workers as the intrinsic critical field. The value of E_c can be found by identifying correctly the parameters α describing the conduction electrons and then solving eqn. (5.122) for the critical field strength E_c.

For a pure homogeneous dielectric Fröhlich developed the so-called "high energy" breakdown criterion, based on the assumption that the dielectric is destroyed by infinitely large multiplication of electrons in the conduction band. In this model the critical field strength (E_c) in the energy balance eqn. (5.122) is obtained by first identifying the parameter α with the electron energy (W_e) such that the balance equation is satisfied and then calculating the critical field strength.

The functional relationship between the parameters in eqn. (5.122) is shown schematically in Fig. 5.54, which shows the average rate of energy gain from the field for various field strengths and the rate of energy loss to the lattice.

For the critical field criterion, eqn. (5.122) becomes

$$A(E_c, T, I) = B(T, I) \qquad (5.123)$$

where I is the ionization energy corresponding to transition of an electron from a valence band to a conduction band. From Fig. 5.54 it is seen that for an electron to remain accelerated and thus lead to instability at any given field it should find itself with an energy which brings it above the curve B so that it gains energy more rapidly than it loses. Equation (5.123) enables us to determine the critical field strength E_c that is required to cause collision ionization from valence to conduction band. For field strength exceeding E_c the electrons gain energy more rapidly from the field than they lose to the lattice and breakdown will result. The above mechanism applies to pure solids in which the equilibrium is controlled by collisions between electrons and the lattice vibrations.

Fröhlich and Paranjape[56] have extended this model to amorphous materials in which the concentration of conduction (or trapped) electrons is high enough to make electron-electron collisions the dominant factor. In this case it is necessary to calculate the electron temperature T_e which will be higher than the lattice temperature T.

The energy balance eqn. (5.122) will then take the form

$$A(E, T_e, T) = B(T_e, T). \qquad (5.124)$$

This relationship is plotted schematically in Fig. 5.55 in which the family of curves plotted for various values of E represents the l.h.s. of the equation and the single curve represents the r.h.s. The intersections give possible solutions for the various electron temperatures.

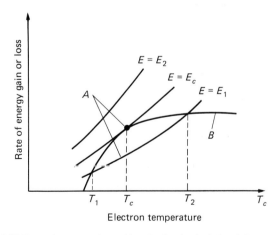

FIG. 5.55. Rate of energy gain and loss for h.t. intrinsic breakdown model.

For the analytical expressions for the critical field strength (E_c) for both of the above two models the reader should refer to reference 57.

To date there has been no direct experimental proof to show whether an observed breakdown is intrinsic or not, except for plastic materials such as Polyethylene and so conceptually it remains an ideal mechanism identified as the highest value obtainable after all secondary effects have been eliminated.

Streamer Breakdown

Under certain controlled conditions in strictly uniform fields with the electrodes embedded in the specimen, breakdown may be accomplished after the passage of a single avalanche. An electrode entering the conduction band of the dielectric at the cathode will drift towards the anode under the influence of the field gaining energy between collisions and loosing it on collisions. On occasions the free path may be long enough for the energy gain to exceed the lattice ionization energy and an additional electron is produced on collision. The process is repeated and may lead to the formation of an electron avalanche similar to gases. Seitz[58] suggested that breakdown will ensure if the avalanche exceeds a certain critical size and derived an expression for a single avalanche breakdown strength. The concept is similar to the streamer theory developed by Raether, and Meek and Loeb for gases discussed earlier.

Electromechanical Breakdown

Substances which can deform appreciably without fracture may collapse when the elctrostatic compression forces on the test specimen exceed its mechanical compressive strength. The compression forces arise from the electrostatic attraction between surface charges which appear when the voltage is applied. The pressure exerted when the field reaches about 10^6 V/cm may be several kN^2/m^2. Following Stark and Garton,[59] if d_0 is the initial thickness of a specimen of material of Young's modulus Y, which decreases to a thickness of $d(m)$ under an applied voltage V, then the electrically developed compressive stress is in equilibrium with the mechanical compressive strength if

$$\varepsilon_0 \varepsilon_r \frac{V^2}{2d^2} = Y \ln \left(\frac{d_0}{d} \right) \tag{5.125}$$

or

$$V^2 = d^2 \frac{2Y}{\varepsilon_0 \varepsilon_r} \ln \left(\frac{d_0}{d} \right)$$

where ε_0 and ε_r are the permittivity of free space and the relative permittivity of the dielectric.

Differentiating with respect to d we find that expression (5.125) has a maximum when $d/d_0 = \exp \left[-\frac{1}{2} \right] = 0.6$. Therefore, no real value of V can produce a stable value of d/d_0 less than 0.6. If the intrinsic strength is not reached at this value, a further increase in V make the thickness unstable and the specimen collapses. The highest apparent strength is then given by

$$E_a = \frac{V}{d_0} = 0.6 \left[\frac{Y}{\varepsilon_0 \varepsilon_r} \right]^{1/2}. \tag{5.126}$$

This treatment ignores the possibility of instability occurring in lower average field because of stress concentration at irregularities, the dependence of Y on time and stress, and also on plastic flow.

Edge Breakdown and Treeing

In practical insulation systems the solid material is stressed in conjunction with one or more other materials. If one of the materials is, for example, gas or liquid, then the measured breakdown voltage will be influenced more by the weak medium than by the solid.

A cross-section of a simplified example is shown in Fig. 5.56 which represents testing of a dielectric slab between sphere-plane electrodes. Ignoring the field distribution, i.e. assuming homogeneous field, if we consider an elementary cylindrical volume of end area dA spanning the electrodes at distance x as shown in Fig. 5.56, then on applying the voltage V between the electrodes, a fraction V_1 of the voltage appears across the ambient given by

$$V_1 = \frac{V d_1}{d_1 + \left(\dfrac{\varepsilon_1}{\varepsilon_2} \right) d_2} \tag{5.127}$$

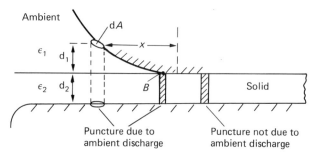

FIG. 5.56. Breakdown of solid specimen due to ambient discharge—edge effect.

where d_1 and d_2 represent the thickness of the media 1 and 2 in Fig. 5.56 and ε_1 and ε_2 are their respective permittivities. For the simple case when a gaseous dielectrics is in series with a solid dielectric stressed between two parallel plate electrodes, the stress in the gaseous part will exceed that of solid by the ratio of permittivities or $E_1 = \varepsilon_r E_2$. For the case shown in Fig. 5.56, the stress in the gaseous part increases further as x is decreased, and reaches very high values as d_1 becomes very small (point B). Consequently the ambient breaks down at a relatively low applied voltage. The charge at the tip of the discharge will further disturb the applied local field and transform the arrangement to a highly non-uniform system. The charge concentration at the tip of a discharge channel has been estimated to be sufficient to give local field of the order of 10 MV/cm, which is higher than the intrinsic breakdown field. A local breakdown at the tips of the discharge is likely, therefore, and complete breakdown is the result of many such breakdown channels formed in the solid and extending step by step through the whole thickness.

The breakdown in general is not accomplished through the formation of a single discharge channel, but assumes a tree-like structure as shown in Fig. 5.57 which can be readily demonstrated in a laboratory by applying an impulse voltage between point-plane electrodes with the point embedded in a transparent solid, e.g. plexiglass. The tree pattern shown in Fig. 5.57 was recorded by Cooper[60] with a 1/30-μsec impulse voltage of the same amplitude. After application of each impulse the channels were observed with a microscope and new channels were recorded. Not every impulse will produce a channel. The time required for this type of breakdown under alternating voltage will vary from a few seconds to a few minutes.

The tree-like pattern discharge is not limited specifically to the edge effect

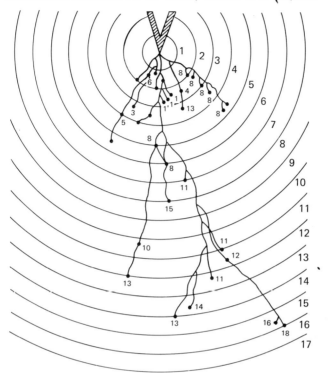

Fig. 5.57. Breakdown channels in perspex between point-plane electrodes. Radius of point = 0.01 in; thickness 0.19 in. Total number of impulses = 190. Number of channels produced = 16; (n) point indicates end of nth channel. Radii of circles increase in units of 10^{-2} in.

but may be observed in other dielectric failure mechanisms in which non-uniform field stresses predominate.

Thermal Breakdown

When an insulation is stressed, because of conduction currents and dielectric losses due to polarization, heat is continuously generated within the dielectric. In general the conductivity (σ) increases with temperature, conditions of instability are reached when the rate of heating exceeds the rate of cooling and the specimen may undergo thermal breakdown. The

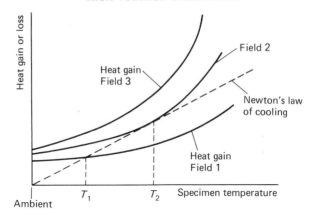

FIG. 5.58. Thermal stability or instability under different applied fields.

situation is illustrated graphically in Fig. 5.58 in which the cooling of a specimen is represented by the straight line and the heating at various field strengths by curves of increasing slope. Field (1) is in equilibrium at temperature T_1, field (2) is in a state of unstable equilibrium at T_2 and field (3) does not reach a state of equilibrium at all. To obtain the basic equation for thermal breakdown let us consider a cube of face area $A(m^2)$ within dielectric. Assume that the heat flow in the x-direction is as shown in Fig. 5.59, then the

$$\text{Heat flow across face (1)} = KA\frac{dT}{dx} \quad (K\text{—thermal conductivity}).$$

$$\text{Heat flow across face (2)} = KA\frac{dT}{dx} + KA\frac{d}{dx}\left(\frac{dT}{dx}\right)\Delta x.$$

The second term represents the heat input into the block.
  Hence

$$\text{heat flow/volume} = K\frac{d}{dx}\left(\frac{dT}{dx}\right) = \text{div } (K \text{ grad } T).$$

The conservation of energy requires that heat input into the element must be equal to the heat conducted away, plus the heat used to raise the temperature T of the solid or

heat generated = heat absorbed + heat lost to surroundings,

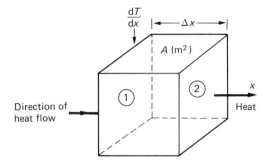

FIG. 5.59. Heat input and output, cubical specimen.

i.e.

$$C_v \frac{dT}{dt} + \text{div } (K \text{ grad } T) = \sigma E^2 \qquad (5.128)$$

where C_v is the thermal capacity of the dielectric, σ is the electrical conductivity and in the case of alternating voltage the heat is generated primarily as a result of dipole relaxation and the conductivity is replaced by $\omega \varepsilon_0 \varepsilon_r''$, where ε_0 represents permittivity of free space and ε_r'', the imaginary component of the complex relative permittivity of the material.

Calculation of the critical thermal situation involves the solution of eqn. (5.128). In solving it, one assumes that a critical condition arises and the insulation properties are lost, when at some point in the dielectric the temperature exceeds a critical temperature T_c. The solution gives the time required to reach T_c for a given field and boundary condition. The equation cannot be solved analytically for the general case since C_v, K and σ may be all functions of temperature (T) and σ may also depend upon the applied field. We consider two extreme cases for the solution of eqn. (5.128).

Case 1. This assumes a rapid build-up of heat so that heat lost to surroundings can be neglected and all heat generated is used in raising the temperature of the solid. We obtain an expression for "impulse thermal breakdown" and eqn. (5.128) reduces to

$$C_v \frac{dT}{dt} = \sigma E^2.$$

To obtain the critical field E_c, assume that we apply a ramp function field.

Then

$$E = \left(\frac{E_c}{t_c}\right) t$$

and

$$\sigma E^2 = C_v \frac{dT}{dE} \frac{dE}{dt}.$$

Also

$$\sigma = \sigma_0 \exp\left[-\frac{u}{kT}\right].$$

σ_0 is the conductivity at ambient temperature T_0. Substituting for σ and rearranging

$$\int_0^{E_c} \frac{t_c}{E_c} \frac{\sigma_0}{C_v} E^2 \, dE = \int_{T_0}^{T_c} \exp\left(\frac{u}{kT}\right) dT$$

for the case when

$$u \gg kT$$

and

$$T_c > T_0 \quad (T_c - \text{critical temperature})$$

the solution of the r.h.s. is

$$\int_{T_0}^{T_c} \exp\left(\frac{u}{kT}\right) dT \rightarrow T_0^2 \frac{k}{u} \exp\left(\frac{u}{kT_0}\right)$$

and that of the l.h.s. is

$$\int_0^{E_c} \frac{t_c}{E_c} \frac{\sigma_0}{C_v} E^2 \, dE \rightarrow \frac{1}{3} t_c \frac{\sigma_0}{C_v} E_c^2.$$

Therefore

$$E_c = \left[\frac{3C_v k T_0^2}{\sigma_0 u t_c}\right] \frac{1}{2} \exp\left(\frac{u}{2kT_0}\right). \tag{5.129}$$

It is seen that reaching the critical condition requires a combination of critical time and critical field and that the critical field is independent of the critical temperature T_c due to the fast rise in temperature.

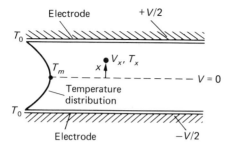

FIG. 5.60. Arrangement for testing a dielectric for minimum thermal B.D. voltage.

Case 2 concerns maximum thermal voltage, i.e. the lowest voltage for thermal breakdown. For this case we assume a thick dielectric slab that is constrained to ambient temperature at its surfaces by using sufficiently large electrodes as shown in Fig. 5.60.

On application of voltage, after some time, a temperature distribution within the dielectric will be established with the highest temperature at the centre (T_1), that at the surface remaining at ambient temperature. On increasing the voltage to a new higher value, an equilibrium will be established at a higher central temperature (T_2). If the process is continued, a thermal runaway will eventually result as shown in Fig. 5.61.

To calculate the maximum thermal voltage, let us consider a point inside

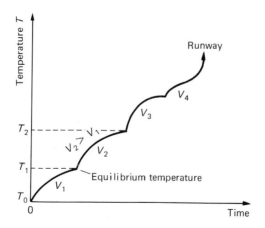

FIG. 5.61. Temperature-time relationship for slow thermal stressing under various applied voltages.

the dielectric distance x from the centre, and let the voltage and temperature at that point be V_x and T_x respectively. For this case we assume that all the heat generated in the dielectric will be carried away to its surroundings through the electrodes. Neglecting the term $C_V(dT/dt)$, eqn. (5.128) becomes

$$\sigma E^2 = \frac{d}{dx}\left(K\frac{dT}{dx}\right).$$

Using the relations of $\sigma E = j$ and $E = -\frac{\partial V}{\partial x}$ (j—current density), and inserting in the above equation, we obtain

$$-j\frac{\partial V}{\partial x} = \frac{d}{dx}\left(K\frac{dT}{dx}\right).$$

Integrating to an arbitrary point x in the dielectric

$$-j\int_0^{V_x} dV = \int_0^x \frac{d}{dx}\left(K\frac{dT}{dx}\right)$$

$$-jV_x = K\frac{dT}{dx}$$

or

$$V_x\sigma\frac{dV}{dx} = K\frac{dT}{dx}.$$

Substituting for $\sigma = \sigma_0 \exp\left[-u/kT\right]$, and integrating from the centre of the dielectric to the electrode,

$$\int_0^{V_c/2} V_x\, dV = \frac{K}{\sigma_0}\int_{T_0}^{T_c}\exp\left[\frac{u}{kT}\right]dT$$

$$V_c^2 = 8\frac{K}{\sigma_0}\int_{T_0}^{T_c}\exp\left[\frac{u}{kT}\right]dT \qquad (5.130)$$

Equation (5.130) gives the critical thermal breakdown voltage, where T_c is the critical temperature at which the material decomposes and the calculation assumes that T_c corresponds to the centre of the slab. The voltage is independent of the thickness of the specimen, but for thin specimens the thermal breakdown voltage becomes thickness dependent and is proportional to the square root of the thickness tending asymptotically to a constant value for thick specimens. Under alternating fields the losses are much greater than under direct fields. Consequently the thermal

TABLE 5.13

Material	Max. thermal voltage in MV/cm	
	d.c.	a.c.
Crystals: Mica muscovite	24	7–18
Rock salt	38	1.4
Quartz: Perp. to axis	12,000	—
Parallel to axis	66	—
Impure	—	2.2
Ceramics: H.V. steatite	—	9.8
L.F. steatite	—	1.5
High-grade porcelain	—	2.8
Organic materials: Capacitor paper		
Ebonite	—	1.45–2.75
Polythene	—	3.5
Polystyrene	—	5
Polystyrene at 1 MC/c	—	0.05
Acrylic resins	—	0.3–1.0

breakdown strength is generally lower for alternating fields, and it decreases with increasing the frequency of the supply voltage. Table 5.13 shows thermal breakdown values for some typical dielectrics under alternating and direct voltages at 20°C. These results correspond to a thick slab of material.

The thermal breakdown is a well-established mechanism, therefore the magnitude of the product $\varepsilon \tan \delta$ which represents the loss is a very essential parameter for the application of insulation material.

Erosion Breakdown

Practical insulations often contain cavities or voids within the dielectric material or on boundaries between the solid and the electrodes. These cavities are usually filled with a medium (gas or liquid) of lower breakdown strength than the solid. Moreover, the permittivity of the filling medium is frequently lower than that of the solid insulations, which causes the field intensity in the cavity to be higher than in the dielectric. Accordingly, under normal working stress of the insulation the voltage across the cavity may exceed the breakdown value and may initiate breakdown in the void.

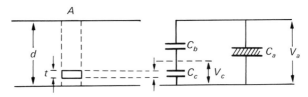

FIG. 5.62. Electrical discharge in cavity and its equivalent circuit.

Figure 5.62 shows a cross-section of a dielectric of thickness d containing a cavity in the form of a disc of thickness t, together with an analogue circuit. In the analogue circuit the capacitance C_c corresponds to the cavity, C_b corresponds to the capacity of the dielectric which is in series with C_c, and C_a is the capacitance of the rest of the dielectric. For $t \ll d$, which is usually the case, and assuming that the cavity is filled with gas, the field strength across C_c is given by the expression

$$E_c = \varepsilon_r E_a$$

where ε_r is the relative permittivity of the dielectric.

For the simple case of a disc-shape dielectric in solid shown in Fig. 5.62, the discharge inception voltage applied across the dielectric can be expressed in terms of the cavity breakdown stress. Assuming that the gas-filled cavity breakdown stress is E_{cb}, then treating the cavity as series capacitance with the healthy part of the dielectric we may write

$$C_b = \frac{\varepsilon_0 \varepsilon_r A}{d-t}$$

$$C_c = \frac{\varepsilon_0 A}{t}.$$

The voltage across the cavity is

$$V_c = \frac{C_b}{C_c + C_b} V_A = \frac{V_A}{1 + \dfrac{1}{\varepsilon_r}\left(\dfrac{d}{t} - 1\right)}.$$

Therefore the voltage across the dielectric which will initiate discharge in the cavity will be given by

$$V_{ai} = E_{cb} t \left\{ 1 + \frac{1}{\varepsilon_r}\left(\frac{d}{t} - 1\right) \right\}. \tag{5.131}$$

In practice a cavity in a material is often nearly spherical, and for such a case the internal field strength is

$$E_c = \frac{3\varepsilon_r E}{\varepsilon_{rc} + 2\varepsilon_r} = \frac{3E}{2} \qquad (5.132)$$

for $\varepsilon_r \gg \varepsilon_{rc}$, where E is in the average stress in the dielectric, under an applied voltage V_a when V_c reaches breakdown value V^+ of the gap t, the cavity may break down. The sequence of breakdowns under sinusoidal alternating voltage is illustrated in Fig. 5.63. The dotted curve shows qualitatively the voltage that would appear across the cavity if it did not break down. As V_c reaches the value V^+, a discharge takes place, the voltage V_c collapses and the gap extinguishes. The voltage across the cavity then starts again increasing until it reaches V^+, when a new discharge occurs. Thus several discharges may take place during the rising part of the applied voltage. Similarly, on decreasing the applied voltage the cavity discharges as the voltage across it reaches V^-. In this way groups of discharges originate from a single cavity and give rise to positive and negative current pulses on raising and decreasing the voltage respectively. For measurements of discharges refer to Chapter 6.

When the gas in the cavity breaks down, the surfaces of the insulation provide instantaneous cathode and anode. Some of the electrons impinging upon the anode are sufficiently energetic to break the chemical bonds of the insulation surface. Similarly, bombardment of the cathode by positive ions may cause damage by increasing the surface temperature and produce local thermal instability. Also channels and pits are formed which elongate through the insulation by the "edge mechanism". Additional chemical

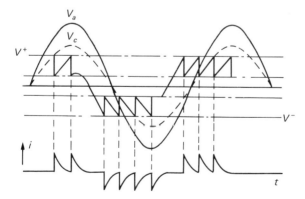

FIG. 5.63. Sequence of cavity breakdown under alternating voltages.

degradation may result from active discharge products, e.g. O_3 or NO_2, formed in air which may cause deterioration. Whatever is the deterioration mechanism operating, the net effect is a slow erosion of the material and a consequent reduction in the thickness of the solid insulation.

When the discharges occur on the insulation surface, the erosion takes place initially over a comparatively large area. The erosion roughens the surface and slowly penetrates the insulation and at some stage will again give rise to channel propagation and "tree-like" growth through the insulation.

For practical application it is important that the dielectric strength of a system does not deteriorate significantly over a long period of time (years). In practice, however, because of imperfect manufacture and sometimes poor design, the dielectric strength (e.g. in cables) decreases with the time of voltage application (or the life) and in many cases the decrease in dielectric strength (E_b) with time (t) follows the empirical relationship

$$tE_b^n = \text{const} \qquad (5.133)$$

where the exponent n depends upon the dielectric material, the ambient conditions, and the quality of manufacture. Figure 5.64 illustrates the case for several m.v. polyethylene cables produced by different manufacturers. The breakdown strength has been plotted against time on a log-log scale.

At this point the weakness of a.c. overvoltage testing should be concentrated upon. Various international specifications call for type test a.c. voltage, which may be several times the working voltage and is usually applied to the equipment for 1 minute or more. The object of this test is to detect major weaknesses in the insulation, but such a test may initiate discharge channels and lower the discharge inception voltage below the working voltage of the system. To overcome this difficulty, in part at least, testing under d.c. voltage and if possible under very low-frequency voltage has been suggested.[61]

Tracking

Tracking is the formation of a permanent conducting path, usually carbon, across a surface of insulation and in most cases the conduction path results from degradation of the insulation. For tracking to occur the insulation must contain some organic substance.

In an outdoor environment insulations will in time become covered with

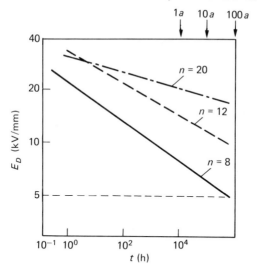

FIG. 5.64. Lifetime (t) stress relationship of polyethylene m.v. cables determined by different manufacturers.[61]

contaminant which may be of industrial or coastal origin. In the presence of moisture the contamination layer gives rise to leakage current which heats the surface and causes interruption in the moisture film; small sparks are drawn between the separating moisture films. This process acts effectively as an extension to the electrodes. The heat resulting from the small sparks causes carbonization and volatilization of the insulation and leads to formation of permanent "carbon track" on the surface. The phenomenon of tracking severely limits the use of organic insulations in the outdoor environment. The rate of tracking depends upon the structure of the polymers and it can be drastically slowed down by adding appropriate fillers to the polymer which inhibit carbonization.

Moisture is not essential to tracking. The conducting path may arise from metallic dust; for example, in oil-immersed equipment with moving parts which gradually wear and deposit on the surface.

5.14.2 Breakdown in Liquids

The general state of knowledge on the electrical breakdown in liquids is less advanced than is in case of gases or even solids. Many aspects of liquid breakdown have been investigated over the last decades, but the findings and conclusions of the many workers cannot be reconciled and so produce a general theory applicable to liquids, as the independent data are at variance and sometimes contradictory. The principle reason for this situation is the lack of comprehensive theory concerning the physical basis of the liquid state which would form the skeleton structure in which observations could be compared and related.

Comprehensive reviews of the published data on the subject have been made periodically and the more recent ones include the reviews of Lewis,[62] Sharbaugh and Watson,[63] Swann,[64] Kok,[65] Krasucki,[66] Zaky and Hawley,[67] and Gallagher.[68] The work falls broadly into two schools of thought. On the one hand there are those who attempt to explain the breakdown of liquids on a model which is an extension of gaseous breakdown, based on the avalanche ionization of the atoms caused by electron collision in the applied field. The electrons are assumed to be ejected from the cathode into the liquid by either a field emission, in which case they are assumed to tunnel out through the surface aided by the field, or by the field enhanced thermionic (Schottky's) effect. This type of breakdown mechanism has been considered to apply to homogeneous liquids of extreme purity, and does not apply to commercially exploited liquid insulations. Conduction studies in highly pure liquids showed that at low fields the conduction is largely ionic due to dissociation of impurities and increases linearly with the field strength. This conduction saturates at intermediate fields. At high field, as we approach breakdown, the conduction increases more rapidly and tends to be unstable. It is believed that this increased current results from electron emission at the cathode by one or both of the above mechanisms, and possibly by field aided dissociation of molecules in the liquid.

It has long been recognized that the presence of foreign particles in liquid insulations has a profound effect on the breakdown strength of liquids. In one approach it has been postulated[65] that the suspended particles are polarizable and are of higher permittivity than the liquid. As a result they experience an electrical force directed towards the place of maximum stress. With uniform field electrodes the movement of particles is presumed to be initiated by surface irregularities on the electrodes, which give rise to local field gradients. The accumulation of particles continues and tends to form a bridge across the gap which leads to initiation of breakdown.

The impurities can also be gaseous bubbles of lower breakdown strength than the liquid, in which case on breakdown of the bubble the total breakdown of the liquid may be triggered. A mathematical model for bubble breakdown has been proposed by Kao.[69]

Electronic Breakdown

Both the field emission and the field enhanced thermionic emission mechanisms discussed earlier have been considered responsible for the current at the cathode. Conduction studies in insulating liquids at high fields show that most experimental data for current fit well the Schottky-type equation [eqn. (5.81)] in which the current is temperature dependent. Breakdown measurements carried out over a wide range of temperatures, however, show little temperature dependence. This suggests that the cathode process is field emission rather than thermionic emission. It is possible that the return of positive ions and particularly positively charge foreign particles to the cathode will cause local field enhancement and give rise to local electron emission.

Once the electron is injected into the liquid it gains energy from the applied field. In the electronic theory of breakdown it is assumed that some electrons gain more energy from the field than they lose in collisions with molecules. These electrons are accelerated until they gain sufficient energy to ionize molecules on collisions and initiate avalanche.

The condition for the onset of electron avalanche is obtained by equating the gain in energy of an electron over its mean free path to that required for ionization of the molecule.

$$eE\lambda = chv \tag{5.134}$$

where E is the applied field, λ the electron mean free path, hv the quantum of energy lost in ionizing the molecule, c an arbitrary constant.

Typical strengths for several highly pure liquids are included in Table 5.14.

TABLE 5.14
Electric Strength of Highly Purified Liquids

Liquid	Strength (MV/cm)
Hexane	1.1–1.3
Benzene	1.1
Good oil	~ 1.0–4.0
Silicone	1.0–1.2
Oxygen	2.4
Nitrogen	1.6–1.88

The electronic theory satisfactorily predicts the relative magnitude of breakdown strength of liquids, but the observed formative time lags are much longer than predicted by electronic theory.[65]

Suspended Solid Particle Mechanism

Solid impurities may be present in the liquid either as fibres or as dispersed solid particles. Let us consider a spherical particle of radius r of permittivity ε to be suspended in dielectric liquid permittivity ε_0. Then in a field the particle will become polarized and it will experience a force given by

$$F_e = r^3 \frac{\varepsilon - \varepsilon_0}{\varepsilon + 2\varepsilon_0} E \text{ grad } E. \tag{5.135}$$

This force is directed towards a place of maximum stress if $\varepsilon > \varepsilon_0$, but for bubbles $\varepsilon < \varepsilon_0$ it has the opposite direction. The force given by eqn. (5.135) increases as the permittivity of the suspended particle (ε) increases, and for a conducting particle for which $\varepsilon \rightarrow \infty$ the force becomes

$$F_e = F_\infty = r^3 E \text{ grad } E. \tag{5.136}$$

Thus the force will urge the particle to move to the strongest region of the field.

In a uniform field gap or sphere gap of small spacing the strongest field is in the uniform region.

In this region grad E is equal to zero so that the particle will remain in equilibrium there. Accordingly, particles will be dragged into the uniform field region. If the permittivity of the particle is higher than that of the medium, then its presence in the uniform field region will cause flux concentration at its surface. Other particles will be attracted into the region of higher flux concentration and in time will become aligned head-to-tail to form a bridge across the gap. The field in the liquid between the particles will be enhanced, and if it reaches critical value breakdown will follow.

The movement of particles by electrical force is opposed by viscous drag, and since the particles are moving into the region of high stress, diffusion must also be taken into account. For a particle of radius r slowly moving with a velocity v in a medium of viscosity η, the drag force is given by Stokes relation

$$F_{\text{drag}} = 6\pi r \eta v(x) \tag{5.137}$$

Equating the electrical force with the drag force ($F_e = F_{drag}$) we obtain

$$v_E = \frac{r^2 E}{6\pi\eta} \frac{dE}{dx} \tag{5.138}$$

where v_E is the velocity of particle towards region of maximum stress.

If the diffusion process is included, the drift velocity due to diffusion will be given by the equation

$$v_d = -\frac{D}{N} \frac{dN}{dx} = -\left(\frac{kT}{6\pi r\eta}\right) \frac{dN}{N\, dx}. \tag{5.139}$$

The relation on the r.h.s. of the equation follows from the Stokes–Einstein relation $D = kT/6\pi r\eta$, where k is Boltzmann's constant and T is the absolute temperature. Equating v_E with v_d gives

$$\frac{r^2}{6\pi\eta} E \frac{dE}{dx} = -\left(\frac{kT}{6\pi\eta r N}\right) \frac{dN}{dx}. \tag{5.140}$$

This introduces breakdown strength dependence in time on concentration of particles N, their radii and the liquid viscosity. The critical value of transverse field $E(x)$, the equilibrium value above which breakdown will occur sooner or later, can be obtained from integration of eqn. (5.140).

$$\left[\frac{r^2 E^2}{2}\right]_{E=E_{(\infty)}}^{E=E_{(x)}} = \left[-\frac{kT}{r} \ln N\right]_{N=N_{(\infty)}}^{N=N_{(x)}}$$

$$\frac{N_{(x)}}{N_{(\infty)}} = \exp\left[r^3 \frac{\{E_{(x)}^2 - E_{(\infty)}^2\}}{2kT}\right]. \tag{5.141}$$

If the increase in the electrostatic energy when the particles drift towards a place of maximum stress is much smaller than their kinetic energy, i.e. $r^3\{E_{(x)}^2 - E_{(\infty)}^2\} \ll 2kT$, the life of the insulation is infinite. The criterion for breakdown resulting from movement of particles towards high stress region corresponds to the condition

$$r^3[E_{(x)}^2 - E_{(\infty)}^2] = 2kT. \tag{5.142}$$

If we consider the case where the initial non-uniformity of field is caused by a hemispherical hump on the electrode, discussed earlier in Chapter 4, and assume that an applied field E_0 will lead to breakdown after a long time of application, then the maximum stress at the tip of the sphere is $3E_0$, or in general the maximum stress is gE_0, where g is a geometrical factor. Then eqn. (5.142) can be written as

$$r^3[g^2-1]E_0^2 = 2kT. \tag{5.143}$$

For $g = 3$ we obtain

$$r^3 E_0^2 = \tfrac{1}{4}kT. \tag{5.144}$$

A more complete theory gives a relation which takes into account the permittivities and is of the form

$$\frac{\varepsilon-\varepsilon_0}{\varepsilon+2\varepsilon_0} r^2 E_0^2 = \tfrac{1}{4}kT.$$

Equation (5.144) gives breakdown strength E_0 after a long time as function of the size of the suspended impurities. This relationship has been checked experimentally and reasonable agreement has been obtained with calculations.

Figure 5.65 shows a plot of eqn. (5.144) for a range of sizes up to 50 Å in radius at temperature $T = 300°K$, for the case where $\varepsilon_0 \ll \varepsilon$.

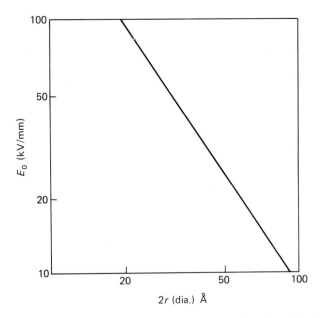

FIG. 5.65. Breakdown strength E_0 after a long duration of time as a function of the diameter $2r$ of foreign particles of high permittivity, with $T = 300°K$.[65]

Cavity Breakdown

Insulating liquids may contain gaseous inclusions in the form of bubbles. The processes by which bubbles are formed include:

(i) gas pockets on the electrode surface,
(ii) changes in temperature and pressure,
(iii) dissociation of products by electron collisions giving rise to gaseous products,
(iv) liquid vaporization by corona-type discharges from points and irregularities on the electrodes.

The electric field in a gas bubble[65] which is immersed in a liquid of permittivity ε_1 is given by:

$$E_b = \frac{3E_0}{\varepsilon_1 + 2} \tag{5.145}$$

where E_0 is the field in the liquid in the absence of the bubble. When the field E_b becomes equal to the gaseous ionization field, discharge takes place which will lead to decomposition of the liquid and breakdown may follow. Kao[69] has developed a more accurate expression for the "bubble" breakdown field strength which is of the form

$$E_0 = \frac{1}{(\varepsilon_1 - \varepsilon_2)} \left\{ \frac{2\pi\sigma(2\varepsilon_1 + \varepsilon_2)}{r} \left[\frac{\pi}{4} \sqrt{\left(\frac{V_b}{2rE_0} \right) - 1} \right] \right\}^{1/2} \tag{5.146}$$

where σ is the surface tension of the liquid, ε_1 and ε_2 are the permittivities of the liquid and the bubble respectively, r is the initial radius of the bubble (initially spherical, which is assumed to elongate under the influence of the field), and V_b is the voltage drop in the bubble. This expression indicates that the critical electric field strength required for breakdown of liquid depends upon the initial size of the bubble which is affected by the external pressure and temperature. A strong dependence of liquid breakdown strength upon the applied hydrostatic pressure has been observed experimentally.[69]

Commercial insulating liquids cannot readily be subjected to highly elaborated purification treatment, and the breakdown strength will usually depend upon the nature of impurities present.

Electroconvection and Electrohydrodynamic Model of Dielectric Breakdown

The importance of electroconvection in insulating liquids subjected to high voltages was not appreciated until recently. Most of the work comes from Felici and his coworkers.[70-72] In highly purified dielectric liquids subjected to high voltage, electrical conduction results mainly from charge carriers injected into the liquid from the electrode surface. The resulting space charge gives rise to Coulomb's force, which under certain conditions causes hydrodynamic instability yielding convecting current. It follows that whenever conduction in a fluid is accompanied by a significant space charge formation, convection motion is very likely to occur. Lacroix *et al.*[70] have studied the conditions under which turbulent motion sets in. Using parallel plate electrodes and controlled injection current, they showed that the onset of instability is associated with a critical voltage. They observed that as the applied voltage is increased near the critical voltage the motion at first exhibits a structure of hexagonal cells. With further increase in voltage the motion becomes turbulent. Thus the interaction between electric field and space charge gives rise to forces creating an eddy motion of the liquid. It has been shown that at voltages close to breakdown the speed of this motion approaches a value given by $\sqrt{\varepsilon/\rho}\, E$ where ε is the permittivity of the liquid, ρ the specific mass and E the electric field strength. In liquids the ratio of this speed to ionic drift velocity (KE), K being the mobility, $M = \sqrt{\varepsilon/\rho}/K$, is always larger than unity and the ratio sometimes is very much larger than unity (see Table 5.15). M is considered to play a dominant

TABLE 5.15.

$$M = \sqrt{\frac{\varepsilon}{\rho}}\bigg/ K$$

Medium	Ion	Relative permittivity	M number
Methanol	H^+	33.5	4.1
Ethanol	Cl^-	25	26.5
Nitrobenzine	Cl^-	35.5	22
Propylene carbonate	Cl^-	69	51
Transformer oil	H^+	2.3	~ 200
Air N.T.P.	O_2^-	1.0	2.3×10^{-2}

role in the theory of electroconvection. Thus, the charge transport will be largely by liquid motion and not by ionic drift. The key condition for the instability onset is that local flow velocity $u\,(=\sqrt{\varepsilon/\rho}\ E)$ exceeds the ionic drift velocity ($u > KE$).

The experimental values for M for various fluid media and common ions obtained by Lacroix et al.[70] are included in Table 5.15. The table contains also the value for air at NTP. It is seen that in this case $M \ll 1$ and the rate of electroconvection is negligible, $M = \sqrt{\varepsilon/\rho}/K$ for various fluids.[70]

Experiments show that electroconvection is prevalent in all experimental settings in dielectric liquids subjected to electric fields irrespective of the gap geometries, provided the applied voltage is high enough. This is true even in thoroughly deionized liquids because of the adequate supply of ions by the high field processes at the electrodes.

Cross et al.[73] have studied electric stress-induced motion in transformer oil under d.c. and 60 Hz stresses. Using high-speed schlieren photography, they found that the turbulent motion was due to injection of positive charges from one electrode. This was confirmed for both d.c. and 60 Hz stresses. They also observed that the delay time in the onset of instability is related to the condition for the injection or creation of charges at the electrode surface. The time delay was found to decrease rapidly with increasing the field strength ranging from a few seconds at 10^6 V/m to a few milliseconds at 6×10^6 V/m. Also as the temperature of the liquid increased, the time delay for given field decreased. Under 60 Hz voltage the time delay was found to reach a minimum value approximately 4 msec, which is to be expected. A 60 Hz wave requires 4.17 msec to reach the peak. From these observations and calculations Cross et al. concluded that under these conditions instability occurs when the injection strength, which is the ratio of the space charge field to the applied field, reaches a large enough value for a critical voltage to develop across the space charge layer within one half-cycle period. The lowest value of the critical voltage occurs where space charge limited conditions prevail at the injecting electrode.

REFERENCES

1. L. B. Loeb. *The Kinetic Theory of Gases*. Wiley, New York, 1963, chapter 2.
2. E. W. McDaniel. *Collision Phenomena in Ionised Gases*. Wiley, New York, 1964.
3. D. Ramp and P. Englander-Golden. *J. Chem. Phys.* **43** (1965), p. 1964.
4. J. S. Townsend. *Electricity in Gases*. Oxford, 1914.

420   HIGH-VOLTAGE ENGINEERING

5. H. Raether. *Z. Phys.* **117** (1941), pp. 375, 524.
6. A. von Angel. *Ionised Gases*, 2nd ed., p. 181. Clarendon Press, 1965.
7. F. H. Sanders. *Phys. Rev.* **44** (1932), p. 667.
8. K. Marsch. *Arch. Elektrotechnik* **26** (1932), p. 598.
9. R. Geballe and M. A. Harrison. *Phys. Rev.* **85** (1952), p. 372.
10. G. K. Kachickas and L. H. Fischer. *Phys. Rev.* **91** (1953), p. 775.
11. M. H. Saha. *Phil. Mag.* **40** (1920), p. 472.
12. L. B. Loeb. *Basic Processes of Gaseous Electronics*. University of California Press, 1955.
13. L. B. Loeb. Formation of negative ions. *Encyclopedia of Physics*, Vol. 16, p. 445. Springer, Berlin, 1956.
14. P. Langevin. *Ann. Chim. Phys.* **8** (1905), p. 238.
15. G. L. Weissler. Photoelectric emission from solids. *Encyclopedia of Physics*, Vol. 16, p. 342. Springer, Berlin, 1956.
16. L. Malter. *Phys. Rev.* **49** (1936), p. 879.
17. O. W. Richardson. *The Emission of Electricity from Hot Bodies*. Longmans Green, London, 1921.
18. W. Schottky. *Ann. Phys.* **44** (1914), p. 1011.
19. R. H. Fowler and L. W. Nordheim. *Proc. Roy. Soc. London* **119** (1928), p. 173; **124** (1929), p. 699.
20. F. Llewellyn Jones and D. E. Davies. *Proc. Phys. Soc.* **B64** (1951), p. 397.
21. J. M. Meek and J. D. Craggs. *Electrical Breakdown of Gases*. Clarendon Press, Oxford, 1953.
22. H. Raether. *Electron Avalanches and Breakdown in Gases*. Butterworths, London, 1964.
23. H. Raether. *Z. Phys.* **112** (1939), p. 464.
24. K. H. Wagner. *Z. Phys.* **189** (1966), p. 466.
25. J. M. Meek. *Phys. Rev.* **57** (1940), p. 722.
26. L. B. Loeb and J. M. Meek. *The Mechanism of Electric Spark*. Stanford University Press, 1940.
27. K. Dehne, W. Khörman and H. Lenne. Measurement of formative time lags for sparks in air, H_2 and N_2. *Dielectrics* **1** (1963), p. 129.
28. D. H. Hale. *Phys. Rev.* **56** (1948), p. 1199.
29. J. J. Thomson and G. P. Thomson. *Conduction of Electricity through Gases*. 2 vols. New York : Dover Publications Inc. 1969 (paper edition).
30. J. Cueilleron. *C.R. Acad. Sci. Paris* **226** (1948), p. 400.
31. W. O. Schumann. *Arch. fur Electrotechnik* **12** (1923), p. 593.
32. H. Sohst. *Zeitsch. fur Angew. Physik* **14** (1962), p. 620.
33. G. A. Schöder, *Zeitsch. fur Angew. Physik* **13** (1961), p. 296.
34. F. M. Penning. *Physica* **1** (1934), p. 1028.
35. F. W. Peek. *Dielectric Phenomena in High Voltage Engineering*, 2nd ed. McGraw-Hill, New York, 1920.
36. W. S. Zaengl and N. U. Nyffenegger. *Proc. 3rd Int. Conf. on Gas Discharges*, 1974, p. 303.
37. R. Geballe and M. L. Reeves. *Phys. Rev.* **92** (1953), p. 867.
38. W. S. Zaengl. *Proc. 10th Symposium on Electrical Insulating Materials*, Tokyo, 1977, p. 13.
39. B. Sangi. Basic discharge parameters in electronegative gases. Ph.D. Thesis, UMIST, Manchester, 1971.
40. L. B. Loeb. *Electrical Coronas*. University of California Press, 1965.
41. G. C. Lichtenberg. *NOVI Comment, Gotingen* **8** (1970), p. 168.
42. E. Nasser. *Fundamentals of Gaseous Ionization and Plasma Electronics*. Wiley-Interscience, 1971.
43. E. Nasser. *IEEE Spectrum* **5** (1968), p. 127.
44. G. W. Trichel. *Phys. Rev.* **55** (1939), p. 382.

45. S. Sangkasaad. Dielectric strength of compressed SF_6 in nonuniform fields. Dissertation, ETH Zurich, No. 5738, 1976.
46. R. L. Hazel and E. Kuffel. *Trans. IEEE Pas.* **95** (1976), p. 178.
47. J. M. Bryant and M. Newman. *Trans. AIEE* **59** (1940), p. 813.
48. L. H. Fischer and B. Benderson. *Phys. Rev.* **81** (1951), p. 109.
49. E. Kuffel and R. M. Radwan. *Proc. IEE* **113** (1966), p. 1863.
50. M. von Laue. *Ann. Phys. Lpz.* **76** (1925), p. 261.
51. K. Zuber. *Ann. Phys. Lpz.* **76** (1925), p. 231.
52. D. M. Taylor and T. J. Lewis. *J. Phys.* **D4** (1971), p. 1346.
53. A. von Hippel. *Ergebn. Exakt. Naturw.* **14** (1935), p. 79.
54. H. Frohlich. *Proc. Roy. Soc.* **160** (1937), p. 230; **A188** (1947), pp. 521, 532.
55. R. Stratton. *Progress in Dielectrics*, Vol. 3, p. 235. Haywood, 1961.
56. H. Frohlich and B. V. Paranjape. *Proc. Phys. Soc. London* **B69** (1956), p. 21.
57. J. J. O'Dwyer. *The Theory of Electrical Conduction and Breakdown in Solid Dielectrics.* Clarendon Press, Oxford, 1973.
58. F. Seitz. *Phys. Rev.* **73** (1979), p. 833.
59. K. H. Stark and C. G. Garton. *Nature, London* **176** (1955), p. 1225.
60. R. Cooper. *Int. J. of Elec. Eng. Education* **1** (1963), p. 241.
61. Conference on Electrical Insulation and Dielectric Phenomena, National Academy of Sciences 1973, p. 247.
62. T. J. Lewis. *Progress in Dielectrics*, Vol. 1. Heywood, London, Wiley, New York 1959.
63. A. H. Sharbaugh and P. K. Watson, *Progress in Dielectrics*, Vol. 4.
64. D. W. Swann. *Brit. J. Appl. Phys.* **135** (1962), p. 208.
65. J. A. Kok. *Electrical Breakdown in Insulating Liquids.* Philips Tech. Library, 1961.
66. Z. Krasucki. Breakdown of commercial liquid and liquid solid dielectrics, *High Voltage Technology* (Alston), p. 129. Oxford University Press, 1968.
67. A. A. Zaky and R. Hawley. *Conduction and Breakdown in Mineral Oils.* Pergamon Press, Oxford, 1973.
68. T. J. Gallagher. *Simple Dielectric Liquids.* Clarendon Press, Oxford, 1975.
69. K. C. Kao. *Trans. AIEEE Elec. Ins.* Vol. E1-11 (1976), pp. 121–128.
70. J. C. Lacroix, P. A. Hen and E. J. Hopfinger. *J. Fluid Mech.* **69** (1975), p. 539.
71. N. J. Felici. *Direct Current* **2** (1971), p. 147.
72. N. J. Felici and J. C. Lacroix. *J. Electrost.* **5** (1978), p. 135.
73. J. D. Cross, M. Nakans and S. Savanis. *J. Electrost.* **7** (1979), p. 361.
74. T. W. Dakin *et al. Electra*, No. 32 (1974), pp. 61–82.

Chapter 6

NON-DESTRUCTIVE INSULATION
TEST TECHNIQUES

This chapter describes some of the ancillary techniques, essential to a h.v. laboratory, used to measure the quality of either a specimen of an insulating material or to test and assess the h.v. insulation on complete equipment. High voltage may be insulated in several ways. A gaseous medium may provide the main insulation, as is the case in overhead transmission lines. If the high voltage is to be insulated within a small space, a compressed gas, solid, liquid or compound insulation is required (e.g. transformers and cables). In all cases the insulation must be designed so that its breakdown strength is high enough to withstand occasional surges which may be several times the working voltage. The dielectric losses must be low and the insulation resistance high in order to prevent thermal breakdown. A further requirement for the satisfactory performance for the insulation is the limitation of internal discharges in voids present within the dielectric which may cause deterioration of the dielectric. The various laboratory techniques for electrical insulation measurement have been reviewed by Baker[1]* and for detailed descriptions the reader is advised to refer to that publication. Additional information is also provided by Schwab.[2]

6.1 HIGH-VOLTAGE DIELECTRIC LOSS AND
CAPACITANCE MEASUREMENTS

6.1.1 The Schering Bridge

One of the most commonly used methods for measuring loss tangent and capacitance is the Schering bridge. The bridge measures the capacitance

* Superscript numbers are to References at the end of the chapter.

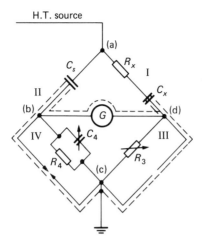

H.T. source

FIG. 6.1. Schering bridge.

and loss angle of a capacitor by comparing it with a gas-filled standard capacitor which has negligible loss over a wide frequency range (see Chapter 3, section 3.5.4). The arrangement is shown in Fig. 6.1. The first arm of the bridge consists of a sample, the dielectric loss and capacitance of which are to be measured. On account of the dielectric loss the current through the capacitor leads the voltage by an angle $(90-\delta)$ which is slightly less than $90°$. The balance conditions are represented by considering that a pure capacitance C_x is connected either in parallel or in series with a hypothetical resistance R_x, the power dissipated in the resistance being the power loss in the actual capacitor. Both models may be used to simulate a loss of capacitance, but the equivalent circuit used must be indicated. It is also well known that the hypothetical resistances—R_s for a series, R_p for a parallel equivalent circuit—are not constant values for the dielectric materials used. The real current causing the phase shift is predominantly due to the frictional work necessary to move the ions and dipoles (ionic and dipolar polarization), the residual conductivity of mostly inhomogeneous dielectrics (interfacial polarization) and sometimes due to the losses caused by partial discharges. The resistances are, therefore, dependent upon frequency and, if partial discharges are present, upon voltage.

For the Schering bridge, the balance conditions are always derived for the series R-C equivalent circuit, which is much simpler to analyze. The derivation is shown below. The comparison of the series- and parallel-equivalent circuit defines the dissipation factor $\tan \delta$ by the following equations:

$$\tan \delta_s = \omega R_s C_s. \tag{6.1}$$

$$\tan \delta_p = \frac{1}{\omega R_p C_p}. \tag{6.2}$$

On the condition that the losses in the two circuits must be equal, the quantities of both circuits may be converted to each other by:

$$C_p = \frac{C_s}{1+\tan^2 \delta_s}; \quad \text{or} \quad \varepsilon_p = \frac{\varepsilon_s}{1+\tan^2 \delta_s}. \tag{6.3}$$

$$R_p = R_s\left(1+\frac{1}{\tan^2 \delta_s}\right). \tag{6.4}$$

The results, provided by a Schering bridge, can thus be always calculated in the parallel equivalent circuit, if necessary. The balance conditions obtained when the indicator shows zero deflection in Fig. 6.1 are:

$$\frac{Z_{ab}}{Z_{bc}} = \frac{Z_{ad}}{Z_{dc}},$$

$$Z_{ad} = R_x - j\frac{1}{\omega C_x}, \quad Z_{ab} = -j\frac{1}{\omega C_s},$$

$$Z_{bc} = \frac{R_4[-j(1/\omega C_4)]}{R_4 - j(1/\omega C_4)}; \quad Z_{dc} = R_3,$$

$$\frac{-j(1/\omega C_s)[R_4 - j(1/\omega C_4)]}{R_4[-j(1/\omega C_4)]} = \frac{R_x - j(1/\omega C_x)}{R_3}.$$

Equating components in quadrature:

$$C_x = C_s \frac{R_4}{R_3} \tag{6.5}$$

and equating components in phase gives:

$$R_x = \frac{C_4 R_3}{C_s}. \tag{6.6}$$

R_3 is a variable resistance and is usually in the form of a six-decade box. Its maximum value is limited to about 10,000 Ω in order to keep the effectiveness of any stray capacitance relatively small.

Substituting for C_s in eqn. (6.5) from eqn. (6.6) and multiplying by ω we obtain:

$$\omega C_x R_x = \omega C_4 R_4.$$

but according to eqn. (6.1)

$$\tan \delta = \omega C_4 R_4. \tag{6.7}$$

In practice R_4 is made constant and C_4 is variable. In a practical bridge C_4 may well be directly calibrated in terms of $\tan \delta$, provided a constant value of the frequency is indicated. To exclude from Z_{bc} and Z_{dc} and the galvanometer branches any currents due to intercapacity between the h.v. and l.v. arms, except those flowing through Z_{ab} and Z_{ad}, the bridge is fully screened as shown in Fig. 6.1. The l.v. arms are usually protected with spark gaps against the appearance of high voltages in the event of failure of Z_I or Z_{II}.

In Fig. 6.1 the network is earthed at the l.v. end of the transformer supplying the high voltage, and by this also the bridge is earthed at (c). Under balance conditions, both sides of the null detector (G) are at the same potential, but the shield is earthed. Therefore partial stray capacitances appear across the branches III and IV, and depending upon the length of the leads to C_s and C_x, these partial capacitances can assume values over a wide limit. These capacitances can be measured and thus their influence on the dissipation factor can be calculated. If C_I is the partial capacitance of branch I, and C_{II} that of branch II, the calculation shows

$$\tan \delta = R\omega(C_4 + C_{II}) - R_3 \omega C_I. \tag{6.8}$$

This procedure is time-consuming and inconvenient, and there are methods available to overcome this effect. The principle of the method may easiest be described by the "Wagner earth" as shown in Fig. 6.2. In this arrangement an additional arm Z is connected between the l.v. terminal of the four-arm bridge and earth. Together with the stray capacitance of the h.v. busbar to earth the arrangement becomes equivalent to a six-arm bridge and a double balancing procedure is required which can be achieved either by using two detectors or a switch arrangement which enables the detector to be switched on into either sets of arms. At balance the terminals of the detector are at earth potential and capacitances between the terminals and screens having no potential difference between them do not affect the balance conditions. Both the detector and the l.v. leads must be screened. The capacitances between the leads and screens are in parallel with the

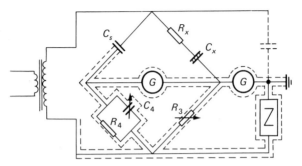

FIG. 6.2. Bridge incorporating "Wagner earth".

impedance Z and as such do not contribute to the balance conditions. For more details see reference 3.

This method, however, is rarely used today, as an electronic device for automatic balancing of "Wagner earth" may be used. The basic circuit is shown in Fig. 6.3. Though the bridge may well be earthed at (c), the potentials of the screens are shifted to the potential of the detector branch by a high-quality amplifier with unity voltage gain. The shields of the leads to C_s and C_x are not grounded, but connected to the output of the amplifier, for which operational amplifiers can be conveniently used. The high input impedance and very low output impedance of the amplifier does not load the detector branch and keeps the screen potential at any instant at an

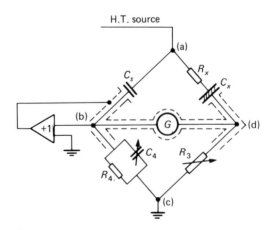

FIG. 6.3. Automatic "Wagner earth" (dividing screen technique).

artificial "ground". A second screen, which is earthed, may be added to prevent disturbances by neighbouring voltage sources.

Measurement of Large Capacitance

When the capacitance to be measured is large, the value of the variable resistance R_3 in eqn. (6.5) capable of passing large currents would be required. To maintain a high value of R_3 it may be shunted by another resistor (A) as shown in Fig. 6.4. An additional resistor (B) is put in series with R_3 to protect it from excessive currents should it accidentally be set to a very low value. With this arrangement it can be shown[1] that the specimen's capacitance and loss tangent become respectively:

$$C_x = C_s \left(\frac{R_4}{R_3} \right) \left[1 + \left(\frac{B}{A} \right) + \left(\frac{R_3}{A} \right) \right] \qquad (6.9)$$

and

$$\tan \delta = \omega C_s R_4 \left(\frac{B}{R_3} \right). \qquad (6.10)$$

The Schering bridge principle is suitable for measurements at frequencies up to some 100 kHz, if the circuit elements are properly designed. Common

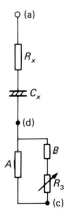

FIG. 6.4. Shunt arrangement for measurement of large capacitance (compare with Fig. 6.1).

Schering bridges for power frequencies may be used at frequencies up to about 10 kHz only. At higher frequencies it becomes necessary to use substitution and resonance methods.[1] Measuring accuracy is in general much higher than 10^{-3} for capacitance values and higher than 10^{-2} for tan δ.

6.1.2 Transformer Ratio-arm Bridge

There are many types of bridges available for precision measurements of impedance over a wide range of frequencies based on transformer coupling. A simple inductively coupled current ratio-arm bridge, suitable for h.v. measurement, is shown in Fig. 6.5. It was originally suggested by Blumlein in 1928.[5] The main part of the bridge circuit consists of a three-winding current comparator or current transformer with very low losses and leakage (core of high permeability) which is carefully shielded against magnetic stray fields and protected against mechanical vibrations. Thus, the particular merit in this arrangement is that there is no net m.m.f. across the windings 1 and 2 at balance conditions. Furthermore, the stray capacitance across the windings and that of the screened l.v. leads does not enter in the balance expression since there is no voltage developed across

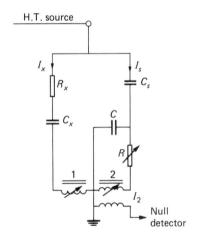

FIG. 6.5. Transformer ratio-arm bridge.

them. This enables long leads to be used without "Wagner earth". The sensitivity of the bridge is higher than that of the Schering bridge.

The balance is indicated by zero voltage induced in the detector coil and corresponds to the conditions when $I_x N_1 = I_2 N_2$ where N_1 and N_2 are the number of turns in series with the sample (C_x) and the standard capacitor (C_s) respectively, and I_x and I_2 are the corresponding currents flowing in C_x and N_2. Again a series equivalent circuit is assumed for the specimen under test.

For a current I_s in the standard capacitor (C_s) the voltage developed across the R-C arm is given by:

$$V = \frac{I_s R}{1 + j\omega CR}.$$

The portion of current I_2 in the coil 2 is

$$I_2 = \frac{I_s}{1 + j\omega CR},$$

and for a unity total applied voltage

$$I_2 = \frac{1}{[\{R/(1+j\omega CR)+(1/j\omega C_s)\}(1+j\omega CR)]} = \frac{j\omega C_s}{1+j\omega(C_s+C)R},$$

therefore:

$$C_x = C_s\left(\frac{N_2}{N_1}\right) \tag{6.11}$$

and

$$\tan \delta = \omega R(C_s + C). \tag{6.12}$$

The capacitance and phase angle balance are obtained by making N_1, N_2 and R variable. The accuracy of this type of bridge is better to that indicated for the Schering bridge.

6.1.3 Loss Measurement on Complete Equipment

It is often required to measure the dielectric loss on specimens one side of which is permanently earthed. There are two established methods used for such measurement. One is the inversion of a Schering bridge, shown in Fig.

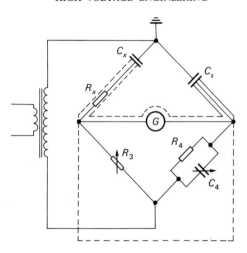

FIG. 6.6. High-voltage bridge with Faraday cage.

6.6 with the operator, ratio arms and null detector inside a Faraday cage at high potential. The system requires the cage to be insulated for the full test voltage and with suitable design may be used up to maximum voltage available. There are, however, difficulties in inverting physically the h.v. standard capacitor and it becomes necessary to mount it on a platform insulated for full voltage.

An alternative method, though limited to lower voltages, employs an artificial earth which differs in potential from a true earth by the voltage developed across each of the l.v. arms as shown in Fig. 6.7. The artificial earth screen intercepts all the field from high potential to earth except in the specimen. It thus requires screening of the h.v. lead and presents difficulties at voltages in excess of about 5 kV.

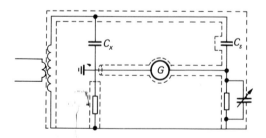

FIG. 6.7. Fully screened bridge.

6.1.4 Null Detectors

The null detector (G) may be a vibration galvanometer of high mechanical Q factor. Though their application is well justified, the sensitivity to mechanical noise (if present) and the limited electrical sensitivity present some disadvantages. Today more sensitive electronic null detectors are commonly used. The possible high sensitivity, however, cannot be utilized in general, as noise voltages from the circuit, or electromagnetically induced voltages from the stray fields of the h.v. circuit, disturb the balance. This electronic null detector reads the voltage across the detector branch. As the balance equations of the bridge are only valid for a particular fixed frequency, the unavoidable harmonic content of the high input voltage of the bridge results in higher harmonic voltages across the null detector, for which the bridge is not balanced. A very pronounced band-pass characteristic is therefore necessary to attenuate these harmonics. The principle of the electronic null detector is thus given by the sketched layout of Fig. 6.8.

A very much improved balance is possible using electronic null detectors, which are also sensitive to the phase. Bridges may only slowly converge,[4] i.e. the magnitude of the detector branch voltage may only slightly change within the individual settings of R_3 and $C_.$ in the Schering bridge or R in the transformer ratio-arm bridge. In the use of phase-sensitive null detectors,

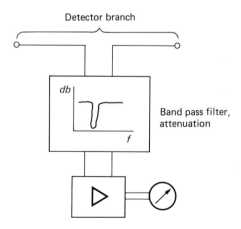

Fig. 6.8. Principle of electronic null detector with bandpass filter.

the balance condition is indicated in terms of magnitude and phase. With a reference voltage in phase with the (high) source voltage, these values describe Lissajou figures at the screen of a CRO used for the display. In this way the balancing procedure is always known and the balance is obtained much faster.

If only unskilled personnel are available or series measurements have to be performed within a production process, a self-balancing of bridges is very convenient. There are many solutions available. Older methods use servo-motor-driven potentiometers controlled from a feedback loop.[6] The capability of electronic circuits provides many different solutions,[7, 8] the most recent of which takes advantage of microcomputer control. Such a circuit published by Seitz and Osvath[9] is briefly described here. Figure 6.9 shows the basic circuit of a ratio-arm bridge. The range windings N_1 (number of turns 1, 10, 100) are relay-switched by the microprocessor as well as the 1000 turns of winding N_2, which are switched by solid state switches. The detector winding N_3 feeds the zero detector amplifier, whose gain is also programmable. The output of this amplifier is processed in a

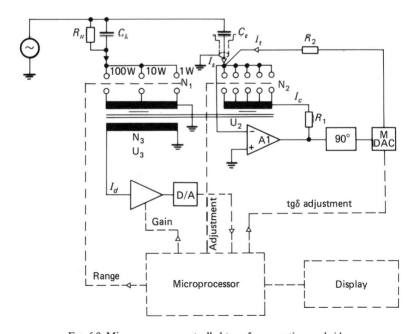

FIG. 6.9. Microprocessor controlled transformer ratio-arm bridge.

complex analogue-to-digital converter providing real and imaginary binary numbers for the microprocessor and thus the exact state of the balance is detected. The behaviour of the R-C branch within the original circuit (Fig. 6.5) is simulated by the amplifier $A1$, whose output voltage is shifted by 90° and applied to the multiplying digital-to-analogue converter M-DAC. This converter attenuates the voltage, which drives a current I_t via R_2 to the summary junction of $A1$. The attenuation of the M-DAC is proportional to the dissipation factor and is controlled by the microprocessor.

The microprocessor is thus used to balance the whole bridge. The output setting of every step is determined by a series of decisions and calculations based upon balanced state within the complex plane. The details may be found in the original paper. The balance procedure takes about 5 sec and it can follow small changes of voltage, capacitance and dissipation factor. The resolution of the system is 10^{-5} and an accuracy of 10^{-4} was achieved in the environment of a h.v. laboratory.

6.2 PARTIAL-DISCHARGE MEASUREMENTS

Partial discharges (PD) are localized electrical discharges within an insulation system, restricted to only a part of the dielectric material, and thus only partially bridging the electrodes. The insulation may consist of solid, liquid or gaseous materials, or of any combination. The term "partial discharge" is relatively new, as it includes a wide group of discharge phenomena: internal discharges may occur in voids or cavities within solid or liquid dielectrics; surface discharges appear at the boundary of different insulation materials; corona discharges are related to discharges in gaseous dielectrics, if strongly inhomogeneous fields are present; the continuous impact of discharges in solid dielectrics forms discharge channels (treeing).

The significance of discharges on the life of insulation has long been recognized. Every discharge event deteriorates the material by the energy impact of high energy electrons or accelerated ions, causing chemical transformations of many types. It is obvious that the actual deterioration is dependent upon the material used. Corona discharges in air will have no influence on the life expectancy of an overhead line; a PD within a thermoplastic dielectric, as PE, may cause breakdown within a few days. It is still the aim of many investigations to relate partial discharge quantities to the lifetime of specified materials. Such a defined relationship is difficult to ensure. PD measurements have nevertheless gained an utmost importance during the last two decades, as at least some levels of PD magnitudes could be found which do not deteriorate an insulation system significantly.

The detection of discharges is based on energy exchanges which take place during the discharge. These exchanges are manifested as (i) electrical impulse currents (with some exceptions, i.e. some types of glow discharges); (ii) dielectric losses; (iii) e.m. radiation (light); (iv) sound (noise); (v) increased gas pressure; (vi) chemical reactions. Discharge detection and measuring techniques may be based on the observation of any of the above phenomena. The oldest and simplest method relies on listening to the noise from the discharge, the "hissing test". The sensitivity is low, however, and difficulties arise in distinguishing between discharges and extraneous noises, particularly when tests are carried out on factory premises. It is also well known that the energy released by PD will increase the dissipation factor; a measurement of tan δ in dependency of voltage applied displays an "ionization knee", a bending of the otherwise straight dependency. This knee, however, is blurred and not pronounced, even with an appreciable amount of PD, as the additional losses generated in very localized sections can be very small in comparison to the volume losses resulting from polarization processes. The use of optical techniques is limited to discharges within transparent media and thus not applicable in most cases. Only modern acoustical detection methods utilizing ultrasonic transducers can successfully be used to localize the discharges.[10–13] These very specialized methods cannot be treated here. Summaries of older methods can be found in the book of Kreuger.[14] The recent developments may be found in reference 33.

The most frequently used and the most successful detection methods are the electrical ones. These methods aim to separate the impulse currents linked with partial discharges from any other phenomena. The adequate application of the different PD detectors presupposes a fundamental knowledge about the electrical phenomena within the test samples and the test circuits.

6.2.1 The PD-equivalent Circuit

The appearance of partial discharges within a closed apparatus can only be measured at its terminals. In Fig. 6.10(a) a simple capacitor arrangement

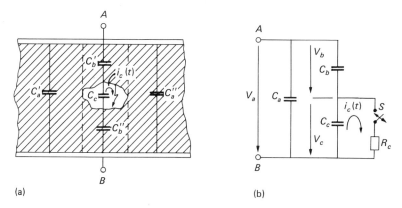

Fɪɢ. 6.10. Simulation of a partial discharge. (a) Scheme of a dielectric comprising a cavity. (b) Equivalent circuit.

is sketched, comprising solid or fluid dielectric material between the two electrodes A and B, and a gas-filled cavity. This void will become the origin of a PD if the applied voltage is increased, as the field gradients in the void are strongly enhanced by the difference in permittivities as well as the shape of the cavity. For an increasing a.c. voltage, the first discharge will appear during the rising part of a half-cycle, causing the cavity capacitance C_c to discharge to a large extent. The discharge current $i_c(t)$, which cannot immediately be measured, has a shape similar to a Dirac function, i.e. the current is a very short pulse in the nsec range. The charges of opposite polarity produced by the discharge will drift to the walls in field direction, thus cancelling the original electric field. If the voltage is still increasing or decreasing by the negative slope of an a.c. voltage, new field lines are built up and hence the discharge phenomena are repeated during each cycle. Field lines starting or ending at the cavity walls form the two capacitances C_b' and C_b'' within the solid or fluid dielectric, and all field lines outside the cavity are represented by $C_a = C_a' + C_a''$. Due to the dimensions involved, and as $C_b = C_b'C_b''/(C_b' + C_b'')$, the magnitude of the capacitances will always be controlled by the inequality

$$C_a \gg C_c \gg C_b. \qquad (6.13)$$

The equivalent circuit of this arrangement is shown in Fig. 6.10(b). The switch S is controlled by the voltage V_c across the void capacitance C_c, and S

is closed only for a very short time, during which the flow of $i_c(t)$ takes place. The resistor R_c simulates finite amplitudes of i_c.

Let us assume that the sample was charged to the voltage V_a, but the terminals A, B are no longer connected to a voltage source. If the switch S is closed, the current $i_c(t)$ releases a charge $\delta q_c = C_c \, \delta V_c$ from C_c, a charge which is lost in the whole system. By comparing the charges within the system before and after this discharge, the voltage drop across the terminals δV_a can easily be computed. The result is

$$\delta V_a = \frac{C_b}{C_a + C_b} \, \delta V_c. \tag{6.14}$$

This voltage drop contains *no* information about the charge δq_c, but it is proportional to $(C_b \, \delta V_c)$, a magnitude vaguely related to this charge, as C_b will increase with the diameter of the cavity.

δV_a is obviously a quantity which could be measured. It is a negative voltage step with a rise time depending upon the duration of $i_c(t)$. The magnitude of the voltage step, however, is quite small, though δV_c is in a range of some 10^2 to 10^3 V; but the ratio C_b/C_a will always be very small $(\lesssim 10^{-3})$ according to eqn. (6.13). As the absolute values of the applied voltages V_a are much higher than δV_c, the ratio $\delta V_a/V_a$ is well below 10^{-3}. Thus a direct detection of this voltage step by a measurement of this input voltage would be a tedious task. The detection circuits are therefore based upon another quantity, which can immediately be derived from a real test circuit shown in Fig. 6.11. The test sample, Fig. 6.10(a), is now connected to a voltage source V, in general an a.c. power supply, though also d.c. PD measurements are sometimes made. An impedance Z, comprising either only the natural impedance of the lead between voltage source and C_K/C_t, or enlarged by a PD-free inductance or filter, may disconnect the "coupling

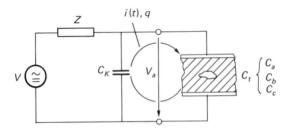

Fig. 6.11. The PD test object C_t within a PD-testing circuit.

capacitor" C_K and the test specimen C_t from the voltage source during the PD phenomena only. Then C_K is a storage capacitor during the short time period of the partial discharge. It releases a charging current $i(t)$ between C_K and C_t which tries to cancel the voltage drop δV_a across $C_t \simeq C_a + C_b$. If $C_K \gg C_t$, δV_a is completely compensated, and the charge transfer is given by

$$q = \int i(t) \, dt = (C_a + C_b) \, \delta V_a. \tag{6.15}$$

With eqn. (6.14), this charge becomes

$$q = C_b \delta V_c. \tag{6.16}$$

q is the "apparent charge" of a partial discharge, as it again is not equal to the amount of charge locally involved at the site of the discharge or cavity C_c. This PD quantity, however, is more realistic than δV_a in eqn. (6.14), as the main capacitance C_a of the test object has no influence on it. The condition $C_K \gg C_a$ is however not applicable in practice, as either C_a is quite large or the loading of an a.c. power supply would be too high and the cost to build such a large capacitor, which must be free of any discharges, are not economical. For a finite value of C_K the charge q or the currents $i(t)$ are reduced, as the voltage across C_K will drop during the charge transfer. Designating this voltage drop by δV_a^*, we may compute this voltage by assuming that the same charge $C_b \delta V_c$ has to be transferred in the circuits of Fig. 6.10(b) and Fig. 6.11. Therefore

$$\delta V_a(C_a + C_b) = \delta V^*(C_a + C_b + C_K). \tag{6.17}$$

Introducing eqn. (6.14) as well as eqn. (6.16), we obtain

$$\delta V^* = \frac{C_b}{C_a + C_b + C_K} \delta V_c = \frac{q}{C_a + C_b + C_K}. \tag{6.18}$$

Again, δV^* is a difficult quantity to be measured. The charge transferred from C_K to C_t by the reduced current $i(t)$ is clearly equal to $C_K \delta V^*$; it is related to the apparent charge which can be measured in practice. If we designate this quantity as q_m, then

$$q_m = C_K \delta V^* = \frac{C_K}{C_a + C_b + C_K} q \approx \frac{C_K}{C_a + C_K} q$$

or

$$\frac{q_m}{q} \simeq \frac{C_K}{C_a + C_K} \approx \frac{C_K}{C_t + C_K}. \tag{6.19}$$

The relationship q_m/q indicates the difficulties arising in PD measurements for test objects of large capacitance values C_t. Though C_K and C_t may be known accurately, the ability to detect small values of q will decrease as all instruments capable of integrating the currents $i(t)$ will have a lower limit for q_m. Equation (6.19), however, must be obeyed to correct the measured quantities, as q is the real apparent charge of the object under test.

6.2.2 PD Currents

Before treating the fundamentals of the measurement of the apparent charge some remarks upon the PD currents $i(t)$ are very useful. Much of the research work has been, and is still, devoted to these currents, which are difficult to measure. The difficulties arise for several reasons:

If V is an a.c. voltage, the main currents flowing within the branches C_K and C_t are displacement currents $C(dV/dt)$, and both are nearly in phase. The PD currents of amplitudes in the range sometimes smaller than 10^{-4} A, are not only small in amplitude, but also of very short duration. If no stray capacitances in parallel to C_K would be present, $i(t)$ would be the same in both branches, but of *opposite* polarity. For accurate measurements, a shunt with matched coaxial cable may be introduced in the circuit as shown in Fig. 6.12. The voltage across the CRO input is then given by $V_m(t) = (i_t + i)Z_0/R$. If the capacitance C_t is small, the voltages referring to the PD currents $i(t)$ may be clearly distinguished from the displacement currents $i_t(t)$, but this is a special case. Even with $R \to \infty$ the sensitivity of the CRO may not be high enough to record $V_m(t)$, as the surge impedance Z_0 of the

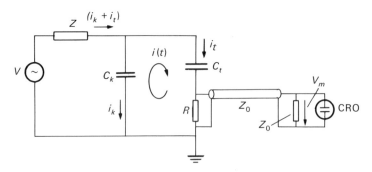

FIG. 6.12. Measurement of PD current $i(t)$: low sensitivity circuit.

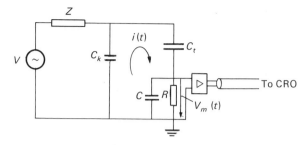

FIG. 6.13. Measurement of PD currents; high sensitivity circuit.

coaxial cable, which is essential to record the current shape as undistorted as possible, is small (50–75 Ω). The crest values of $V_m(t)$ are therefore very small.

Improvements are possible by inserting an amplifier (active voltage probe) of very high bandwidth at the input end of the signal cable. In this way the signal cable is electrically disconnected from R. High values of R, however, will introduce measuring errors, which are explained with Fig. 6.13. A capacitance C of some 10 pF, which accounts for the lead between C_t and earth as well as for the input capacitance of the amplifier or other stray capacitances, will shunt the resistance R and thus bypass or delay the very high-frequency components of the current $i(t)$. Thus, if $i(t)$ is a very short current pulse, the amplitude or crest value is heavily decreased. Furthermore, with R within the discharge circuit, the current pulse will be lengthened, as the charge transfer even with $C = 0$ will be delayed by a time constant $RC_tC_K/(C_t+C_K)$. Both effects are influencing the shape of the original current pulse, and thus the measurement of $i(t)$ is a tedious task.

All measured data on current shapes published in many papers are suffering from this effect. One may, however, summarize the results by the following statements. Partial discharges originated by voids within solids or liquids can excite very short current pulses with durations $\lesssim 5$ nsec. This may be understood, as the gas discharge process within a very limited space is developed in a very short time and is terminated by the limited movement of the charge carriers. Discharges within a homogeneous dielectric material, i.e. a gas, excite currents with a very short rise-time ($\lesssim 5$ nsec) and a longer tail. Whereas the fast current rise is produced by the fast avalanche processes and the electron current produced, the decay of the current can be attributed to the drift velocity of attached electrons and positive ions within the material. Discharge pulses in atmospheric air provide current durations of less than about 100 nsec in general. Longer current pulses have only been measured for partial discharges in fluid or solid materials without pronounced voids, if a number of discharges take place within a short time. In most of these cases the total duration of $i(t)$ is less than about 2 μsec, with only some exceptions.

All the above statements refer to testing circuits with very low inductance and proper damping effects within the loop $C_K - C_t$. The current $i(t)$, however, may easily oscillate, as oscillations are exicted by the sudden voltage drop across C_t. Test objects with inherent inductances or internal resonant circuits, e.g. transformer or reactor windings, will always cause oscillatory PD currents.

These statements illustrate the reasons why the measurement of PD currents is not recommendable in factory premises. The distortions of the current, however, do not change the transferred charge magnitudes, as no discharge resistor is in parallel to C_K or C_t. If the displacement currents $i_t(t)$ or $i_K(t)$ are suppressed, the distorted PD currents can be filtered, integrated and displayed.

6.2.3 PD-measuring Circuits for Apparent Charge

Depending upon the type of apparatus or insulation system under PD test, the sensitivity of the PD-measuring device necessary to detect dangerous magnitudes may vary. The actual lower limits range between 0.1 to 1 pC. These charge quantities are obviously very low. PD-measuring circuits applicable for practical testing must be designed for environmental conditions that are not ideal.

Testing circuits may be set up within well electromagnetically shielded laboratories using filtered mains for the h.v. power supplies as well as in industrial plants with simple testing areas. In the first case the test circuit will experience only a negligible disturbance, as no electromagnetic noise will be present. In practice, many types of interferences will influence the measurements: the power supply voltage may contain many harmonics and switching transient voltages. Poor contacts in the supply circuits may cause high-frequency current oscillations of small magnitudes in the vicinity of the current zeros. Stray electric and magnetic fields caused by neighbouring h.v. circuits or power lines may induce interference voltages in the PD-testing circuit. The electromagnetic waves from radio stations penetrate into the testing areas and induce interference voltages. Loose metal or conducting parts placed in the neighbourhood of the test circuit will be charged by the electrical fields surrounding the circuit and may be discharged by tiny sparks if they are not earthed in advance. Finally, apart from the partial discharges of the object under test, discharges may occur within the actual test circuit, i.e. within the h.v. power supply, the coupling capacitor, or at any of the h.v. leads used for the interconnection of the circuit elements.

Thus it is obvious that the distinction between PD caused by the test object and all other interfering currents would be impossible if no attempt was made to suppress the interference voltages and currents as much as possible. The interferences may be subdivided into harmomic and pulsed events. The first type of interference is due to higher harmonics in the supply voltage or electromagnetic waves' impact, and the second due to impulse phenomena similar to PD currents. The continuous alternating currents of any frequency would steadily disturb the integration procedure of the measuring circuits, and hence the suppression of this current is of utmost importance. This task is solved by using filtering circuits, which may be practically independent of the actual integration circuit. Two possibilities for using so-called "straight PD test circuits" are then available shown in Fig. 6.14(a) and (b): A coupling or measuring impedance Z_m, sometimes referred to as a "coupling two-port", is connected either in series within the test objects or the coupling capacitors ground lead. (The significance of the calibration circuit C_0 in series with the step voltage generator is explained later on.) If there were no stray capacitances in parallel with C_K and C_t, and no PD leakage currents across the h.v. power supply, the high-frequency PD currents detected by Z_m would be equal for both circuits. In practice, the series connection of Z_m with the test object C_t provides higher sensitivity, as the PD currents excited from C_t are best picked up by this circuit. The disadvantage is the possibility of damage to the PD-measuring circuit, if the test object fails. The series connection of Z_m with the especially provided coupling capacitor C_K eliminates these disadvantages and is more commonly in use. Not all PD currents excited by C_t, however, will pass through the measuring impedance, Z_m, as they are bypassed by all stray capacitances between h.v. leads and ground potential.

The coupling impedance Z_m and the coaxial signal cable to the main instrument M, so far not discussed, are integral parts of the whole PD-measuring circuit. Apart from some specialized circuits used for integrating the PD currents, only the following two fundamental circuits are in general use.

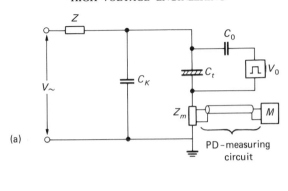

(a)

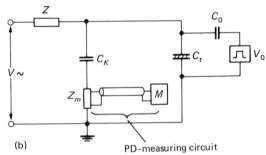

(b)

FIG. 6.14. Straight PD-detection circuits, complete test arrangements, including connections for calibration.

Wide-Band PD-detection Circuits

Figure 6.15 shows the principle of these circuits. The coupling impedance Z_m (Fig. 6.15a) is in general a parallel R-L-C resonance circuit (Fig. 6.15b) whose quality factor is relatively low. In spite of this, such a coupling impedance provides two important qualities: a simple calculation of the ratio output voltage V_0 to input current I_i in dependency of frequency would easily demonstrate an adequate suppression of low- and high-frequency currents in the neighbourhood of its resonance frequency. For a quality factor of $Q = 1$, this attenuation is -20 dB per decade and could be greatly increased close to resonance frequency by increasing the values of Q. This parallel circuit also performs, however, an integration of the PD currents $I_i = \mathscr{L}\{i(t)\}$, as every filter characteristic may be used as an integrating device. Let us assume that $i(t)$ would not be influenced by the

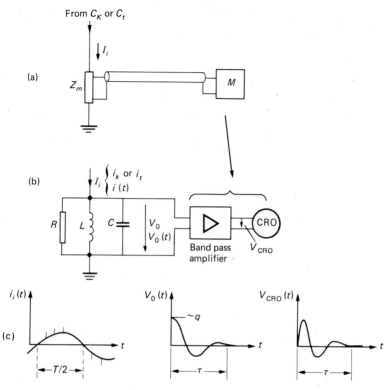

FIG. 6.15. Principle of "wide-band" PD-measuring circuit. (a) PD-measuring circuit according to Fig. 6.14. (b) Simplified equivalent circuit. (c) Typical time-dependent quantities within (b) (T = period of power frequency; τ = resolution time).

coupling impedance and is given by a Dirac function, comprising the apparent charge q. Then the calculation of the output voltage $V_0(t)$ according to Fig. 6.15(b) results in:

$$V_0(t) = \frac{q}{C} e^{-\alpha t} \left[\cos \beta t - \frac{\alpha}{\beta} \sin \beta t \right] \qquad (6.20)$$

where

$$\alpha = \frac{1}{2RC}; \quad \beta = \sqrt{\frac{1}{LC} - \alpha^2}$$

$$= \omega_0 \sqrt{1 - \alpha^2 LC}.$$

Equation (6.20) shows a damped oscillatory output voltage, whose amplitudes are proportional to q. The integration of $i(t)$ is actually performed instantaneously ($t = 0$) by the capacitance C, but the oscillations, if not damped, would heavily increase the "resolution time" τ of the measuring circuit, i.e. the time necessary to calm the circuit response and to provide a proper integration of consecutive PD events. With a quality factor of $Q = 1$, i.e. $R = \sqrt{L/C}$, a very efficient damping can be achieved, as then $\alpha = \omega_0/2 = \pi f_0$. For a resonance frequency f_0 of typically 100 kHz, and a resolution time $\tau \simeq 3/\alpha$, this time becomes about 10 μsec. For higher Q values, τ will be longer, but also the filter efficiency will increase and therefore a compromise is necessary. The resonance frequency f_0 is also influenced by the main test circuit elements C_K and C_t, as their series connection contributes to C. The RLC input units must therefore be changed according to specimen capacitance and to achieve a bandwidth or resonance frequency f_0 within certain limits. These limits are postulated by the band pass amplifier connected to this resonant circuit. These amplifiers are typically designed for lower and upper cut-off frequencies (-3 dB values) between 30 kHz and some 100 kHz, and the bandwidth or bandpass frequency range may also be switched from some 10 kHz up to about 150 kHz. In general the fixed cut-off frequencies are thus within a frequency band not used by radio stations, and higher than the harmonics of the power supply voltages. This limited bandwidth of the amplifier again suppresses harmonic interferences. The bandpass characteristic of the amplifier is also able to integrate short input voltage pulses (see next section); in this application, however, the amplifier is mainly used to increase the sensitivity of the whole measuring circuit. The amplification can in general be continuously tuned to feed the CRO following the amplifier with adequate magnitudes. These amplified discharge impulses are—though integrated—not heavily distorted, as only the rise-time will be decreased and the resonance frequency f_0 of the RLC circuit is well within the bandpass amplification. For a clearer understanding the time-dependent quantities (input current, voltages before and after amplification) are sketched in Fig. 6.15(c).

Finally, the amplified discharge pulses are in general displayed oscillographically superimposed on a power frequency elliptic time base, as shown in Fig. 6.16. The magnitude of the individual discharges is quantified by comparing the pulse crest values with those produced from the calibration circuit shown in Fig. 6.14. This circuit comprising a voltage step generator V_0 and a series capacitance C_0 simulates the apparent charge q with no voltage applied to the PD-testing circuit, as charges with magnitudes $\delta V C_0$ (δV = magnitude of voltage step) are injected into the circuit.

It should be emphasized that the slope of the pulses displayed on the CRO is completely different from the slope of the original *PD* currents $i(t)$, which have twice been integrated. If the duration of the PD currents would

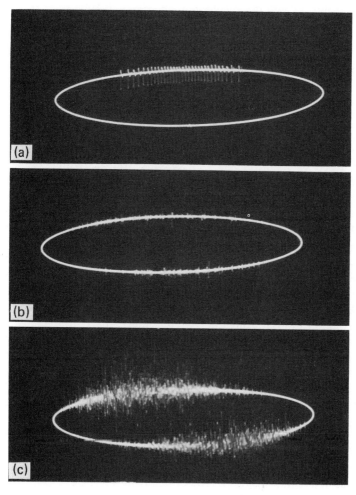

FIG. 6.16. Elliptical display. (a) Point plane. (b) Void breakdown at inception. (c) Void breakdown at twice inception voltage.

be longer than about one-tenth of $1/f_0$, the correct integration is no longer achieved. The pattern on the CRO display can often be used to recognize the origin of the PD sources. The typical pattern of Trichel pulses can be seen in Fig. 6.16(a). Figure 6.16(c) is also typical for the case, for which the resolution time τ is too large to distinguish between individual impulses. In such a case, the reading of the crest values can be completely erroneous, i.e. the amplitudes are not proportional to the real, individual apparent charge magnitudes, due to the superposition of the individual discharges. This superposition can increase or decrease the peak output voltages of the measuring impedance or the bandpass amplifier, depending upon the individual time delays between consecutive PD events.

Narrow-band PD-detection Circuits

It is well known that radio transmission or radiotelephony may heavily be disturbed by high-frequency interference voltages within the supply mains to which receivers are connected or by disturbing electromagnetic fields picked up by the aerials. It was early recognized, for instance, that corona discharges at h.v. transmission lines are the source of such interferences. The measurement of "radio noise" in the vicinity of such transmission lines is thus an old and well-known technique (see, for instance, reference 15), and also publications of Koske[16, 17] supported the application of this measurement technique to detect insulation failures, i.e. partial discharges, within h.v. apparatus of any kind.

The methods for the measurement of radio noise have been subject to many modifications during the past decades. Apart from many older national or international recommendations, the measuring apparatus preferably applicable for the detection of all types of interferences within a frequency range of 10 kHz to 1000 MHz are now described in the CISPR Publication 16.[18] As defined in this specification, the expressions "radio interference voltages" (RIV) or "radio noise voltages" will be used to characterize the measured interference quantity.

Narrow-band PD detectors used for the measurement of the apparent charge are very similar or even identical to RIV meters, which are applied for radio noise measurements in the frequency range of 100 kHz to 30 MHz. As the application of such receivers often causes some confusion for the user, a brief description of their use in RIV meters as well in PD measurements will be presented. Broadcasts are transmitted within narrow frequency bands, and thus the aim of a RIV measurement is to provide an objective assessment of interference signals effective in similar narrow frequency range of interest. The majority of interferences show themselves in the form of repeated impulses, each of which is short in duration. The frequency spectrum of an individual impulse, however, contributes to short duration interferences effective within a broad frequency band. A RIV receiver or RIV meter should quantify these pulses in accordance to the physiological noise response of the human ear (psophometric weighting).

To fulfil this requirement, the main part of a RIV meter is a selective voltmeter of high sensitivity which can be tuned within the frequency range of interest. The selectivity may be reached by a narrow bandpass filter characteristic similar to long or medium wave broadcast receivers. The RIV meter is thus primarily a superheterodyne-type receiver, though also a straight type narrow-band receiver may be used. In any case, the meter can be treated as a high-quality linear amplifier with a bandpass filter characteristic and of an adequate amplification to give high sensitivity. The mid-band frequency f_m of the filter should be continuously variable, a quality easy to perform by the superheterodyne principle (scc Fig. 6.17a). This frequency may also be treated as a resonance frequency f_0 as this is done in the new IEC Recommendations for PD measurements.[19] The bandwidth Δf of such a bandpass receiver is the width of the overall selectivity curve at a level 6 dB below the mid-band response; according to reference 18 this bandwidth is 9 kHz, and the selectivity curve for other frequencies will lie within narrow limits. According to this limit, a sinusoidal input voltage which is 10 kHz apart from f_m is attenuated at least by 20 dB, i.e. by a factor of 10, and attenuations of 50 to 60 dB are typical for $f_m \pm 20$ kHz values.

This main part of a RIV meter described so far is obviously an integration device for input voltage pulses. To demonstrate this behaviour, we assume an input voltage $v_1(t) = V_0 \exp(-t/T)$, i.e. an exponentially decaying input pulse which starts suddenly with amplitude V_0 (see Fig. 6.17b). The complex frequency spectrum of this impulse is then given by applying the Fourier integral

$$V_1(j\omega) = \int_{-\infty}^{+\infty} v_1(t) \exp(-j\omega t)\, dt = \frac{V_0 T}{1+j\omega T} \tag{6.21}$$

and the amplitude frequency spectrum $|V_1(j\omega)|$ by

$$|V_1(j\omega)| = \frac{V_0 T}{\sqrt{1+(\omega T)^2}}. \tag{6.22}$$

As $\int_0^\infty v_1(t)\,dt = V_0 T$, the relative amplitudes of the spectrum are thus proportional to the integrated input voltage with respect to time, the voltage-time area of the impulse or pulse area. From the amplitude frequency spectrum [eqn. (6.22)] sketched in Fig. 6.17c it can easily be seen that the amplitudes will decay more than -3 dB for the angular frequency of $\omega_c > 1/T$. This critical frequency f_c is still quite high for $T < 0.1$ μsec, i.e. $f_c = 1.6$ MHz, a value which can be assumed for many impulse disturbances. It should be mentioned that every amplitude frequency spectrum of a time-limited pulse contains the information about the pulse area. These spectra are in general constant starting from very low frequencies ($\omega \to 0$),

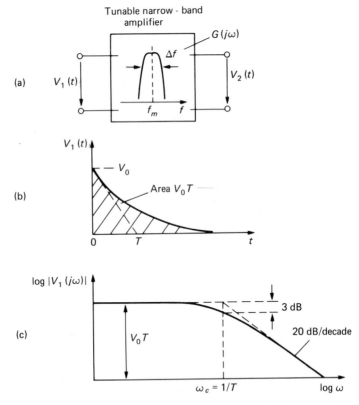

FIG. 6.17. Narrow-band amplifiers: some explanations to the impulse response. (a) Block diagram. (b) Input voltage, example, $V_1(t)$. (c) Amplitude frequency spectrum from $V_1(t)$. (d) Idealized transfer function of narrow-band amplifier. (e) Computed impulse response according to eqn. (6.24) for $f = 150$ kHz and $\Delta f = 8.33$ kHz.

(d)

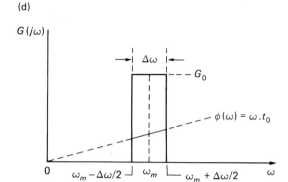

(e)

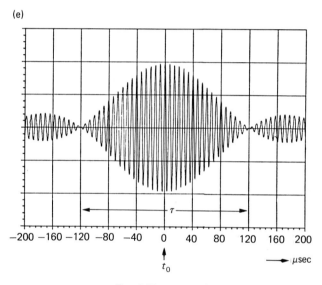

FIG. 6.17.—*continued*

extending to higher frequencies before they deviate to higher (resonances, i.e. oscillating pulses) or lower values. In addition, as long as the shape of an impulse does not change, every amplitude of the spectrum is proportional to the pulse area; the deviating amplitude, however, must then be compared with the low-frequency value to quantify the pulse area.

For the calculation of the output voltage $v_2(t)$ of a tunable narrow-band system we thus may assume that the input voltage is equivalent to a Dirac impulse or delta function of magnitude $V_0 T = S_0$. As the spectrum of an impulse function is constant for all frequencies, the response $v_2(t)$ is then proportional to S_0 as long as the overall sensitivity curve of our narrow-band amplifier fits into the constant part of the spectrum $|V_1(j\omega)|$. The impulse response of the amplifier is of course dependent upon the exact transfer function $G(j\omega)$ of the system; we may, however, approximate the bandpass characteristic by an idealized one as shown in Fig. 6.17d, with a mid-band angular frequency ω_m, an angular bandwidth $\Delta\omega$ and the constant amplitude G_0 within $\omega_m \pm (\Delta\omega/2)$. For such ideal bandpass systems and especially narrow-band receivers the phase shift $\phi(\omega)$ may well be assumed to be linear with frequency as indicated, at least within the bandpass response. In this approximation no phase distortion is assumed, and t_0 (see Fig. 6.17d) is equal to the delay time of the system.[20] The impulse response with S_0 as input pulse appearing at $t = 0$ can then be evaluated[20, 35] from

$$v_2(t) = \frac{1}{\pi} \int_{\omega_m - \Delta\omega/2}^{\omega_m + \Delta\omega/2} S_0 G_0 \cos\left[\omega(t - t_0)\right] d\omega. \tag{6.23}$$

This integral can easily be solved; the result is

$$v_2(t) = \frac{S_0 G_0 \Delta\omega}{\pi} \text{ si} \left[\frac{\Delta\omega}{2}(t - t_0)\right] \cos \omega_m(t - t_0) \tag{6.24}$$

where $\text{si } x = \sin x / x$.

Equation (6.24) shows an oscillating response whose main frequency is given by $f_m = \omega_m / 2\pi$, the amplitudes are essentially given by the si x function which is the envelope of the oscillations. The example for such a response is shown in Fig. 6.17e. The maximum value will be reached for $t = t_0$ and is clearly given by

$$V_{2\max} = \frac{S_0 G_0 \Delta\omega}{\pi} = 2S_0 G_0 \Delta f \tag{6.25}$$

where Δf is the idealized bandwidth of the system. The two main disadvantages of narrow-band receivers can easily be seen: first, for $\Delta\omega \ll \omega_m$ the positive and negative peak values of the response are equal and therefore the polarity of the input pulse cannot be detected. The second disadvantage is related to the long duration of the response. Though more realistic narrow-band systems will effectively avoid increased response amplitudes outside of the first zero values of the $(\sin x)/x$-function, the length τ of the response, with τ defined by Fig. 6.17e, becomes

$$\tau = \frac{2}{\Delta f} = \frac{4\pi}{\Delta\omega}, \qquad (6.26)$$

which becomes quite large for small values of Δf. The time τ gives the resolution time of the system, as subsequent input pulses within a time shorter than τ must lead to an overlapping of the equal individual pulse responses. Measured responses from a RIV meter taken from the output of the intermediate-frequency amplifier, i.e. before the weighting circuit, are shown in Fig. 6.18 to demonstrate an actual response from a narrow-band amplifier as well as the overlapping effect.

RIV meters comprise, in addition to the system described so far, a weighting circuit to quantify the magnitudes of repeated impulses in accordance with the physiological noise response of the human ear, as mentioned before. In most cases, a quasi-peak detection is made as the early work of CISPR led to the conclusion that this would be the best measure for repeated impulse interferences. Subsequent experience has shown also that a r.m.s. voltmeter connected to the output of narrow-band amplifier might give even more accurate assessment of the disturbances. The quasi-peak-type RIV meter comprises at the output of the narrow-band amplifier essentially a nonlinear element (for example a diode) in association with a resistance (forward resistance), followed by a capacitance in shunt with a discharge resistance. The voltage across the capacitance, which will be charged by the impulse response (Fig. 6.18) by a time constant of typically 1 msec, is measured by an indicating instrument (for arithmetic mean values) which is also critically damped. The electrical discharge time constant of the quasi-peak circuit as well as the mechanical time constant of the indicating instrument are defined to be 160 msec. By this procedure the indication of the instrument is dependent upon the *pulse repetition rate n*.

This indication will be a nonlinear function of n and will be accurate only if the input pulses are *equidistant* and of *equal amplitude*. For these assumptions the nonlinear function $f(n)$ is presented in Fig. 6.19 according to references 18 or 19. The calibration point is given by $n = 100$, i.e. with input pulses repeated at a frequency of 100 Hz, and it can be seen that for a very high repetition rate ($n \gg 1000$) the function $f(n)$ would saturate for $f(n) = 2$. For this case, which cannot be reached experimentally due to an overlapping of subsequent responses (see Fig. 6.18), the quasi-peak circuit would be charged to the maximum value, V_{2max}, according to eqn. (6.25). The quasi-peak RIV meters are calibrated in such a way that the response

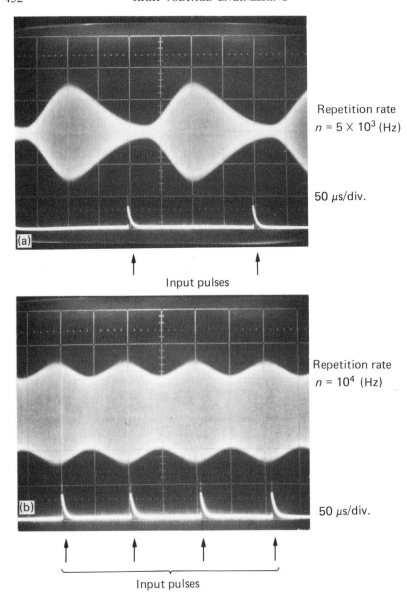

Repetition rate
$n = 5 \times 10^3$ (Hz)

50 μs/div.

Input pulses

Repetition rate
$n = 10^4$ (Hz)

50 μs/div.

Input pulses

FIG. 6.18. Measured pulse response of an actual narrow-band detector (RIV meter). Signals taken from the intermediate frequency amplifiers for repetitive input signals (a) with adequate and (b) inadequate time distances. Bandwidth $\Delta f \approx 9$ kHz.

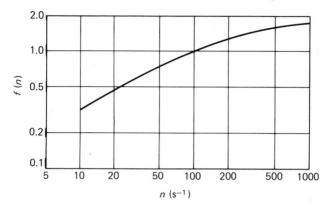

FIG. 6.19. Variation of CISPR radio interference meter reading with repetition rate, n, for constant pulses.

to adequate short input pulses of 0.316 μVs voltage-time-area repeated at $n = 100$ Hz is equal to an unmodulated sine-wave signal at the tuned frequency having an e.m.f. of 2 mV r.m.s. from a signal generator having the same output impedance as the pulse generator and the input impedance of the RIV meter. By this procedure the impulse voltages as well as the sine-wave signal are halved in value, an input voltage pulse of 0.158 μVs equal to a 1 mV r.m.s. input signal. This relationship follows from eqn. (6.25), as we may rewrite this equation taking into account the reduced indicated value by the instrument E_r for $n = 100$ by a factor of 2 and taking the r.m.s. reading into account:

$$E_r = \frac{1}{2\sqrt{2}} 2 S_0 G_0 \Delta f = \frac{S_0 G_0 \Delta f}{\sqrt{2}}. \qquad (6.27)$$

As $G_0 = 1$ for a proper calibration, and $\Delta f = 9$ kHz, $S_0 = 0.158$ μVs, the indicated quantity is $S_0 \Delta f / \sqrt{2} = 1$ mV or 60 dB(μV), as the usual reference quantity is 1 μV.

For a long time and even today partial discharge measurements are made with RIV or radio-noise meters, also according to national standards. The measured PD quantities are then "microvolts" due to the indication of the receivers used. Many experiments and attempts have been made to relate the indication of quasi-peak RIV meters with PD detectors measuring the individual charges of PD currents according to wideband PD-detection circuits described before. Such comparisons may be found in the literature (see for example references 21 and 22). It is obvious, however, that no definite relationship will exist, though RIV meters are also principally integrating devices. However, actual partial discharge currents are in general not equal in amplitude and equidistant, so that the correction factor $f(n)$, Fig. 6.19, can only be used approximately to convert the μV reading to charge quantities, even if a mean value of impulses per second, $\bar{n}$, is known. Further on this relationship is dependent upon the equivalent input resistance of the RIV meter, i.e. the resistance value which converts the PD currents into input voltages. If this input resistance is provided by an impedance Z_m, the real value of which $|Z_m|$ is constant for the frequency range under consideration, the quantity S_0 in eqn. (6.27) may also be written as

$$S_0 = \int v_1(t)\,dt = |Z_m| \int i_1(t)\,dt = |Z_m|q_m, \qquad (6.28)$$

where q_m is the measured charge quantity for an impulse current $i_1(t)$ flowing through the input impedance. A conversion factor between the measured charge, q_m, and the indicated voltage by a RIV meter can therefore be derived directly from eqns. (6.28) and (6.27) for fixed conditions, i.e. $n = 100$ and $\Delta f = 9$ kHz. If the RIV meter reads 1 mV, $S_0 = 0.158$ μVs and therefore $q_m = S_0/|Z_m|$. For $Z_m = 60$ (or 150) Ω $q_m \simeq 2.6$ (or 1) nC, a relationship also confirmed experimentally.[22]

The voltage reading E_r of a quasi-peak RIV meter for equidistant and equal input current pulses of charge q_m each, whose spectrum is still uniform in the range of the mid-band frequency used to obtain the information on the integrated pulse [see eqn. (6.21)], is therefore

$$E_r = \frac{1}{\sqrt{2}} f(n)|Z_m|q_m\Delta f. \qquad (6.29)$$

The foregoing described fully narrow-band detection circuits. In Fig. 6.20 a block diagram of such a circuit is sketched, recalling again the differences between a pure narrow-band detector and the RIV meter. In practice, the coupling impedance Z_m for PD measurements is formed by a parallel arrangement of an inductance and a resistance, which in general are in parallel to the input resistance of the narrow-band detector, that matches the connecting coaxial cable. The inductance (L) reduces the voltage input for low frequencies and so suppresses the effects of the low-frequency displacement currents through the coupling capacitor C_K or the test object C_t

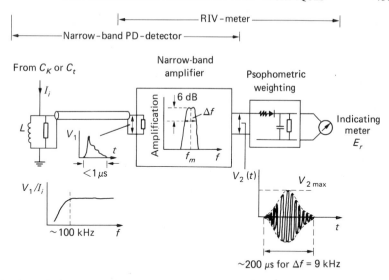

FIG. 6.20. Block diagram of a narrow-band PD detector including psochometric weighting (RIV meter, quasi-peak).

(see Fig. 6.14). The magnitude of L must be such that $|Z_m|$ remains constant in the range of f_m used. All further suppression of disturbing signals not related to partial discharges is made by the narrow-band filter circuit. A pure charge quantity measurement can be made not using the weighting circuits [see eqns. (6.25) and (6.28)]; otherwise the reading is directly proportional to the charge only for certain conditions [see eqn. (6.29)]. The main advantage of narrow-band circuit is the large suppression of sinusoidal interference voltages outside the midband frequency band f_m $\pm(2-3)\Delta f$ used. As f_m can be continuously changed, one may easily find a frequency band in which the lowest amount of disturbances are present. Adequate midband frequencies may be found between about 100 kHz to 2 MHz, but for the higher frequency values the consistency of the PD pulse spectra should be checked. If PD currents are oscillating, as is often the case for samples with distributed capacitances and inductances (i.e. transformer windings, cables), constant spectra are not available. Then f_m may be tuned to the frequency of the oscillations which provides high sensitivity but in general no adequate proportionality to the charge of the PD currents. The main disadvantage is the large resolution time [see eqn. (6.26)] for the small bandwidth Δf. If superposition effects are not controlled by an additional measurement of the time distances between the PD pulses, erroneous applications of RIV meter or narrow-band circuits are unavoidable.[23] Finally, the disadvantage that the polarity of the pulses cannot be detected should be again emphasized; however, the polarity will contribute strongly to the possibility of detecting PD sources within a test circuit.[24]

In this section the application of RIV meters with quasi-peak indication and the psophometric weighting was discussed and compared with the pure narrow-band circuit. It is unfortunate that quasi-peak detectors are still in use which have been developed to quantify the interference on radio reception only. However, many RIV meters are also equipped to measure the pure peak values of the pulse response and can thus be used to measure the charge of PD's more adequately.

6.2.4 Suppression of Disturbances: Special Methods

The deficiency of the straight PD-detection circuits shown in Fig. 6.14 is obvious: any discharge within the entire circuit, including h.v. source, which is not generated in the test specimen itself, will be detected by the measuring impedance Z_m. Therefore, such "external" disturbances are not rejected. A blocking of the mains interferences at the l.v. side of the h.v. testing transformer is possible using filters. The testing transformer itself should be PD-free as far as possible, as h.v. filters or inductors providing the blocking impedance Z in Fig. 6.14 are expensive. It is also difficult to avoid any partial discharges at the h.v. leads of the test circuit, if the voltages are very high. A basic improvement of the straight detection circuit may therefore become necessary.

The improvement is possible with a bridge circuit similar to a Schering bridge. In Fig. 6.21 the coupling capacitor C_K and test specimen C_t form the h.v. arm of the bridge, and the l.v. arms are basically analogous to a Schering bridge. As C_K is not a standard capacitor, the dissipation factor $\tan \delta_K$ may also be higher than that of C_t, and therefore the capacitive branch may be switched to any of the two bridge arms. The bridge can be adjusted for balance for all frequencies at which $\tan \delta_K = \tan \delta_t$. If the frequency dependence of the dissipation factors are different in the two capacitors, a complete balance within a large frequency range is not possible. Nevertheless, a fairly good balance can be reached and therefore most of the sinusoidal or transient voltages appearing at the input ends of C_K

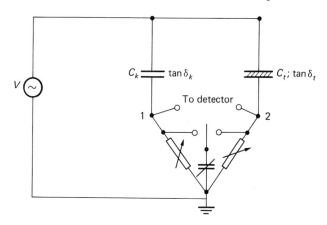

FIG. 6.21. Differential discharge bridge.

and C_t cancel out between the points 1 and 2. A discharge within the test specimen, however, will contribute to voltages of opposite polarity across the l.v. arms, as the PD current is flowing in opposite directions within C_K and C_t. The method is referred to as the differential method or balanced circuit.

The detection circuit connected to the points 1 and 2 may be identical to the circuits discussed earlier (see Figs. 6.15 and 6.20). The measuring impedances Z_m including detectors, however, must be able to remain at a small floating potential. As the bridge circuit itself suppresses sinusoidal voltages within a high-frequency range to a large extent, a better rejection of all types of external disturbances is achieved. Whereas the capacitances C_K and C_t need not be equal, the same insulation media within both capacitors are preferable, as then the frequency dependency of their dissipation factors are essentially the same. The use of a partial discharge free sample for C_K of the same type as is used in C_t is thus advantageous.

Apart from this extensively used method, some other procedures are applied to suppress interference pulses. Commercially available today are so-called window gating facilities, i.e. electronically switched "windows" suppressing input voltages of the detector during time intervals, for example in the vicinity of the voltage zeros of the test voltage. With such adjustable gates discrete interference pulses which would give false reading of the PD detector may be set to blank off (for instance Discharge Detector Model 5, Robinson Electronic Instruments, England). Apart from the possibility to discriminate partial discharges within C_K or C_t by visual observation of their polarity with reference to the polarity of the test voltage only, such a pulse discrimination system may be made by electronic circuits in connection with wide-band PD detectors.[25, 26] Such a system compares the polarity of a current pulse in the test component with that in a parallel capacitor, this means within C_t and C_K. If the pulses are of equal polarity, the indication of the PD detector is suppressed by a logic system.

6.2.5 Other PD Quantities

The measurement of the apparent charge q as a fundamental PD quantity is widely acknowledged today. The individual charge magnitudes of subsequent pulses are different, however, as well as the number of partial discharges within a given reference time interval. The deterioration process within an insulation system is certainly a result of *all* discharges and is not limited to the maximum values only, though only the largest apparent charges are in general taken as a specified value. Much recent research work has been related to the measurement of all single PD impulses and to the evaluation of the results on a statistical basis. Measuring systems of such kind are known as PD pulse analyzers and depending upon the extent of the detection and analyzing systems, the number of pulses, the pulse intervals and the amplitudes of the individual impulses may be detected. The large amount of information available by the great number of events and therefore distributions makes it necessary to incorporate electronic multichannel pulse analyzers into the system, and also the evaluation of the results will preferably be made by computers. Only some references are provided for further information.[27–29,37]

For the application of such systems, the proper measurement of the apparent charge q as described before is a prerequisite. The magnified PD pulses can then easily be counted by any type of pulse counter or rate meter, indicating either an average number of pulses per second or the total number of pulses in a given time. In this way the "pulse repetition rate" $\bar{n}$ as a mean value may be detected, provided that the resolution time τ of the PD detector is sufficiently short to distinguish between the individual pulses. The repetition rate can also be related to the charge magnitude, as the counters may be set to react only for given amplitude ranges. In any case, care is needed to avoid more than one count per PD pulse as the pulse response of most PD detectors is oscillatory.

Another specified PD quantity is the average discharge current, I, expressed in coulombs per second or amperes, and defined by

$$I = \frac{1}{T}|q_1 + q_2 + \ldots q_m| = \frac{1}{T}\sum_{i=1}^{m}|q_i| \qquad (6.30)$$

where T is a reference time interval and q_i are the individual apparent charges. By this definition a quantity is available which includes all individual PD pulses as well as the pulse repetition rate. The measurement of this quantity is possible based upon either linear amplification and rectification of the PD discharge currents (without interferent currents) or by processing the output quantities of the apparent charge detectors by integration and averaging.[30] This average discharge current was not investigated extensively up to now, though the investigations available show quite interesting additional information about the impact on the lifetime of insulation.[31] The correct measurement of this quantity is not easy if also pulseless PD pulses are present.

Further specified PD quantities are the quadratic rate, D, defined by

$$D = \frac{1}{T}|q_1^2 + q_2^2 + \ldots q_m^2| \qquad (6.31)$$

and the discharge power, P, defined by

$$P = \frac{1}{T}|q_1\mu_1 + q_2\mu_2 + \ldots q_m\mu_m|. \qquad (6.32)$$

where T and q are defined as in eqn. (6.30) and $\mu_1, \mu_2 \ldots \mu_m$ are the absolute instantaneous values of the test voltage at the instants of discharges $q_1, q_2 \ldots q_m$. The quadratic rate, D, appears to have no advantages as compared to the measurement of the maximum values of q_{max} only.[32] More important is the measurement of the discharge power, but according to eqn. (6.32) this needs the measurements of the instantaneous voltages also including multiplication and averaging. Therefore, this quantity was also not very much investigated up to now.[33] Measurement apparatus are in general, therefore, developed individually[34] and are not commercially available.

6.2.6 Calibration of PD-Dectectors in a Complete Test Arrangement

It was shown on p. 442 that the PD measuring circuit comprises a measuring impedance Z_m as well as a measuring instrument (M in Fig. 6.14), and that for wide-band or narrow-band detection circuits an interaction of both elements takes place. A calibration of this measuring circuit is usually done by the manufacturers, and a detailed recalibration should only be performed after major repairs or for control purposes, i.e. within longer time intervals. Calibration devices injecting short current pulses of any convenient but known charge magnitudes through the measuring impedance are often built in within the discharge detector. The pulses may be produced by means of a voltage generator providing rectangular step voltages of magnitudes V_0 in series with a small capacitance of known value C_0. Under these conditions the injected calibration pulse is equivalent to a charge $q_0 = C_0 V_0$, if the current pulse is sufficiently short.

If the PD-measuring circuit is placed within the complete test arrangement, the PD current pulses $i(t)$ produced by a PD within the object under test, C_t (see Fig. 6.11), are dependent upon the test circuit parameters. For known effective values of the coupling capacitance, C_K, the relationship between the *measured* charge quantity q_m and the apparent charge q inherent in the discharge mechanism within C_t could easily be calculated using eqn. (6.19). In reality C_K may be shunted by stray capacitances according to the h.v. leads within the circuit or capacitances involved in the h.v. power supply, which may be unsatisfactorily disconnected by the impedance or filter, Z. For a consistent measurement of the apparent charge q it is thus necessary to calibrate the measuring circuit or instrument within the complete test arrangement. This is done by a routine calibration, primarily in the circuits of Fig. 6.14, in which the calibration pulse generating circuit (V_0, C_0) is shown to be in parallel with the test object, C_t. This generating circuit acts by this method similar to the equivalent circuit of partial discharges within an insulation system (Fig. 6.10), and thus it may well be understood that C_0 should be small ($\lesssim 10\%$) in comparison to $C_t + C_K$. The value $q_0 = C_0 V_0$ of the injected calibration pulse is then equivalent to an artificial apparent charge, q, and the indication of the instrument of the PD detector can thus be calibrated in terms of apparent charge. By this calibration procedure a scale factor $k = q_m/q$ similar to eqn. (6.19) can be determined, and this scale factor would be smaller for the PD-detection circuit (Fig. 6.14b) than that for the circuit (Fig. 6.14a) due to the stray capacitances. Taking the stray inductances of the leads within the test and calibration arrangement into account, the injected current pulses may oscillate, so that the amplitude frequency spectrum of the current pulses detected by Z_m contains resonance frequencies. Narrow-band detectors will react to these resonances, and thus the existence of such phenomena has to be checked by changing the midband frequency. To avoid unnecessary inductances, the calibration circuit should therefore be located as close as possible to the test object.

C_0 can be a l.v. capacitor if the calibration procedure is performed without the test voltage. Otherwise C_0 must be a PD-free h.v. capacitor similar to C_K. For further details refer to reference 19.

REFERENCES

1. W. P. Baker. *Electrical Insulation Measurements*. Newnes International Monographs on Electrical Engineering and Electronics, 1965.
2. A. J. Schwab. *High Voltage Measurement Techniques*. M.I.T. Press, 1972.
3. B. Hague. *Alternating-Current Bridge Methods*, 5th ed. Pitman & Sons, London, 1959.
4. F. W. Rutloh. Convergence of bridges for dissipation-factor measurements of capacitors. *ETZ-A* **86** (1965), pp. 596–599.
5. H. A. M. Clark and P. B. Vandermlyn. Double ratio a.c. bridges with inductively coupled ratio arms. *Proc. IEE* **96** (1949), pp. 365–378.
6. N. Hemmer. Universal-*C*-tan δ-Messbruecke mit schreibendem Schnellabgleich. *Siemens-Z.* **38** (1964), pp. 500–506.
7. R. Calvert and J. Mildwater. Self-balancing transformer ratio arm bridges. *Electronic Engn.* **35** (1963), pp. 782–787.
8. O. Peterson. A self-balancing high-voltage capacitance bridge. *Trans. IEEE* **IM13** (1964), pp. 216–224.
9 P. Seitz and P. Osvath. Microcomputer controlled transformer ratio-arm bridge. 3rd Int. Symp. on High Voltage Engg., Milan, 1979, Report 43.11.
10. J. G. Anderson. *Trans. IEEE*, Part III, *Power Applications & Systems*, **33** (1957), p. 1066.
11. P. Moro and J. Poittevin. Localization des de charges partielles dans le transformateurs par detection des ondes ultrasonores emises. *Rev. Generale de l'Electricite* **87** (1978), pp. 25–35.
12. E. Howells and E. T. Norton. Detection of partial discharges in transformers using emission techniques. *Trans. IEEE* **PAS97** (1978), pp. 1538–1549.
13. R. T. Harrold. Acoustic waveguides for sensing and locating electrical discharges in H.V. power transformers and other apparatus. *Trans. IEEE* **PAS98** (1979), pp. 449–457.
14. F. H. Kreuger. *Discharge Detection in High Voltage Equipment*. Heywood, London, 1964; Elsevier, New York, 1964.
15. *Methods of Measuring Radio Noise*. NEMA Publication No. 107, 1940.
16. B. Koske. *Pruefung der Isolation von Hochspannungsfreileitungen und Schaltanlagen*. Girardet, Essen, 1951.
17. B. Koske. Ueber die Pruefung von Hochspannungsisolationen auf dem Profstand mit HF-Messmethoden. *Energietechnik* **2** (1952), pp. 181–186.
18. C.I.S.P.R. Specifications for Radio Interference Measuring Apparatus and Measurement Methods (edited by IEC, Int. Special Committee on Radio Interference), 16 (1977).
19. IEC Standard, Publication 270: Partial Discharge Measurements, 1981.
20. A. Papoulis. *The Fourier Integral and its Applications*. McGraw-Hill, 1962.
21. E. Buchmann, B. Gänger and A. Goldstein. Messanordnung zur Erfassung innerer Ionization. *Bull. SEV* **57** (1966), pp. 511–517.

22. E. M. Dembinski and J. L. Douglas. Calibration of partial-discharge and radio-interference measuring circuits. *Proc. IEE* **115** (1968), pp. 1332–1340.
23. R. T. Harrold and T. W. Dakin. The relationship between the picocoulomb and microvolt for corona measurements on hv transformers and other apparatus. *Trans. IEEE* **PAS 92** (1973), pp. 187–198.
24. Th. Praehauser. Lokalisierung von Teilentladungen in Hochspannungsapparaten. *Bull. SEV* **63** (1972), pp. 893–905.
25. British Patent No. 6173/72. Improvements in or Relating to High Voltage Component Testing Systems.
26. I. A. Black. A pulse discrimination system for discharge detection in electrically noisy environments. 2nd Int. High Voltage Symposium, Zurich, 1975, pp. 239–243.
27. R. Bartnikas. Use of multichannel analyzer for corona pulse-height distribution measurements on cables and other electrical apparatus. *Trans. IEEE* **IM-22** (1973), pp. 403–407.
28. S. Kärkkainen. Multi-channel pulse analyzer in partial discharge studies. 2nd Int. High Voltage Symposium, Zurich, 1975, pp. 244–249.
29. K. Umemoto, E. Koyanagy, T. Yamada and S. Kenjo. Partial discharge measurement system using pulse-height analyzers. 3rd Intern. Symp. on High Voltage Engg., Milan, 1979, Report 43.07.
30. E. Lemke. Gerätesystem zur Messung von Teilentladungen. *Elektrie* **26** (1972), pp. 165–167.
31. B. Kübler. Investigation of partial discharge measuring techniques using epoxy resin samples with several voids. IEEE Intern. Symp. on El. Insulation, 1978, 78 CH 1287-2EI (see also Ph.D. Thesis, Techn. Universität Braunschweig, 1978).
32. J. Carlier et al. Ageing under voltage of the insulation of rotating machines: influence of frequency and temperature. CIGRE-Rapport No. 15-06, 1976.
33. R. Bartnikas and E. J. McMahon. Corona measurement and interpretation. *Engineering Dielectrics*, Volume 1, ASTM STP 669, 1979.
34. K.-V. Boos. Die Energiebilanz von Teilentladungen und ihr Einfluss auf das Durchschlagsverhalten von Polyäthylene-Isolierstoffen. Ph.D. Thesis, Techn. Universität Karlsruhe, 1975.
35. K. Kuepfmueller. *Die Systemtheorie der elektrischen Nachrichtenuebertragung*. S. Hirzel-Verlag, Stuttgart, 1968.
36. E. Kuffel and M. Abdullah. *High Voltage Engineering*. Pergamon Press, Oxford, 1970.
37. A. G. Millar et al. Digital acquisition, storage and processing of partial discharge signals. 4th Int. Symp. on High Voltage Engng., Athens 1983, Report 63.01.

Chapter 7

OVERVOLTAGES AND INSULATION COORDINATION

Power systems are often subjected to overvoltages that have their origin in atmospheric discharges in which case they are called external or lightning overvoltages, or they are generated internally by connecting or disconnecting the system, or due to the systems fault initiation or extinction. The latter type are called internal overvoltages. This class may be further subdivided into (i) temporary overvoltages, if they are oscillatory of power frequency or harmonics, and (ii) switching overvoltages, if they are heavily damped and of short duration. Temporary overvoltages occur almost without exception under no load or very light load conditions. Because of their common origin the temporary and switching overvoltages occur together and their combined effect has to be taken into account in the design of h.v. systems insulation.

The magnitude of the external or lightning overvoltages remains essentially independent of the system's design, whereas that of internal or switching overvoltages increases with increasing the operating voltage of the system. Hence, with increasing the system's operating voltage a point is reached when the switching overvoltages become the dominant factor in designing the system's insulation. Up to approximately 300 kV, the system's insulation has to be designed to withstand primarily lightning surges Above that voltage, both lightning and switching surges have to be considered. For ultra h.v. systems, 765 kV and above switching overvoltages in combination with insulator contamination becomes the predominating factor in the insulation design.[1]* For the study of overvoltages occurring in power systems, a thorough knowledge of surge

---

* Superscript numbers are to References at the end of the chapter.

propagation laws is needed which can be found in a number of text-books[2, 3] and will not be discussed here.

7.1 THE LIGHTNING MECHANISM

Physical manifestations of lightning have been noted in ancient times, but the understanding of lightning is relatively recent. Franklin carried out experiments on lightning in 1744–1750, but most of the knowledge has been obtained over the last 50 years. The real incentive to study lightning came when electric transmission lines had to be protected against lightning. The methods include measurements of (i) lightning currents, (ii) magnetic fields, (iii) voltages, (iv) use of high-speed photography.

Fundamentally, lightning is a manifestation of a very large electric spark. Several theories have been advanced to explain accummulation of electricity in clouds and are fully discussed in reference 4. The present section reviews briefly the lightning discharge processes. For a more detailed review the reader should consult reference 5.

In an active thunder cloud the larger particles usually possess negative charge and the smaller carriers are positive. Thus the base of a thunder cloud generally carries a negative charge and the upper part is positive, with the whole being eletrically neutral. As will be discussed later, there may be several charge centres within a single cloud. Typically the negative charge centre may be located anywhere between 500 m and 10,000 m above ground. Lightning discharge to earth is usually initiated at the fringe of a negative charge centre.

To the eye a lightning discharge appears as a single luminous discharge, although at times branches of variable intensity may be observed which terminate in mid-air, while the luminous main channel continue in a zig-zag path to earth. High-speed photographic technique studies reveal that most lightning strokes are followed by repeat or multiple strokes which travel along the path established by the first stroke. The latter ones are not usually branched and their path is brightly illuminated.

The various development stages of a lightning stroke from cloud to earth as observed by high-speed photography is shown diagrammatically in Fig. 7.1 together with the current to ground. The stroke is initiated in the region of the negative charge centre where the local field intensity approaches ionization field intensity ($\simeq 30$ kV/cm in atmospheric air, or ~ 10 kV/cm in the presence of water droplets).

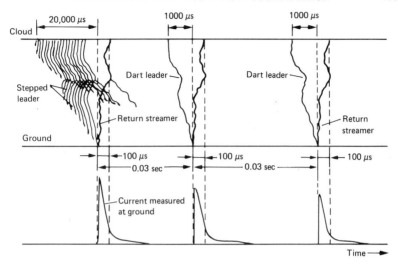

FIG. 7.1. Diagrammatic representation of lightning mechanism and ground current.[3]

During the first stage the leader discharge known as the "stepped leader" moves rapidly downwards in steps of 50 m to 100 m, and pauses after each step for a few tens of microseconds. From the tip of the discharge a "pilot streamer" having low luminosity and current of a few amperes propagates into the virgin air with a velocity of about 1×10^5 m/sec. The pilot streamer is followed by the stepped leader with an average velocity of about 5×10^5 m/sec and a current of some 100 A. For a stepped leader from a cloud some 3 km above ground shown in Fig. 7.1 it takes about 60 msec to reach the ground. As the leader approaches ground, the potential difference induces a charge in the earth. This charge is augmented by point discharges from earth objects such as tall buildings, trees, etc. At some point the charge concentration at the earthed object is high enough to initiate an upwards positive streamer. At the instance when the two leaders meet, the "main" or "return" stroke starts from ground to cloud, travelling much faster ($\sim 50 \times 10^6$ m/sec) along the previously established ionized channel. The current in the return stroke is in the order of a few kA to 250 kA and the temperatures within the channel are 15,000°C to 20,000°C and is responsible for the destructive effects of lightning giving high luminosity and causing explosive air expansion. The return stroke causes the destructive effects generally associated with lightning.

The return stroke is followed by several strokes at 10- to 300-msec intervals. The leader of the second and subsequent strokes is known as the "dart leader" because of its dart-like appearance. The dart leader follows the path of the first stepped leader with a velocity of about 10 times faster than the stepped leader. The path is usually not branched and is brightly illuminated.

A diagrammatic representation of the various stages of the lightning stroke development from cloud to ground in Fig. 2(a) to (f) gives a clearer appreciation of the process involved. In a cloud several charge centres of high concentration may exist. In the present case only two negative charge centres are shown. In (a) the stepped leader has been initiated and the pilot streamer and stepped leader propagate to ground, lowering the negative charges in the cloud. At this instance the striking point still has not been decided; in (b) the pilot streamer is about to make contact with the upwards positive streamer from earth; in (c) the stroke is completed, a heavy return stroke returns to cloud and negative charge of cloud begins to discharge; in (d) the first centre is completely discharged and streamers begin developing in the second charge centre; in (e) the second charge centre is discharging to ground via the first charge centre and dart leader, distributing negative charge along the channel. Positive streamers are rising up from ground to meet the dart leader; (f) contact is made with streamers from earth, heavy return stroke proceeds upwards and begins to discharge negatively charged space beneath the cloud and the second charge centre in the cloud.

Lightning strokes from cloud to ground account only for about 10% of lightning discharges, the majority of discharges during thunderstorms take place between clouds. Discharges within clouds often provide general illumination known as "sheath lightning".

Measurements of stroke currents at ground have shown that the high current is characterized by a sharp rise to crest (1 to 10 μsec) followed by a longer decay time 50–1000 μsec to half-time. Figure 7.3 gives the probability distribution of times to crest for lightning strokes as prepared by Anderson.[7] There is evidence that very high stroke currents do not coincide with very short times to crest. Field data [3, 20] indicate that 50% of stroke currents including multiple strokes have a rate of rise exceeding 20 kA/μsec and 10% exceed 50 kA/μsec. The mean duration of stroke currents above half value is 30 μsec and 18% have longer half-times than 50 μsec. Thus for a typical maximum stroke current of 10,000 A a transmission line of surge impedance (say) $Z = 400\ \Omega$ and assuming the strike takes place in the middle of the line with half of the current flowing in each direction ($Z \simeq 200\ \Omega$) the lightning overvoltage becomes $V = 5000 \times 400 = 2$ MV. Based on

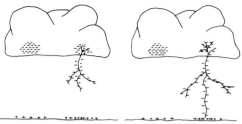

(a) Charge centers in cloud; pilot streamer and stepped leader propagate earthward; outward branching of streamers to earth. Lowering of charge into space beneath cloud.

(b) Process of (a) almost completed; pilot streamer about to strike earth.

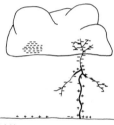

(c) Heavy return streamer; discharge to earth of negatively charged space beneath cloud.

(d) First charge center completely discharged; development of streamers between charge centers within cloud.

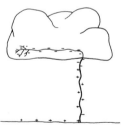

(e) Discharge between two charge centers; dart leader propagates to ground along original channel; dart leader about to strike earth; negative charge lowered and distributed along stroke channel.

(f) Heavy return streamer discharge to earth of negatively charged space beneath cloud.

FIG. 7.2. Schematic representation of various stages of lightning stroke between cloud and ground.[6]

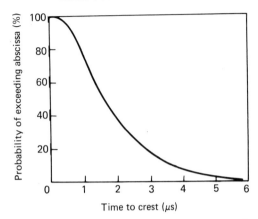

Fig. 7.3. Distribution of times to crest of lightning stroke currents (after Anderson[7]).

many investigations the AIEE Committee[8] has produced the frequency distribution of current magnitudes, shown in Fig. 7.4, which is often used for performance calculations. Included in Fig. 7.4 is a curve proposed by Anderson.[7]

The data on lightning strokes and voltages has formed the basis for establishing the standard impulse or lightning surge for testing equipment in laboratories. The standard lightning impulse waveshape will be discussed later in this chapter.

Energy in Lightning

To estimate the amount of energy in a typical lightning discharge let us assume a value of potential difference of 10^7 V for a breakdown between a cloud and ground and a total discharge of 20 coulombs. Then the energy released is 20×10^7 Ws as about 55 kW-hr in one or more strokes that make the discharge. The energy of the discharge dissipated in the air channel is expended in several processes. Small amounts of this energy are used in ionization of molecules, excitations, radiation, etc. Most of the energy is consumed in the sudden expansion of the air channel. Some fraction of the total causes heating of the struck earthed objects. In general, lightning processes return to the global system the energy that was used originally to create the charged cloud.

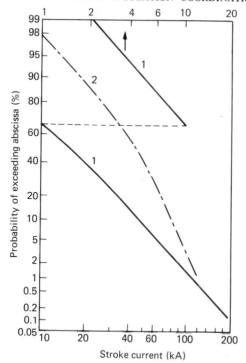

FIG. 7.4. Cumulative distributions of lightning stroke current magnitudes: 1. After AIEE Committee.[8] 2. After Anderson.[6]

Nature of Danger

The degree of hazard depends on circumstances. To minimize the chances of being struck by lightning during thunderstorm, one should be sufficiently far away from tall objects likely to be struck, remain inside buildings or be well insulated.

A direct hit on a human or animal is rare. Most frequently it is due to indirect striking, usually when the subject is (a) close to a parallel hit or other tall object, (b) due to an intense electric field from stroke which can induce sufficient current to cause death, (c) lightning terminating on earth can set up high potential gradients over the ground surface in an outwards direction from the point or object struck. Figure 7.5 illustrates qualitatively

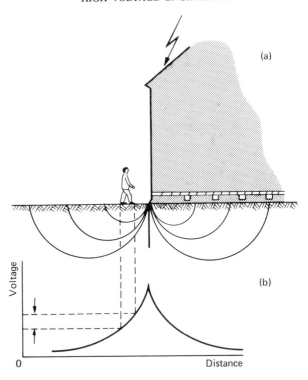

F<small>IG</small>. 7.5. Current distribution and voltage distribution in ground due to lightning stroke to a building (after Golde[9]).

the current distribution in the ground and the voltage distribution along the ground extending outwards from the edge of a building struck by lightning.[9] The potential difference between the person's feet will be largest if his feet are separated along a radial line from the source of voltage and will be negligible if he moves at a right angle to such a radial line. In the latter case the person would be safe due to element of chance.

7.2 SIMULATED LIGHTNING SURGES FOR TESTING

The danger to electric systems and apparatus comes from the potentials that lightning may produce across insulation. Insulation of power systems may be classified into two broad categories: external and internal insulation. External insulation is comprised of air and/or porcelain, etc., such as conductor to tower clearances of transmission lines or bus supports. If the potential caused by lightning exceeds the strength of insulation, a flashover or puncture occurs. Flashover of external insulation generally does not cause damage to equipment. The insulation is "self-restoring". At the worst a relatively short outage follows to allow replacement of a cheap string of damaged insulation. Internal insulation most frequently consists of paper, oil or other synthetic insulation which insulates h.v. conductors from ground in expensive equipment such as transformers, generators, reactors, capacitors, circuit-breakers, etc. Failure of internal insulation causes much longer outages. If power arc follows damage to equipment it may be disastrous and lead to very costly replacements.

The system's insulation has to be designed to withstand lightning voltages and be tested in laboratories prior to commissioning.

Exhaustive measurements of lightning currents and voltages and long experience has formed the basis for establishing and accepting what is

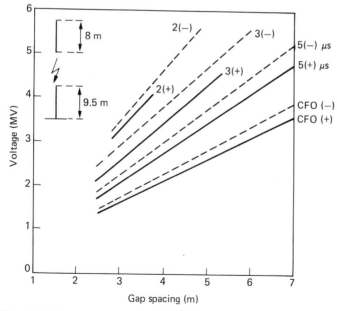

FIG. 7.6. Impulse (1.2/50 μsec) flashover characteristics of long rod gaps corrected to STP (after Udo[10]).

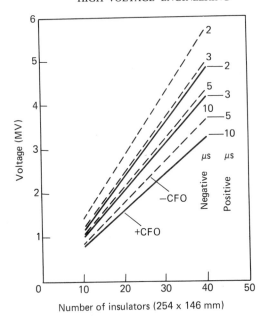

FIG. 7.7. Impulse (1.2/50 μsec) flashover characteristics for long insulator strings (after Udo[10]).

known as the standard surge or "impulse" voltage to simulate external or lightning overvoltages. The international standard lightning impulse voltage waveshape is an aperiodic voltage impulse that does not cross the zero line which reaches its peak in 1.2 μsec and then decreases slowly (in 50 μsec) to half the peak value. The characteristics of a standard impulse are its polarity, its peak value, its front time and its half value time. These have been defined in Chapter 2, Fig. 2.24.

Extensive laboratory tests have shown that for external insulation the flashover voltages are substantially proportional to gap length and that positive impulses give significantly lower flashover values than negative ones. In addition, for a particular test arrangement, as the applied impulse crest is increased the instant of flashover moves from the tail of the wave to the crest and ultimately to the front of the wave giving an impulse voltage-time characteristic as was discussed in Chapter 5, Fig. 5.34. Figures 7.6 and 7.7 show typical impulse spark over characteristics for long rod gaps and suspension insulators obtained by Udo[10] at various times to flashover. These figures include the critical or long time flashover characteristics

(CFO) occurring at about 10 μsec on the wave tail as well as the characteristics corresponding to shorter time lags near the wave crest. Data for both polarities are shown. The values plotted in Figs. 7.6 and 7.7 have been corrected to standard atmospheric conditions.

7.3 SWITCHING SURGE TEST VOLTAGE CHARACTERISTICS

In power transmission systems with systems voltages of 245 kV and above, the electrical strength of the insulation to switching overvoltages becomes important for the insulation design. A considerable amount of data on breakdown under switching surges is available. However, a variety of switching surge waveshapes and the correspondingly large range of flashover values make it difficult to choose a standard shape of switching impulses. Many tests have shown that the flashover voltage for various geometrical arrangements under unidirectional switching surge voltages decreases with increasing the front duration of the surge, reaching the lowest value somewhere in the range between 100 and 500 μsec. The time to half-value has less effect upon the breakdown strength because flashover almost always takes place before or at the crest of the wave. Figure 7.8 illustrates a typical relationship for a critical flashover voltage per metre as function of time to flashover for a 3-m rod-rod gap and a conductor-plane gap respectively.[11] It is seen that the standard impulse voltages give the

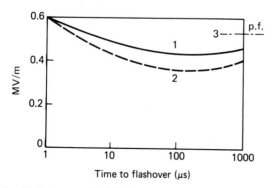

Fig. 7.8. Relationship between vertical flashover voltage per metre and time to flashover (3 m gap). 1. Rod-rod gap. 2. Conductor plane gap. 3. Power frequency.

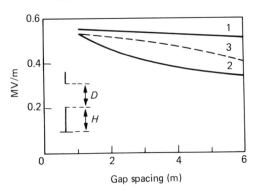

FIG. 7.9. Relationship between flashover voltage (MV/m) and gap length for 1: 1.2/50 μsec
impulses, 2: 200/2000 μsec switching surges and 3: power frequency voltages.

highest flashover values, with the switching surge values of crest between
approx. 100 and 500 μsec falling well below the corresponding power
frequency flashover values.

The relative effect of time to crest upon flashover value varies also with
the gap spacing and humidity.[21] Figure 7.9 compares the positive
flashover characteristics of standard impulses and 200/2000 μsec with
power frequency voltages for a rod-rod gap plotted as flashover voltage per
metre against gap spacing.[11] We observe a rapid fall in switching surge
breakdown strength with increasing the gap length. This drastic fall in the
average switching surge strength with increasing the insulation length leads
to costly design clearances, especially in the ultra h.v. regions. All
investigations show that for nearly all gap configurations which are of
practical interest, positive switching impulses result in lower flashover
voltage than negative ones. The flashover behaviour of external insulations
with different configurations under positive switching impulse stress is
therefore most important. The switching surge voltage breakdown is also
affected by the air humidity. Kuffel et al.[22] have recently reported that over
the range from 3 to 16 g/m³ absolute humidity, the breakdown voltage of
positive rod gaps increases approximately 1.7% per 1 g/m³ increase in
absolute humidity.

For testing purposes the standard switching surge recommended by
IEEE St-4-1978 Publication[12] and IEC Publication 70[13] has a front time
$T_1 = 250$ μsec $\pm 20\%$ and half-time value $T_2 = 2500$ μsec $\pm 60\%$. The general designation for a standard switching impulse is given as 250/2500 μsec.

The front is counted from the actual beginning of the impulse till the peak value is reached. Full characteristics of a standard switching test surge have been defined in Chapter 2, Fig. 2.25.

It was shown in Chapter 5, section 5.9 that in non-uniform field gaps the shape of both electrodes affects the formation and propagation of streamers and directly influences the flashover values. This explains the different flashover values observed for various insulating structures, especially under switching surges. Much of the laboratory flashover data for large gaps under switching surges have been obtained for rod-plane gaps. Subsequently, several attempts have been made to relate data for other structures to rod-plane gap data. Several investigators[14,15] have shown that the positive 50% switching surge voltage of different structures in air in the range from 2 to 8 m follow the expression

$$V_{50} = k500\,d^{0.6} \text{ kV} \tag{7.1}$$

where d is the gap length in metres, k is gap factor relating to the electrodes geometry. For rod-plane gaps the factor k is accepted as unity. Thus, the factor k represents a proportionality factor of the 50% flashover voltage of any gap geometry to that of a rod-plane gap for the same distance or

$$k = \frac{V_{50}}{V_{50} \text{ rod-plane}} \tag{7.2}$$

Expression (7.1) applies to data obtained under switching impulse of constant time to crest. A more general expression which gives minimum strength and applies to longer times to crest has been proposed by Gallet and Leroy[16] as follows:

$$V_{50} = \frac{k3450}{1+\dfrac{8}{d}} \text{ kV} \tag{7.3}$$

where k and d have the same meaning as in expression (7.1).

In expression (7.2) only the function V_{50} rod-plane is influenced by the switching impulse shape, while the gap factor k depends only on the gap geometry and hence upon the field distribution in the gap. The parameters influencing the gap factor (k) have been fully discussed by Schneider and Weck.[17] These authors have measured the gap factor (k) for different gap geometries and spacings using a large three dimensional electrolytic tank

TABLE 7.1
Geometric Gap Factor for Various Structures

Configuration	Figure	$d = 2$ m k	$d = 3$ m k	$d = 4$ m k	$d = 6$ m k
Rod-plane	a	1	1	1	1
Rod-structure	b	1.08	—	1.07	1.06
Rod-rod vertical					
$\quad H = 2$ m	c	1.27	1.26	1.21	1.14
Conductor-plane	d	1.08	—	1.14	1.15
Conductor-cross					
$\quad$ arm end	e	1.57	1.68	1.65	1.54
Conductor-2 m rod	f	1.47	—	1.40	1.25
Conductor-7 m rod	g	1.55	—	1.54	1.40

and modelling scaled down gaps. Their data are included in Table 7.1. The corresponding geometric configurations are shown in Fig. 7.10(a) to (f).

Expressions (7.1) and (7.3) together with data presented in Table 7.1 can be used in estimating required clearances in designing e.h.v. and u.h.v. structures. Refinements to these expressions are being introduced as more data becomes available.

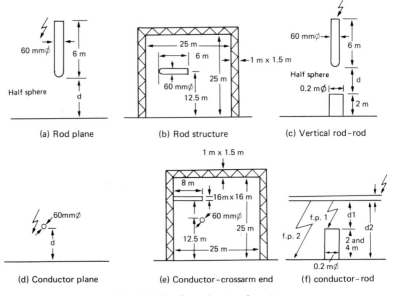

FIG. 7.10. Configuration (gap factor).

7.4 INSULATION COORDINATION

Insulation coordination is the correlation of insulation of electrical equipment with the characteristics of protective devices such that the insulation is protected from excessive overvoltages. In a substation, for example, the insulation of transformers, circuit breakers, bus supports, etc., should have insulation strength in excess of voltage provided by protective devices.

Electric systems' insulation designers have two options avilable to them : (i) choose insulation levels for components that would withstand overvoltages, (ii) devise protective devices that could be installed at the sensitive points in the system that would limit overvoltages there. The first alternative is unacceptable especially for e.h.v. and u.h.v. operating levels because of the excessive insulation required. Hence, there has been great incentive to develop and use protective devices. The actual relationship between the insulation levels and protective levels is a question of economics. Conventional methods of insulation coordination provide a margin of protection between electrical stress and electrical strength based on predicated maximum overvoltage and minimum strength, the maximum strength being allowed by the protective devices. "Insulation level"— insulation level is defined by the values of test voltages which the insulation of equipment under test must be able to withstand.

In the earlier days of electric power, insulation levels commonly used were established on the basis of experience gained by utilities. As laboratory techniques improved, so that different laboratories were in closer agreement on test results, an international joint committee, the Nema-Nela Committee on Insulation Coordination, was formed and was charged with the task of establishing insulation strength of all classes of equipment and to establish levels for various voltage classification. In 1941 a detailed document[18] was published giving basic insulation levels for all equipment in operation at that time. The presented tests included standard impulse voltages and 1-minute power frequency tests.

In today's systems for voltages up to 245 kV the tests are still limited to lightning impulses and 1-minute power frequency tests. Above 300 kV, tests include in addition to lightning impulse and the 1-minute power frequency tests, the use of switching impulse voltages. Tables 7.2 and 7.3 list the standardized test voltages adopted for testing equipment by European and other countries and the North American countries for voltages up to

TABLE 7.2
Standardized Test Voltages for Rated Voltages up to 245 kV

IEC Publication 71, 1972: Coordination of insulation
Drafts 17A (C.O.) 103 and 104: New specifications for d-electric tests

European practice and other countries					U.S.A. and Canada						
Rated voltage	Test voltage 50 Hz, 1 min		Impulse voltage 1.2/50 μsec		Rated voltage	Test voltage 60 Hz				Impulse voltage 1.2/50 μsec	
		across		across		to earth		across open contacts*			across
	to earth	open contacts*	to earth	open contacts*		dry 1 min	wet 10 sec	dry 1 min	wet 10 sec	to earth	open contacts*
V_m kV†	kV†	kV‡	kV‡	kV‡	V_m kV†	kV†	kV†	kV†	kV†	kV‡	kV‡
3.6	10	12	20§ / 40	23§ / 46	4.76 I	19	—	21	—	60	70
7.2	20	23	40§ / 60	46§ / 70	8.25 I	26		29		75	80
					8.25 F	35	30	39	33	95	105
12	28	32	60§ / 75	70§ / 85	15 I	36	—	40	—	95	105
17.5	38	45	75§ / 95	85§ / 110	15.5 I	50		55		110	125
					15.5 F	50	45	55	50	110	125
24	50	60	95§	110§	25.8 I	60	—	60	—	125	140

Vm	70	80	125	145		70	60	77	66	150	165
52	95	110	145§	165§	25.8 F	80	–	88	–	150	165
72.5	140	160	170	195	38 I	95	80	105	88	150	165
100 E	150	175	250	290	38 F	120	100	132	110	200	220
100	185	210	325	375	48.3 F	175	145	195	160	250	275
123 E	185	210	380	440	72.5 F					350	385
123	230	265	450	520							
145 E	230	265	450	520							
145	275	315	550	630							
170 E	275	315	550	630							
170	325	375	650	750							
245 E	325	375	650	750							
245 E	360	415	750	860							
245 E	395	460	750	860							
245	460	530	850	950							
245			950	1050							
245			1050	1200							

Above V_m = 100 kV as per European practice

* Only for isolators and earthing switches.
† RMS value
‡ Peak value.
§ For effectively earthed neutral with additional overvoltage protection or lightning arresters.
V_m = Max. service voltage of the network between phases.
I = Indoor execution.
F = Outdoor execution.
E = Reduced insulation, permissible only for effectively earthed neutral.

TABLE 7.3
Standardized Test Voltages for Rated Voltages Above 300 kV

IEC Publication 71, 1972:	Coordination of insulation
Drafts 17A (C.O.) 103 and 104:	New specifications for dielectric tests

Rated voltage	to earth			across open contacts					
			Switching surge 250/ 2500		Bias test: IS + 50 Hz Lightning surge + 0.7 × $V_m(\sqrt{2}/\sqrt{3})$ 1.2/50 μsec		Switching surge 250/ 2500	Bias test: SS + 50 Hz Switching surge + $V_m(\sqrt{2}/\sqrt{3})$ 250/2500 μsec	
	Test voltage 50 Hz, 1 min	Impulse voltage 1.2/50 μsec		Test voltage 50 Hz, 1 min					
V_m kV*	kV*	kV†	kV†	kV*	kV†	kV†	kV†	kV†	kV†
300	380	950	750	435	950	+170	850	700	+245
		1050	850		1050	+170			
362	450	1050	850	520	1050	+205	950	800	+295
		1175	950		1175	+205			
420	520	1300	950	610	1300	+240	1050	900	+345
		1425	1050		1425	+240			
525	620	1425	1050	760	1425	+300	1175	900	+430
		1550	1175		1550	+300			
765	830	1800	1300	1100	1800	+435	1550	1100	+625
		2100	1425		2100	+435			

* RMS value.
† Peak value.
V_m = max. service voltage of the network between phases.
IS = Lightning surge.
SS = Switching surge.

245 kV and above 300 kV respectively. For V_m (maximum voltage between phases) above 100 kV the European and North American practices use the same test voltages (Table 7.2). The values given in column 3 of Tables 7.2 and 7.3 correspond to impulse test voltage (1.2/50 μsec) and are usually referred to as the "Basic Insulation Levels" (BILs), defined as the impulse voltage which the insulation of any electrical equipment for a given rated voltage must be able to withstand, also commonly known as "Impulse Withstand Level".

Test Procedures

(a) *Proof of lightning impulse withstand level.* Details of test procedures applicable to particular types of test objects are specified by the appropriate apparatus standards (ASTM). The recommended procedure depends on the nature of the subject whether it has self-restoring insulation only or a combination of self-restoring and non-self-restoring.

For self-restoring insulation the test procedures are in common use for impulse withstand voltage establishments: (i) fifteen impulses of the rated voltage and of each polarity are applied—up to two disruptive discharges are permitted. (ii) In the second procedure the 50% flashover technique described in section 5.13 is used. The object is deemed to have withstood the test provided the withstand probability is not less than 90%, which in turn is given by the expression[11]

$$V_{w90\%} = V_{50\%}(1 - 1.30\sigma) = 0.96V_{50\%} \qquad (7.4)$$

where σ is the standard deviation $\sigma = 0.03$, with normal distribution being assumed.

In tests on non-self-restoring insulation three impulses are applied at the rated withstand voltage level of the specified polarity. The requirements of the test are satisfied if no indication of failure is obtained using methods of detection specified by the appropriate apparatus standards.

(b) *Testing with switching impulses.* These tests are foreseen, as mentioned before, for equipment for rated voltages for 300 kV and above. The testing procedure is similar to that outlined for lightning impulses applying 15 impulses. The tests are carried out on objects in clean and dry conditions such as applied for indoor equipment, while outdoor equipment is usually tested under positive switching impulses only. In some cases, such as in testing of circuit isolators or circuit breakers which in service may experience combined voltage stresses (power frequency and switching surge), the "biased" tests are used to simulate these conditions. The switching impulse tests are carried out with the equipment energized from a power frequency transformer. The acceptable insulating capability requires 90% withstand probability.

(c) *Testing with power frequency voltage.* To assess the effect of overvoltages that insulation may experience over long periods in service, it has become a standard practice to perform a "1-minute test" with power frequency voltages at levels such as specified in Tables 7.2 and 7.3. It has often been argued that these test levels are excessive and not experienced in practice. The question is presently under review by the IEC Committee. The power frequency tests of indoor equipment are carried out in dry conditions, while outdoor equipment is tested under conditions of standard rain. The IEC prescribes the conditions for standard rain as folllows: precipitation rate 1–

1.5 mm/min, with the resistivity of water (collected) $\rho = 100$ Ωm; earlier European specifications called for precipitation of 3 mm/min and $\rho = 100$ Ωm.

Statistical Approach to Insulation Coordination

In the early days insulation levels for lightning surges were determined by evaluating the 50% flashover values for all insulations and providing sufficiently high withstand levels for all insulations. This approach is difficult to apply at e.h.v. and u.h.v. levels, particularly for external insulations.

Present-day practices of insulation coordination rely on a statistical approach which relates directly the electrical stress and the electrical strength.[19] This approach requires a knowledge of the distribution of both the anticipated stresses and the electrical strengths.

The statistical nature of overvoltages, in particular switching overvoltages, makes it necessary to compute a large number of overvoltages in order to determine with some degree of confidence the statistical overvoltages on a system. The e.h.v. and u.h.v. systems employ a number of nonlinear elements, but with today's availability of digital computers the distribution of overvoltages can be calculated. A more practical approach to determine the required probability distributions of system's overvoltages employs a comprehensive systems simulator interfaced with a hybrid computer, e.g. as described in reference 23, the IREQ simulator.

The dielectric strengths of external self-restoring insulations are determined through tests carried out in laboratories and the data on withstand provide the basis for establishing withstand levels. It was shown in Chapter 5 that the development of electrical breakdown is governed by statistical laws and has a random character; furthermore, it is found that the distribution of breakdowns for a given gap follows with some exceptions approximately normal or Gaussian distribution, as does the distribution of overvoltages on the system. For the purpose of coordinating the electrical stresses with electrical strengths it is convenient to represent the overvoltage distribution in the form of probability density function and the insulation breakdown probability by the cumulative distribution function as shown in Fig. 7.11. The knowledge of these distributions enables us to determine the "risk of failure". As an example, let us consider a case of a spark gap for which the two characteristics in Fig. 7.11 apply. At an

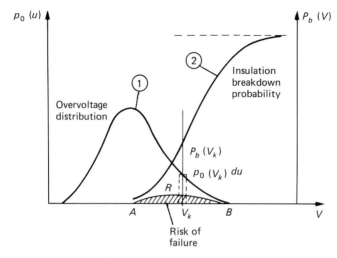

Fig. 7.11. Method of describing the risk of failure. 1. Probability density function

$$p_0(V) = \frac{1}{\sigma\sqrt{2\pi}}\, e^{-[(V_k-V_a)^2/2\sigma^2]}.$$

V_a average value of overvoltage; V_k Kth value of overvoltage; σ standard deviation. 2. Cumulative distribution function $P_b(V) = \int_0^\infty P_b(V_k)\,du$.

overvoltage V_k the probability of occurrence of overvoltage is $p_0(V_k)\,du$, whereas the probability of breakdown in $P_b(V_k)$ or the probability that the gap will breakdown at an overvoltage V_k is $P_b(V_k)p_0(V_k)\,du$. For the total voltage range we obtain for the total probability of failure of "risk of failure"

$$R = \int_0^\infty P_b(V_k)p_0(V_k)\,du. \tag{7.5}$$

The risk of failure will thus be given by the shaded area under the curve R.

In engineering practice it would become uneconomical to use the complete distribution functions for the occurrence of overvoltage and for the withstand of insulation and a compromise solution is accepted as shown in Fig. 7.12(a) and (b) for guidance. Curve (a) represents probability of occurrence of overvoltages of such amplitude (V_s), that only 2% (shaded area) has a chance to cause breakdown. V_s is known as the "statistical overvoltage". In Fig. 7.13(b) the voltage V_w is so low that in 90% of applied impulses, breakdown does not occur and such voltage is known as the "statistical withstand voltage" V_w.

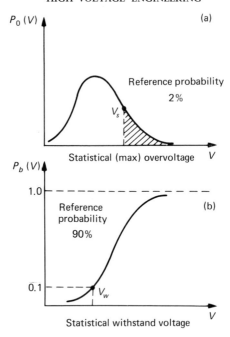

$P_0(V)$ (a)

Reference probability
2%

V_s

Statistical (max) overvoltage V

$P_b(V)$

1.0

Reference probability 90%   (b)

0.1 V_w

Statistical withstand voltage V

FIG. 7.12. Reference probabilities for overvoltage and for insulation withstand strength.

In addition to the parameters "statistical overvoltage V_s" and the "statistical withstand voltage V_w" we may introduce the concept of statistical safety factor γ. This parameter becomes readily understood by inspecting Fig. 7.13(a) to (c) in which the functions $P_b(V)$ and $p_0(V_k)$ are plotted for three different cases of insulation strength but keeping the distribution of overvoltage occurrence the same. The density function $p_0(V_k)$ is the same in (a) to (c) and the cumulative function giving the yet undetermined withstand voltage is gradually shifted along the V-axis towards high values of V. This corresponds to increasing the insulation strength by either using thicker insulation or material of higher insulation strength. As a result of the relative shift of the two curves [$P_b(V)$ and $P_0(V_k)$] the ratio of the values V_w/V_s will vary. This ratio is known as the statistical safety factor or

$$\frac{V_w}{V_s} = \gamma \qquad (7.6)$$

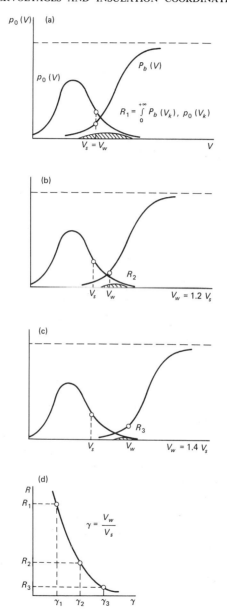

FIG. 7.13. The statistical safety factor and its relation to the risk of failure (R).

In the same figure (d) is plotted the relation of this parameter to the "risk of failure". It is clear that increasing the statistical safety factor (γ) will reduce the risk of failure (R), but at the same time will cause increase in insulation costs. The above treatment applies to self-restoring insulations. In the case of non-self-restoring insulations the electrical withstand is expressed in terms of actual breakdown values. The statistical approach to insulation, presented here, leads to withstand voltages (i.e. probability of breakdown is very small), thus giving us a method for establishing the "insulation level".

Correlation Between Insulation and Protection Levels

"The protection level" provided by (say) arresters is established in a similar manner to "insulation level" the basic difference is that the insulation of protective devices (arresters) must not withstand the applied voltage. The concept of correlation between insulation and protection levels can be readily understood by considering a simple example of an insulator string being protected by a spark gap, the spark gap (of lower breakdown strength) protecting the insulator string. Let us assume that both gaps are subjected to the same overvoltage represented by the probability density function $p_0(V)$, Fig. 7.14. The probability distribution curves for the spark gap and the insulator string are presented by $P_g(V)$ and $P_i(V)$ respectively in Fig. 7.14. The statistical electrical withstand strength of the insulator string is given by a curve identical with Fig. 7.12. The probability of breakdown of this insulation remains in the area R which gives "risk of failure". Since the string is protected by a spark gap of withstand probability $P_g(V)$, the probability that the gap will operate (its risk of failure) is obtained from integrating the product $P_g(V)p_0(V)\,dV$. In Fig. 7.14 this probability is denoted (qualitatively) by $P_p(V)$. As is seen the probability is much higher than the probability of insulation damage—probability of failure R. In the same figure is shown the traditional margin of safety corresponding to the voltage difference between the 50% flashover values of the protecting gap and the protected gap.

For overvoltages of the highest amplitude (extreme right of Fig. 7.14) the probability curves of insulation failure and that of protective spark gap breakdown overlap. In reality such cases will not arise. Figure 7.14 is simplified in that it contains information pertaining to the amplitude of the overvoltage, and it ignores the effect of time of voltage application on the breakdown of both the protective gap and the insulation. In practice, the

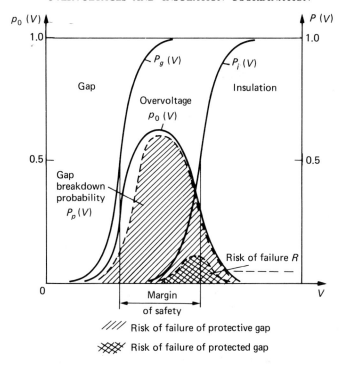

FIG. 7.14. Distribution functions of breakdown voltages for protective gap and protected insulation both subjected to an overvoltage $p_0(V)$.
P_p Risk of failure of protective gap.
R Risk of failure of protected gap.

protective gap will break down before the insulation and will cause a reduction (to a safe limit) in overvoltage reaching the protected insulation.

REFERENCES

1. Hydro-Quebec Symposium on Extra-High Voltage Alternating Current, October 1973.
2. L. V. Bewley. *Travelling Waves on Transmission Systems.* Dover Publications, New York, N.Y., 1963.
3. *Electrical Transmission and Distribution.* Westinghouse Electric Co., Pittsburgh, Penn., 1964.
4. W. W. Lewis. *The Protection of Transmission Systems against Lightning.* Dover Publication Inc., New York 1965.
5. R. H. Golde (editor) *Lightning*, Vol. I: *Physics of Lightning*; Vol. II: *Lightning Protection.* Academic Press, London/New York/San Francisco 1977.

6. B. F. J. Schonland. Progressive lightning, IV. The Discharge mechanism. *Proc. Roy. Soc.* Series A, **164** (1938), p. 132.
7. *E.H.V. Transmission Lines.* Reference Book General Electrical Company, Edison Electrical Institute, New York, 1968, p. 288.
8. AIEE Committee Report. Method for Estimating Lightning Performance of Transmission Lines. *Trans. AIEE* Part III, **69** (1950), p. 1187.
9. R. H. Golde. A plain man's guide to lightning protection. *Electronics and Power*, March 1969.
10. T. Udo. Sparkover characteristics of long gaps and insulator strings. *Trans. IEEE* **PAS 83** (1964), p. 471.
11. W. Diesendorf. *Insulation Coordination in High Voltage Electric Power Systems.* Butterworths, 1974.
12. IEEE St-4-1978, Standard Techniques for High Voltage Testing. IEEE Inc. publication.
13. International Electrotechnical Commission, Technical Com. 28 (Central Office), 35 (1970).
14. L. Paris. Influence of air gap characteristics on line to ground switching surge strength. *Trans. IEEE* **PAS 86** (1967), p. 936.
15. L. Paris and R. Cortina. Switching surge characteristics of large air gaps and long insulator strings. *Trans. IEEE* **PAS 87** (1968), p. 947.
16. G. Gallet and G. Leroy. Expression for switching impulse strength suggesting the highest permissible voltage for AC systems. IEEE—Power, Summer Power Meeting, 1973.
17. K. H. Schneider and K. H. Weck. *Electra* No. 35 (1974) p. 25.
18. Standard Impulse, Basic Insulation Levels. A Report of the Joint Committee on Coordination of Insulation AIEE, EEI and NEMA. EEI Publication No. H-9, NEMA Publication #109, AIEE Transactions, 1941.
19. Dielectric Stresses and Coordination of Insulation. Brown Boveri Publication No. CH-A0500 20E No. 4, 1972.
20. K. Berger. Method und Resultate der Blitzforschung auf dem Monte San Salvatore bei Lugano in den Jahren 1963–1971.
21. W. Büsch. The effect of humidity on the dielectric strength of long air gaps of UHV-configurations subjected to positive impulses. Ph.D. thesis, E.T.H., Zurich, 1982, (see also: W. Büsch, *Trans. IEEE* **PAS 97** (1978), pp. 2086–2093).
22. J. Kuffel, R. G. van Heswijk and J. Reichman. Atmospheric influences on the switching impulse performance of 1-m gaps. *Trans. IEEE* **PAS 102** (7), July 1983.
23. P. C. S. Krischnayya, M. M. Gavrilovic and N. L. Nakra. Power systems simulation facilities at IREQ. Int. Conf. on Overvoltages and Compensation on Integrated AC-DC Systems, Winnipeg, 1980, p. 114.

AUTHOR INDEX

SUBJECT INDEX